Biology

A Reference Guide

Staff for This Book

Dan Franck *Content Specialist*
Suzanne Montazer *Art Director*
Lisa Dimaio Iekel *Production Manager*
Carol Leigh *Designer*
Christopher Yates *Cover Designer*
Dan Perkins *Visual Designer*
Henrik de Gyor *Illustrations Editor*
Bruce Hunter *Illustrations Editor*
Bud Knecht *Text Editor*
Susan Raley *Text Editor, Quality Control Specialist*
Karen Sweet *Instructional Designer*
Phil George *Instructional Designer*
Ralf Provant *Instructional Designer*
Craig Ruskin *Project Manager*
Corey Maender *Project Manager*
Connie Moy *Quality Control Manager*

Bror Saxberg *Chief Learning Officer*
John Holdren *Senior Vice President for Content and Curriculum*
Maria Szalay *Senior Vice President for Product Development*
Jennifer Thompson *Director of Product Delivery*
Tom DiGiovanni *Senior Director of Instructional Design*
Kim Barcas *Creative Director*
John G. Agnone *Director of Publications*
Charles Kogod *Director of Media and IP Management*
Jeff Burridge *Managing Editor*
Steve Watson *Product Manager*

About K12 Inc.

Founded in 1999, K12 Inc. is an elementary and secondary school service combining rich academic content with powerful technology. K¹² serves students in a variety of education settings, both public and private, including school classrooms, virtual charter schools, home schools, and tutoring centers. K¹² currently provides comprehensive curricular offerings in the following subjects: Language Arts/English, History, Math, Science, Visual Arts, and Music. The K¹² curriculum blends high quality offline materials with innovative online resources, including interactive lessons, teacher guides, and tools for planning and assessment. For more information, call 1-888-YOUR K12 or visit www.K12.com.

ISBN: 1-931728-98-4

Printed by RR Donnelley, Shenzhen, China, March 2011, Lot 032011

Biology

A Reference Guide

Contents

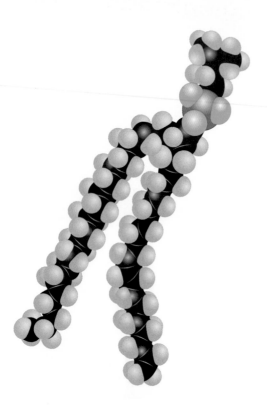

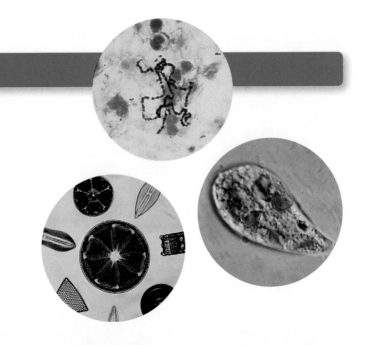

Unit 3 Cell Biology

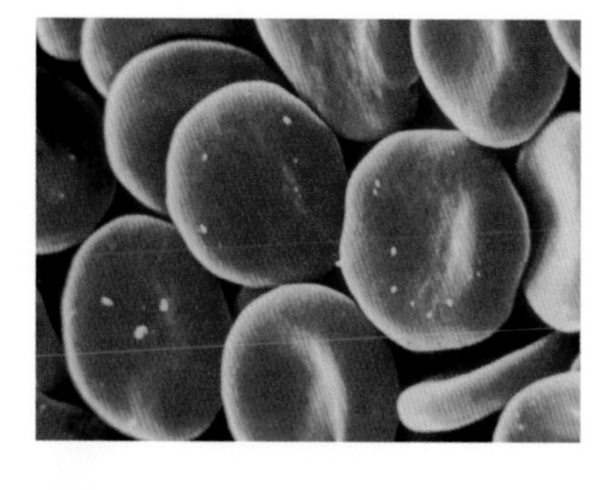

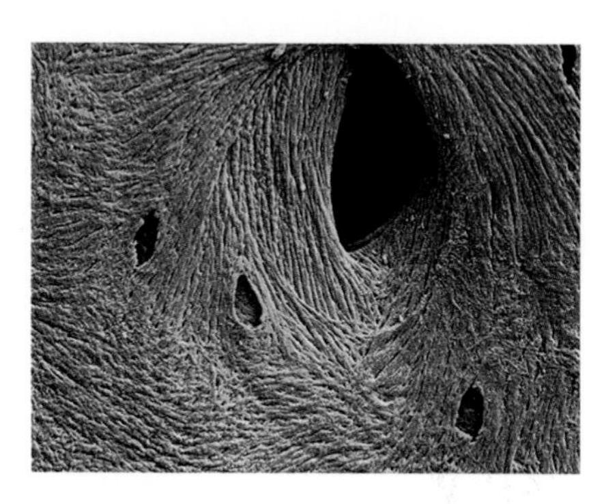

Unit 4 Mendelian Genetics

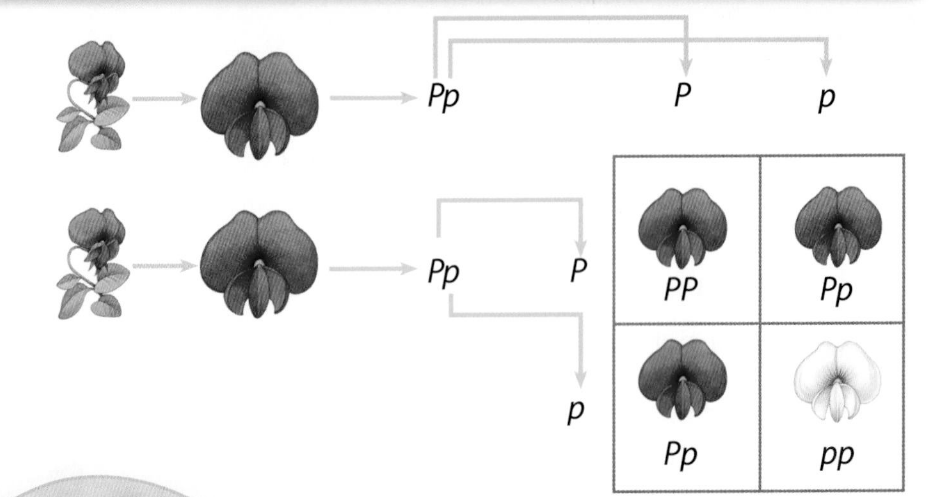

Unit 5 Molecular Genetics

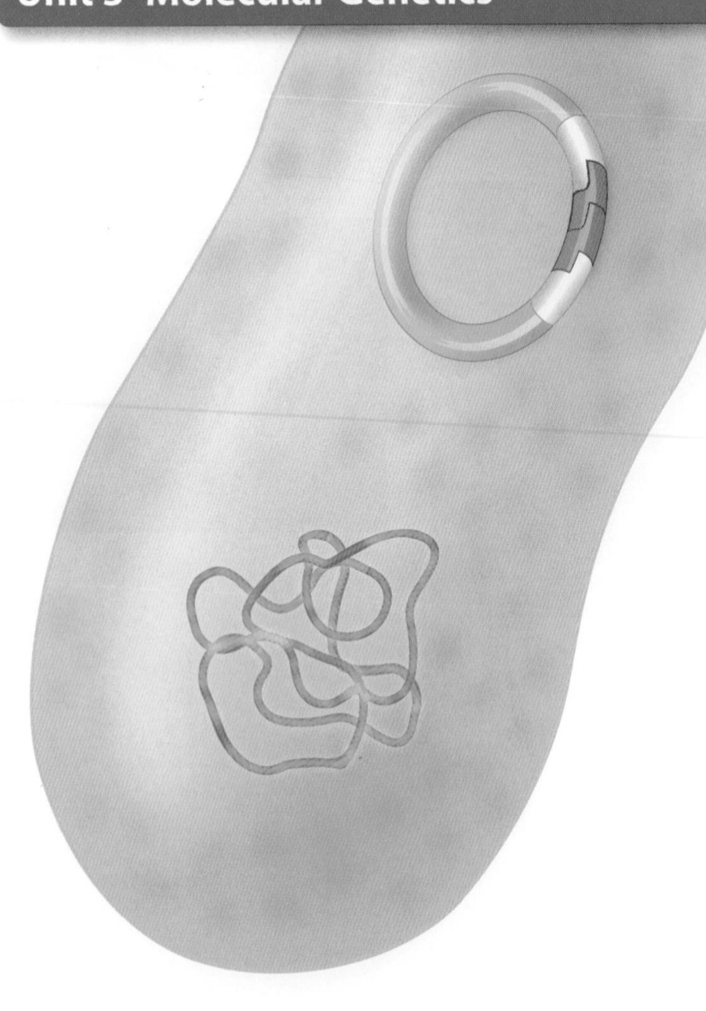

Unit 6 Evolution

Unit 7 Survey of Living Things 1

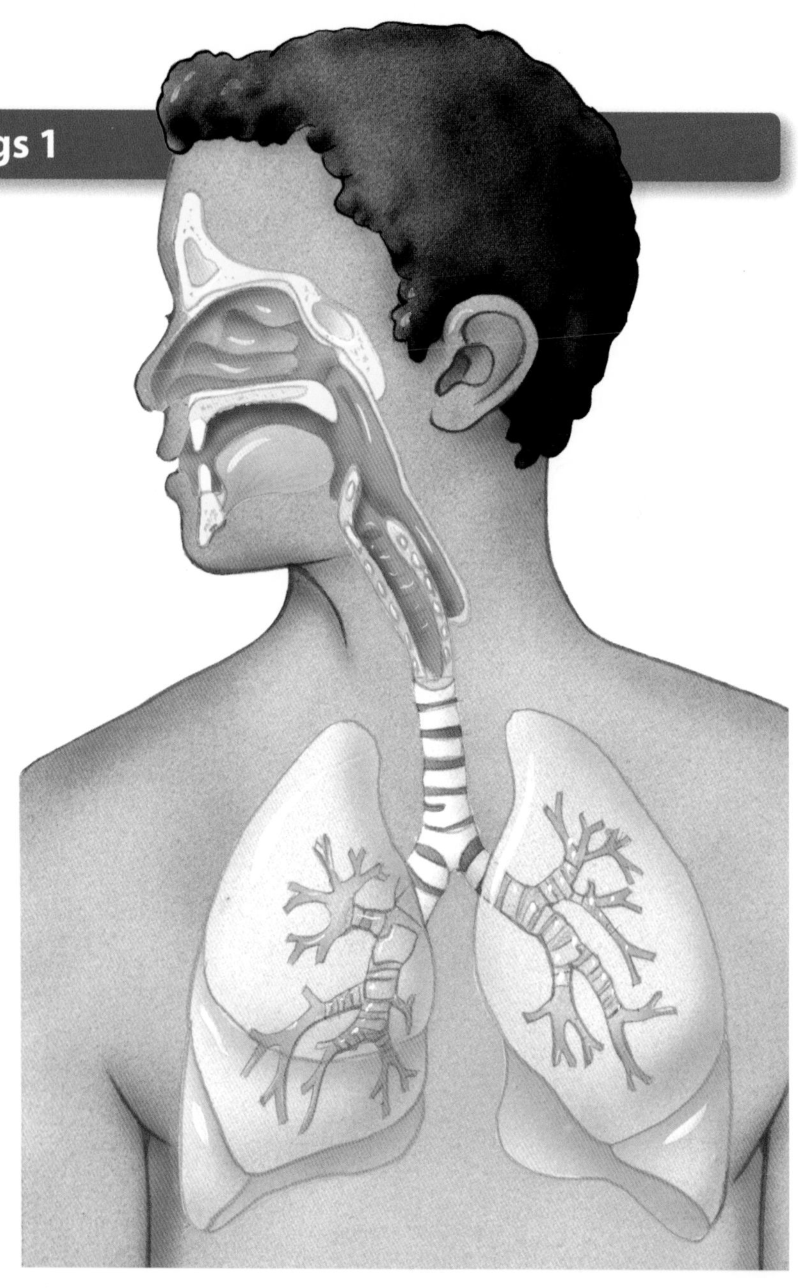

Unit 8 Survey of Living Things 2

Unit 9 Ecology and the Environment

How to Use This Book

Welcome to *Biology: A Reference Guide*

This book serves as a reference guide for any student of biology. It was also developed as a companion to the online portion of K12 Inc.'s High School Biology program.

Each two-page spread of this book uses words and pictures to present an overview of a Key Idea. You can use this book to familiarize yourself with some aspects of biology, or to review materials you're studying in other books or online sources.

How This Book Is Organized

Units of Study

This book is organized in the following units of study:

- The Science of Biology
- The Chemistry of Life
- Cell Biology
- Mendelian Genetics
- Molecular Genetics
- Evolution
- Survey of Living Things 1
- Survey of Living Things 2
- Ecology and the Environment

Pronunciation Guide

To learn how to pronounce scientific terms, see the Pronunciation Guide on page 216.

Glossary

See pages 217–220 for a Glossary with brief definitions of some key terms.

Index

An Index is provided on pages 221–233.

Navigating a Page

Subject Each two-page spread explores a Key Idea in biology.

Key Idea What's the Key Idea on these pages? Start reading here to find out.

Further Explanation This text provides more detailed information about the Key Idea.

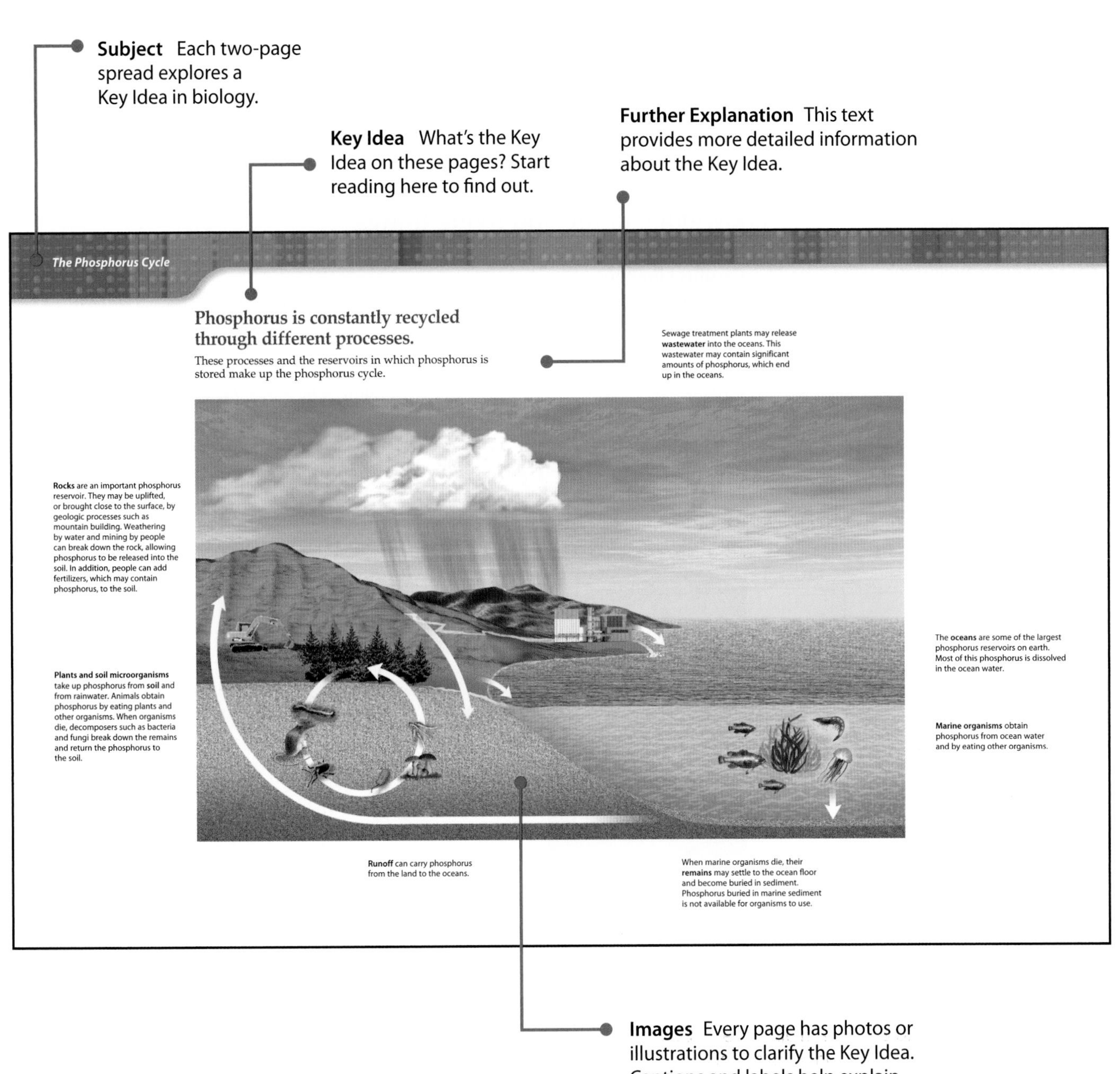

The Phosphorus Cycle
Phosphorus is constantly recycled through different processes.
These processes and the reservoirs in which phosphorus is stored make up the phosphorus cycle.
Sewage treatment plants may release wastewater into the oceans. This wastewater may contain significant amounts of phosphorus, which end up in the oceans.
Rocks are an important phosphorus reservoir. They may be uplifted, or brought close to the surface, by geologic processes such as mountain building. Weathering by water and mining by people can break down the rock, allowing phosphorus to be released into the soil. In addition, people can add fertilizers, which may contain phosphorus, to the soil.
Plants and soil microorganisms take up phosphorus from soil and from rainwater. Animals obtain phosphorus by eating plants and other organisms. When organisms die, decomposers such as bacteria and fungi break down the remains and return the phosphorus to the soil.
The oceans are some of the largest phosphorus reservoirs on earth. Most of this phosphorus is dissolved in the ocean water.
Marine organisms obtain phosphorus from ocean water and by eating other organisms.
Runoff can carry phosphorus from the land to the oceans.
When marine organisms die, their remains may settle to the ocean floor and become buried in sediment. Phosphorus buried in marine sediment is not available for organisms to use.

Images Every page has photos or illustrations to clarify the Key Idea. Captions and labels help explain details in the images.

Individuals throughout history have made scientific observations about the natural world.

Some important discoveries in biology have occurred by accident, while others came about through many years of careful experimentation. The discoveries below are just a few of the many contributions to biology that have increased knowledge of life and living things.

William Harvey carried out detailed studies of the circulatory systems of humans and other animals. He concluded that the heart is a pump and that blood is continually recirculated through the body, not created and consumed with every heartbeat as previously thought.

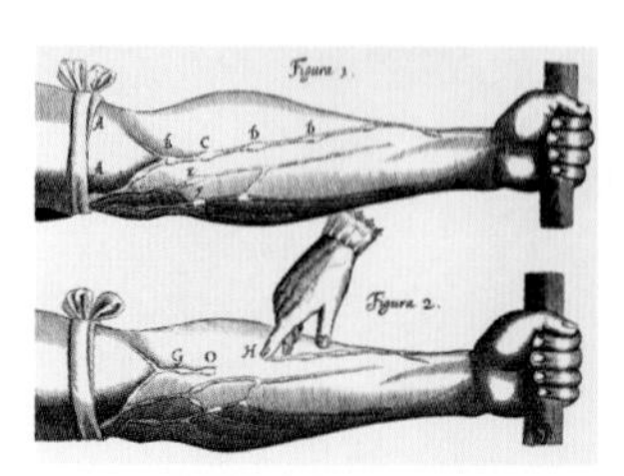

1628

Robert Hooke used a microscope to examine bits of cork and discovered tiny compartments in the plant tissue. He called these compartments *cells*. Other scientists built upon this initial discovery to formulate the cell theory.

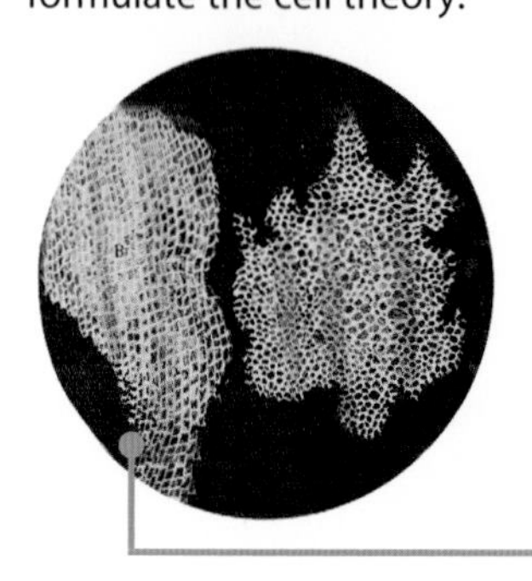

1665

Carolus Linnaeus published his *Systema Naturae,* an attempt to classify and describe all known living things. He replaced the cumbersome system of long, descriptive names with binomial nomenclature—a system in which each species is assigned a unique, two-part Latin name.

1735

Building on the work of earlier scientists, **Theodor Schwann** outlined the first two parts of the cell theory, a major unifying concept in biology: Living things are made of one or more cells, and the cell is the basic unit of life. The third part of the cell theory, proposed later by Rudolf Virchow, states that all cells come from existing cells.

1839

After his voyage on HMS *Beagle*, **Charles Darwin** worked for more than 20 years before publishing his evidence for what he called *descent with modification*. His work is the basis for what is known today as the *theory of evolution by natural selection*. Darwin's ideas met with great resistance during his lifetime. Today, however, most scientists accept natural selection as a primary mechanism for evolution.

1858

Gregor Mendel, an Austrian monk, carried out extensive studies on pea plants to examine how traits are passed from parents to offspring. His work established the field of modern genetics.

1866

Melvin Calvin used radioactive carbon as a tracer to follow the path carbon takes through a plant during photosynthesis. The series of reactions in photosynthesis known as the *Calvin cycle* is named for him.

Kary Mullis invented a procedure known as the *polymerase chain reaction* (PCR). PCR allows scientists to copy, or amplify, small amounts of DNA for study. Two of the most common applications of PCR are the diagnosis of inherited diseases and the study of crime scene evidence.

When a plate culture of *Staphylococcus* became contaminated with bread mold spores, **Alexander Fleming** discovered that mold could inhibit bacterial growth. This mold, called *Penicillium notatum*, is used today to produce the antibiotic penicillin.

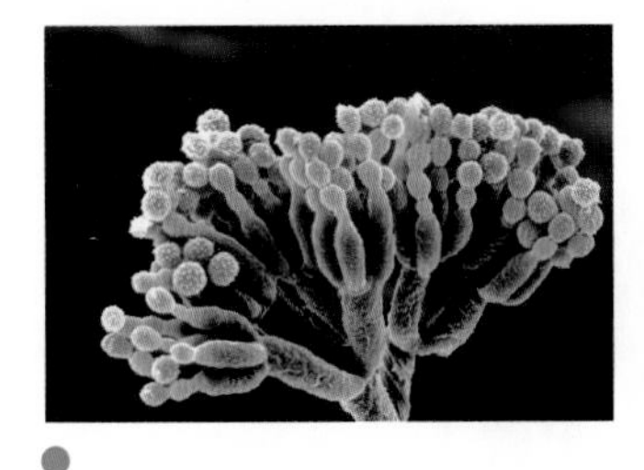

Using Rosalind Franklin's X-ray diffraction data, **James Watson and Francis Crick** proposed a double helix as the structure of DNA.

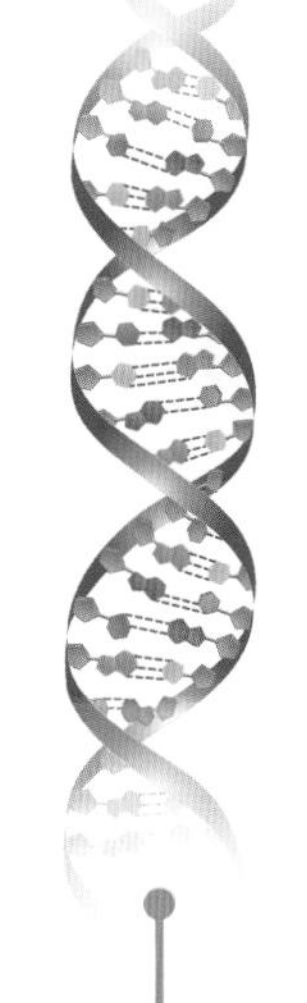

Christiaan Barnard, a South African surgeon, performed the first human heart transplant. Although the surgery itself was successful, the patient died of pneumonia 18 days later. Since that time, heart transplants have become a standard procedure.

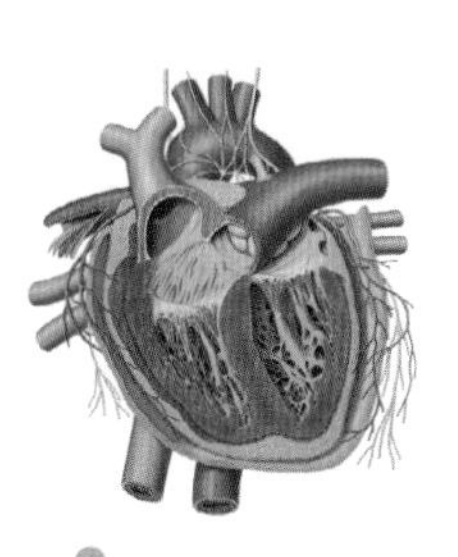

Ian Wilmut cloned the first adult mammal. The cloned offspring, a lamb named Dolly, received her genetic material from a mammary cell of a ewe.

Building on the earlier work of Louis Pasteur, who showed that diseases are caused by bacteria and viruses, **Robert Koch** established the germ theory of disease. Koch's extensive studies of disease transmission revolutionized the field of medicine.

1882 | 1928 | 1945 | 1953 | 1967 | 1992 | 1996

Scientific ideas develop and change over time as new information becomes available to scientists.

Our modern scientific understanding of evolution took centuries to develop. As early as the sixth century B.C., Greek thinkers like Anaximander and Aristotle put forth the idea that organisms change over time. In the eighteenth and nineteenth centuries, discoveries in geology suggested that earth might be much older than people had previously believed. Scientists like Lamarck and Darwin proposed theories about how life changes over time. The discovery of deoxyribonucleic acid (DNA) opened the door to an even greater scientific understanding of how populations of organisms evolve.

Carolus Linnaeus tackled the monumental task of naming all living things. In his *Systema Naturae*, Linnaeus presented his naming system (now called *binomial nomenclature*), which gives each species in the world a two-part Latin name that includes a genus and species descriptor.

1735

Thomas Malthus's *An Essay on the Principle of Population* stated that much of human suffering was due to human populations' increasing faster than their supply of food and other resources.

1798

In *Philosophie Zoologique*, **Jean-Baptiste de Lamarck** stated that an individual could acquire characteristics during its lifetime and pass those characteristics on to its offspring. That principle was later proven incorrect.

1809

One of the first dinosaur fossils described scientifically was ***Megalosaurus***. Fossils discovered since then have provided evidence that different kinds of organisms have existed on earth at different times.

Based on his observation of rock layers and layering, **Charles Lyell** suggested that earth is extremely old. He provided evidence for the principle of uniformitarianism—that is, processes observed today have been occurring since earth formed.

Charles Darwin published *On the Origin of Species*, a groundbreaking work that described natural selection as a mechanism for evolution. Influenced by Malthus's essay, Darwin suggested that the "struggle for existence" is a driving force in natural selection. Darwin was unable to suggest a mechanism for variation in populations.

1824 | **EARLY 1830s** | **1859**

Our scientific understanding of evolution continued to grow as scientists learned more about genetics and inheritance.

Studies in genetics accelerated scientists' understanding of the mechanisms of evolution. Mendel's experiments on the transmission of traits from parents to offspring laid the foundation for later work on DNA structure and function. Both were important in the scientific understanding of evolution.

Gregor Mendel, an Austrian monk, studied pea plants to discover how traits are passed from parents to offspring. His work helped scientists understand heredity.

1856

The first fossil specimen of ***Archaeopteryx***, thought to be about 150 million years old, was discovered in Germany. *Archaeopteryx* had characteristics of both dinosaurs and modern birds.

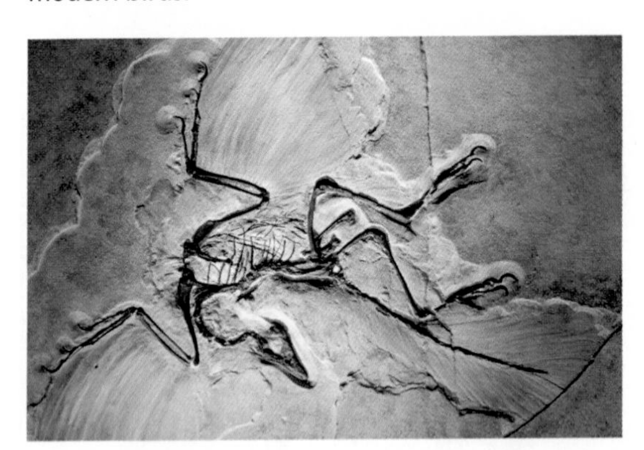

1861

Godfrey Hardy and Wilhelm Weinberg described the characteristics of a population that is not evolving. Their principle of genetic equilibrium allowed scientists to examine the forces that cause a population to evolve.

$$p^2 + 2pq + q^2 = 1$$

1908

1953

James Watson and Francis Crick published their description of the double helix structure of DNA. Their breakthrough allowed scientists to understand the underlying changes in genetic material and how they affect the evolutionary process.

1974

In the Afar Valley region of Africa, anthropologist Donald Johanson discovered a 3.2 million-year-old hominid fossil, later nicknamed **Lucy**. Lucy's species, *Australopithecus afarensis,* is one of the oldest known ancestors of modern humans. Scientists have deduced from fossil remains that *Australopithecus* walked upright and may have used simple stone tools.

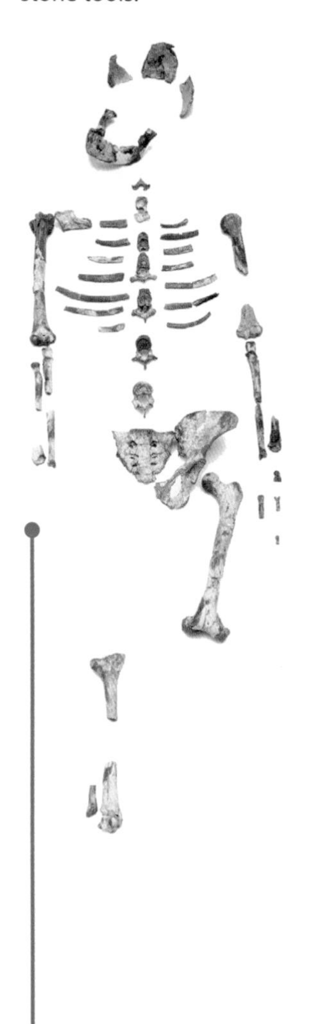

TODAY

Geneticists sample DNA from various organisms and organize life-forms into **phylogenetic trees**. The diagrams show evolutionary connections for a range of species that has a common ancestor. Through genetic sequencing, scientists learn the language of the gene and how all life is both closely related and incredibly diverse.

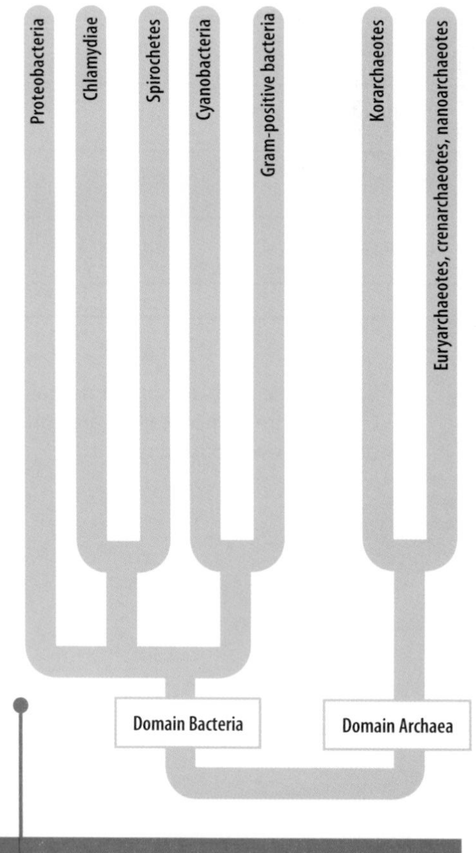

Although many people in the United States use units such as inches, feet, or pounds to express measurements, scientists use a different system.

This system of measurement is called the *Système International d'Unités* (International System of Units), and it is based on the metric system. Scientists often refer to this measurement system as SI.

SI BASE UNITS

QUANTITY	BASE UNIT	SYMBOL
Time	Second	s
Mass	Kilogram	kg
Length	Meter	m
Electric current	Ampere	A
Amount of a substance	Mole	mol
Temperature	Kelvin	K
Luminous intensity	Candela	cd

Seven **base units** are fundamental to the SI. Other, more complex units are combinations of these seven base units.

SI PREFIXES

PREFIX	ABBREVIATION	FACTOR
pico-	p	0.000000000001
nano-	n	0.000000001
micro-	µ	0.000001
milli-	m	0.001
centi-	c	0.01
deci-	d	0.1
deka-	da	10
hecto-	h	100
kilo-	k	1,000
mega-	M	1,000,000
giga-	G	1,000,000,000

The **prefix** of a unit indicates its relationship to the base unit.

The SI organizes units by **powers of 10**. This organization makes the system easy for all scientists to work with.

COMMON MEASUREMENTS

LENGTH		*AREA*	
1 kilometer (km)	1,000 m	1 square kilometer (km^2)	100 ha
1 meter (m)	standard unit	1 hectare (ha)	10,000 m^2
1 centimeter (cm)	0.01 m	1 square meter (m^2)	standard unit
1 millimeter (mm)	0.001 m	1 square centimeter (cm^2)	0.0001 m^2
1 micrometer (µm)	0.000001 m		
MASS		***LIQUID VOLUME***	
1 kilogram (kg)	1,000 g	1 kiloliter (kL)	1,000 L
1 gram (g)	standard unit	1 liter (L)	standard unit
1 milligram (mg)	0.001 g	1 milliliter (mL)	0.001 L
1 microgram (µg)	0.000001 g	1 mL	1 cm^3

Converting from One Temperature Scale to Another

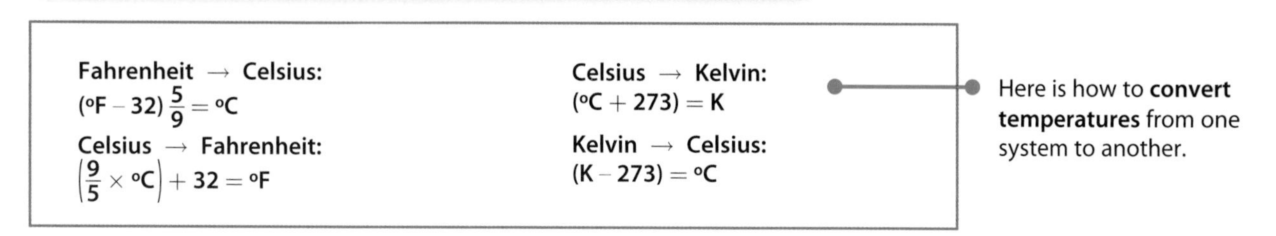

Fahrenheit → Celsius:
$(°F - 32)\frac{5}{9} = °C$

Celsius → Fahrenheit:
$\left(\frac{9}{5} \times °C\right) + 32 = °F$

Celsius → Kelvin:
$(°C + 273) = K$

Kelvin → Celsius:
$(K - 273) = °C$

Here is how to **convert temperatures** from one system to another.

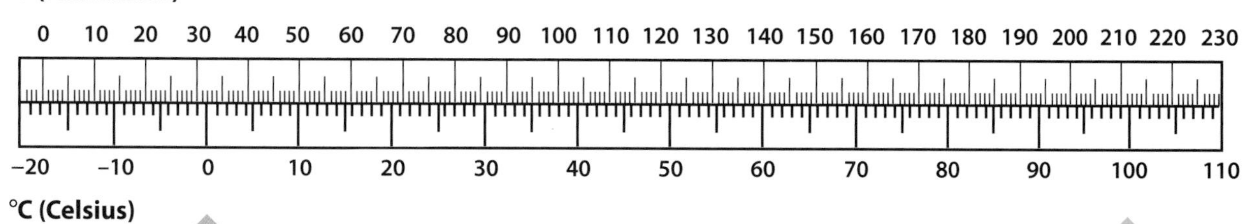

Most people in the United States **express temperature** in degrees Fahrenheit. Scientists in the United States and throughout the world, however, express temperature in degrees Celsius. The Celsius scale is based on the freezing point and boiling point of water.

Scientists use scientific methods to answer their questions about the natural world.

Although there is no single scientific method, scientists usually follow all or some of the following processes: observing and questioning, forming hypotheses, experimenting, gathering and analyzing data, and drawing conclusions. Often a scientist needs to repeat certain processes within one inquiry. For example, the scientist may begin an experiment and then find that she has to modify her hypothesis or form a new hypothesis, then design new experiments.

Make Observations → **Form a Hypothesis** → **Perform an Experiment**

Make Observations: A scientist notices that the plants under the fluorescent lights in her office grow at a different rate from that of the plants by the window in her house.

Form a Hypothesis: The scientist does research and learns that sunlight contains a lot of red and blue light, while certain fluorescent lights contain only small amounts of red and blue light.

Perform an Experiment: The scientist decides to experiment by growing 10 snapdragons under different kinds of light. She grows all of the plants under the same conditions, but she places 5 plants where they will receive sunlight only and 5 plants where they will receive fluorescent light only.

"If the plants by the window are taller than those in my office, then I hypothesize that plants exposed to natural light grow more quickly than those exposed to this type of fluorescent light."

Theory

In everyday conversation, people often use the word *theory* to mean a guess. In science, however, theory has a very different meaning. A scientific theory represents hypotheses that have been tested repeatedly and confirmed by different scientists. A theory is a general statement backed up by a large body of facts.

Gather and Analyze Data

Every week, the scientist measures the snapdragons and calculates the average growth rate of the plants in the different light treatments. She carefully records and analyzes the data.

Draw Conclusions

After analyzing the data, the scientist makes conclusions about the differences in plant growth and presents the findings to her colleagues.

Alter the Hypothesis/ Form a New Hypothesis

The scientist decides to perform another experiment, adding a group of plants that will be exposed only to black light. Black light is limited to a narrow band of ultraviolet frequencies and emits little visible light. Because black light contains no red or blue light, the scientist hypothesizes that the plants will grow even more slowly than those exposed to fluorescent light.

"The plants on the window sill grew more rapidly. I conclude that the higher levels of red and blue light in sunlight help plants grow faster."

A microscope lets you see objects and details far smaller than you can see with your unaided eye.

There are several types of microscopes that allow for different degrees of magnification. Scientists choose a particular microscope based on the specimen they are studying and the level of detail they need to see.

A bacterium like ***Streptococcus*** may be around 1 µm long. A light microscope can reveal the shape of these tiny organisms, but generally does not have a high enough magnification to show fine details.

Diatoms are typically 10–200 µm long. A light microscope can reveal the colors and intricate shapes of these tiny organisms.

Single-cell ***Euglena*** may be 80–150 µm long. In this image from a light microscope, you can see some internal structures of *Euglena*, such as chloroplasts and the nucleus.

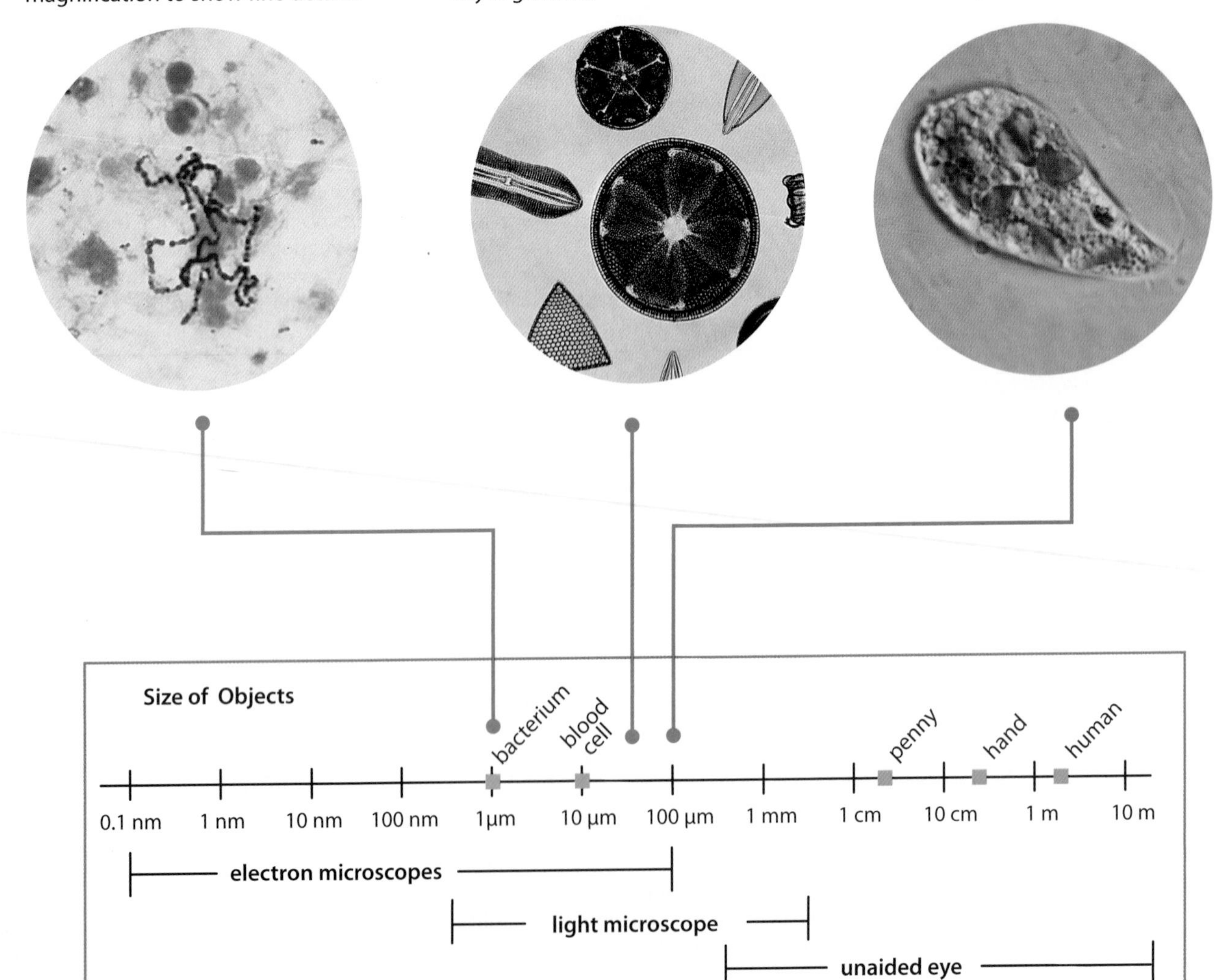

Light Microscope

Beams of light pass through one or more lenses to enlarge the image of a specimen. This light microscope has **two types of lenses**: an ocular lens and an objective lens.

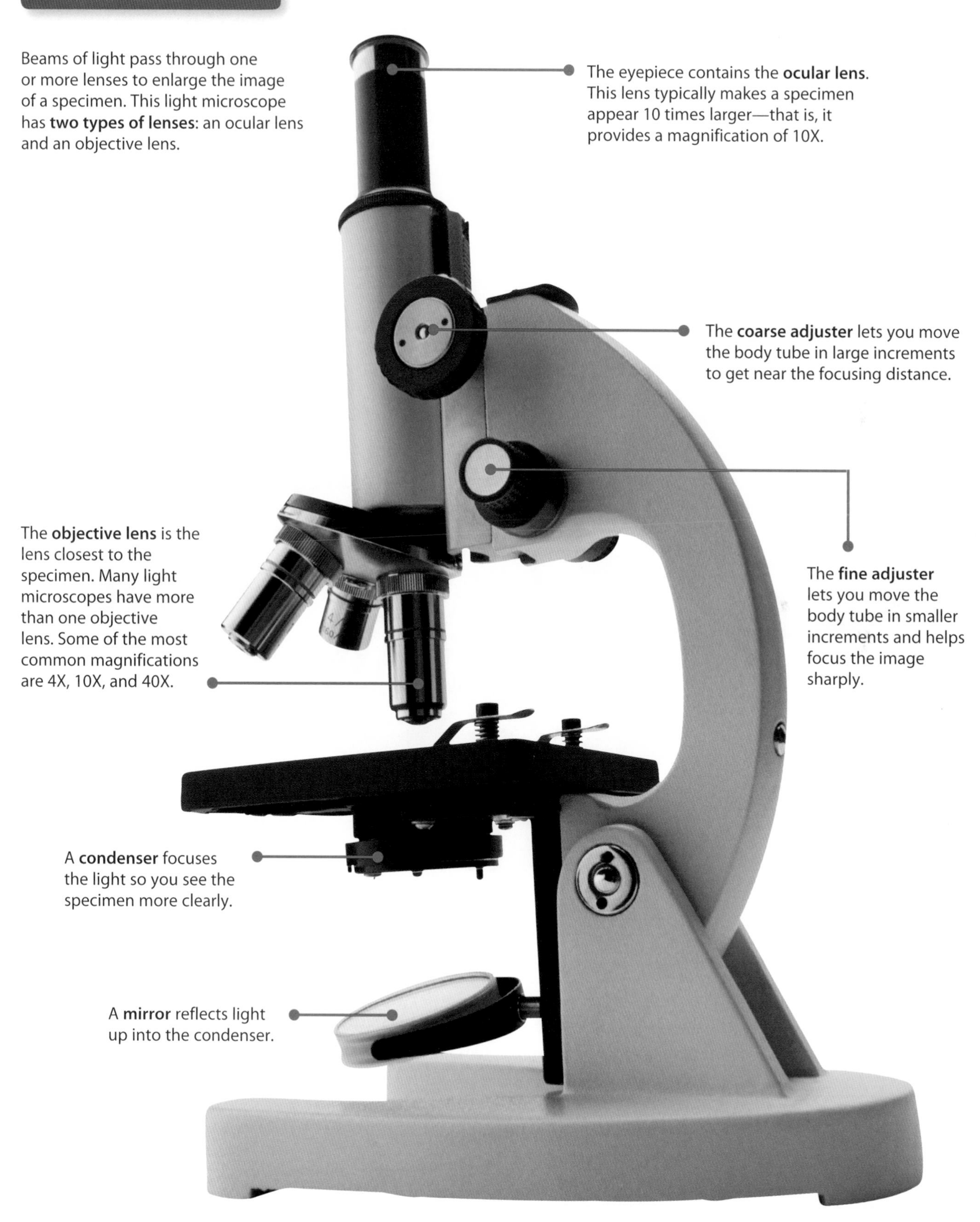

The eyepiece contains the ocular lens. This lens typically makes a specimen appear 10 times larger—that is, it provides a magnification of 10X.
The coarse adjuster lets you move the body tube in large increments to get near the focusing distance.
The fine adjuster lets you move the body tube in smaller increments and helps focus the image sharply.
The objective lens is the lens closest to the specimen. Many light microscopes have more than one objective lens. Some of the most common magnifications are 4X, 10X, and 40X.
A condenser focuses the light so you see the specimen more clearly.
A mirror reflects light up into the condenser.

Instead of passing light through lenses as in a light microscope, an **electron microscope** sends a beam of electrons through the specimen itself. The wave-length of the electron beam is shorter than wavelengths of light. Shorter wavelengths allow for the projection of finer details.

Even with the strongest objective lenses, a light microscope can magnify a specimen only about 1,000 times.

An electron microscope can magnify a specimen hundreds or thousands of times. Transmission electron microscopes (TEMs) and scanning electron microscopes (SEMs) are the most common kinds of these powerful microscopes.

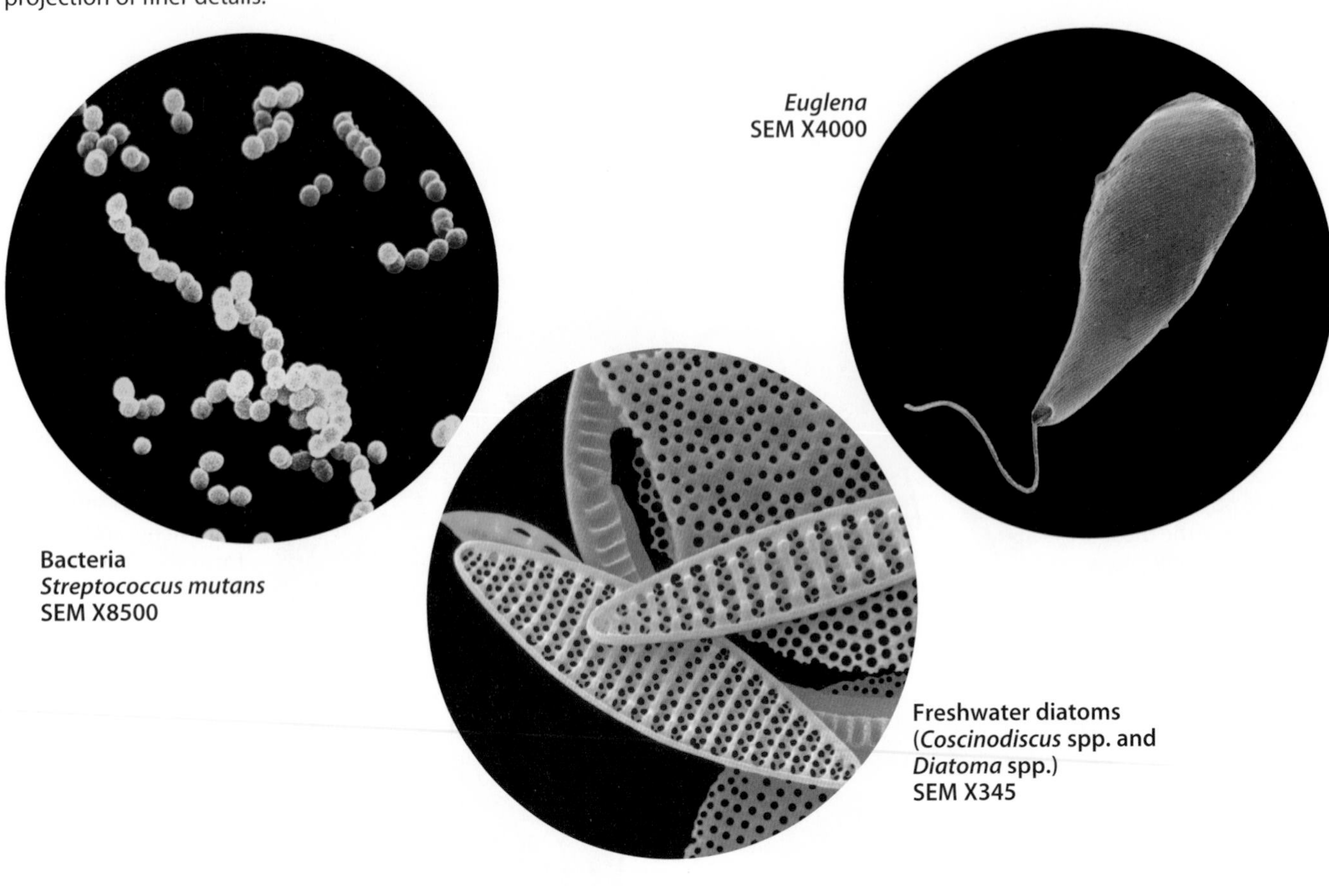

Euglena
SEM X4000

Bacteria
Streptococcus mutans
SEM X8500

Freshwater diatoms
(*Coscinodiscus* spp. and
***Diatoma* spp.)**
SEM X345

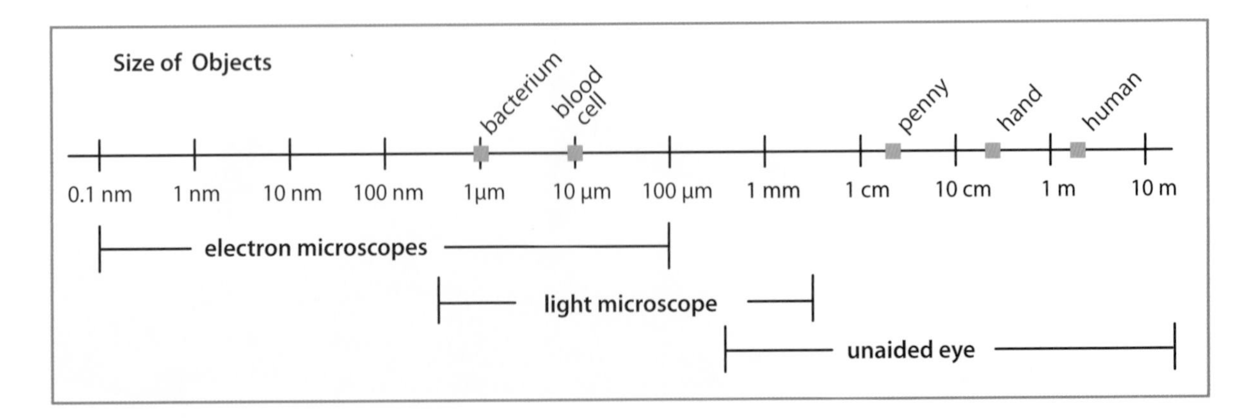

Transmission Electron Microscope

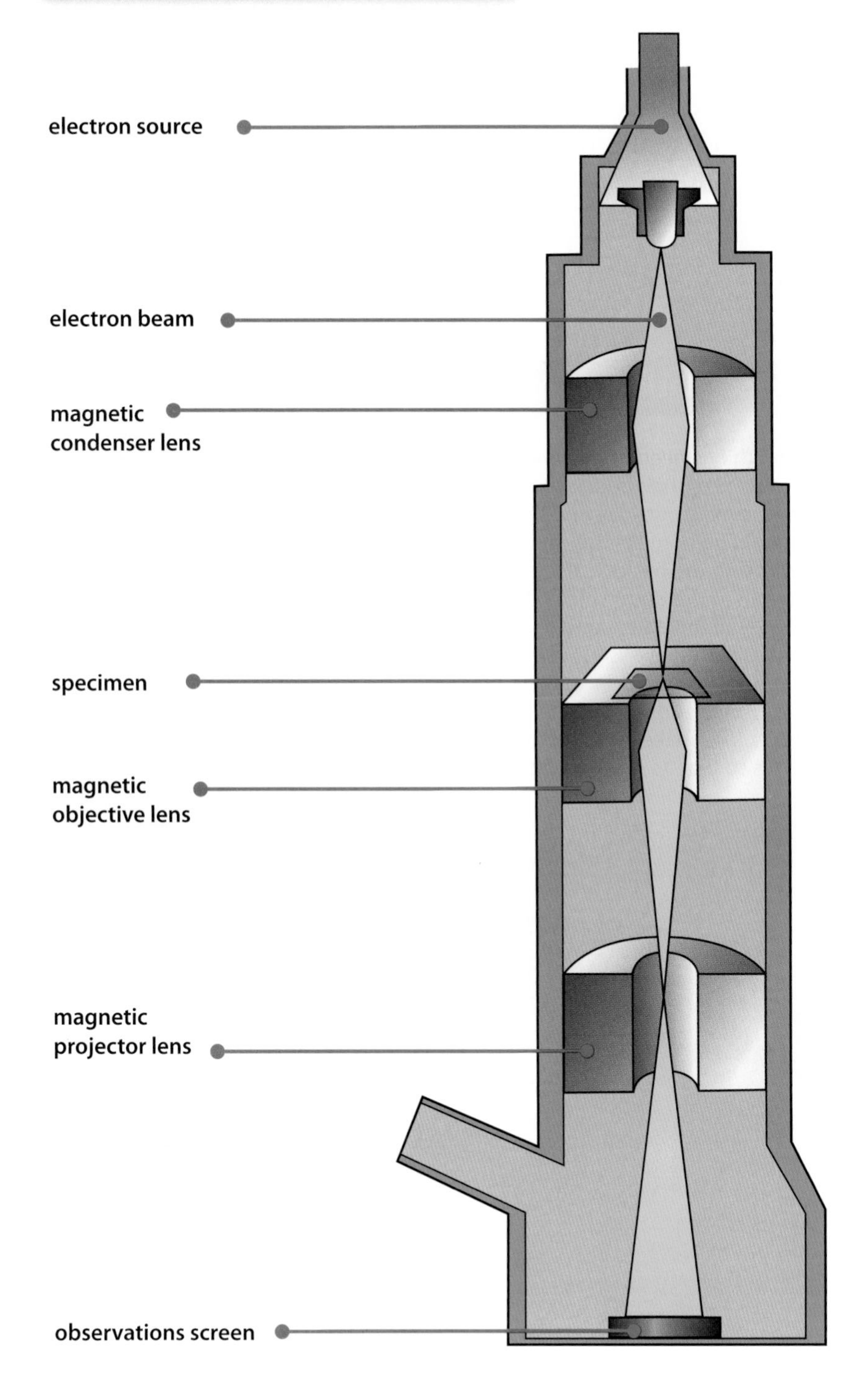

A TEM can magnify an image as much as 2 million times. An SEM can magnify an image as much as 50,000 times. While light microscopes can produce color images, images from electron microscopes are black and white. The images on these pages have been artificially colored to clarify details.

Since an electron beam cannot pass through thick specimens or samples, a **TEM** is suitable only for viewing very thin objects. A scientist prepares thin sections in the laboratory.

An **SEM** provides images of the surface of thicker specimens such as a *Euglena*. An SEM detects electrons emitted from the surface of the sample when the SEM electron beam excites them. A TEM may have greater magnification, but an SEM reveals finer details of the surface of the specimen and provides a good representation of its 3-D structure.

All living things share seven basic characteristics.

They are made of cells. Their cells carry out chemical reactions. They grow and develop. They respond to changes in their environment. They maintain homeostasis. They reproduce. They carry genetic information that can be passed on to offspring.

Homeostasis

Living things need to maintain the internal conditions of their bodies within a narrow range, even if outside conditions change. Maintaining homeostasis involves controlling the balance of water and minerals in the body, responding to changes in the environment, and controlling metabolism. For example, this snake's cells produce waste products as they break down food molecules for energy. The snake must get rid of these wastes so that its cells remain functional.

Heredity

Like every organism, this snake received genetic information from its parents. It can pass the information on to its offspring. This information carries instructions for almost all of the snake's characteristics, including patterns of development, physical appearance, and even many behaviors such as hunting and basking in the sun.

Reproduction

To make more of their kind, living things reproduce. Reproduction may be either asexual or sexual. Snakes reproduce only sexually, requiring genetic material from two parents. After two red boas mate, embryos develop inside the mother's body. The eggs eventually hatch inside the mother's body or immediately after the eggs are laid.

Growth and Development

All living things grow and develop. These processes are controlled by genetic information contained in the cells. Snakes shed their skin as they grow and may change in appearance.

Cellular Organization

All living things are made of cells. Some organisms, such as bacteria, are unicellular. Other organisms, such as the snake, are multicellular. This snake's body is made up of billions of cells.

Metabolism

Metabolism is the sum of all chemical processes required to maintain life. For example, one set of chemical reactions in this snake's body produce venom. For all necessary chemical reactions to take place in the body, such as digesting food and making proteins, an animal's body temperature must be relatively high. Unlike mammals, which maintain a fairly stable body temperature, snakes are ectotherms—that is, they must absorb heat from their surroundings to warm their bodies. Snakes often bask in the sun to raise their body temperatures and retreat to shady areas to cool down.

Response

All living things respond to changes in their environment. Responses may include behaviors directed at other organisms, such as the threat posture described above. Living things also respond to changes in the nonliving environment, such as changes in temperature.

Like all matter, the matter of living things is made up of elements.

Scientists have identified 92 elements that occur in nature. Of these, about 25 are essential to life. The elements highlighted in red are some of the most important for living things. Three of these elements—carbon, oxygen, and hydrogen—account for most living matter.

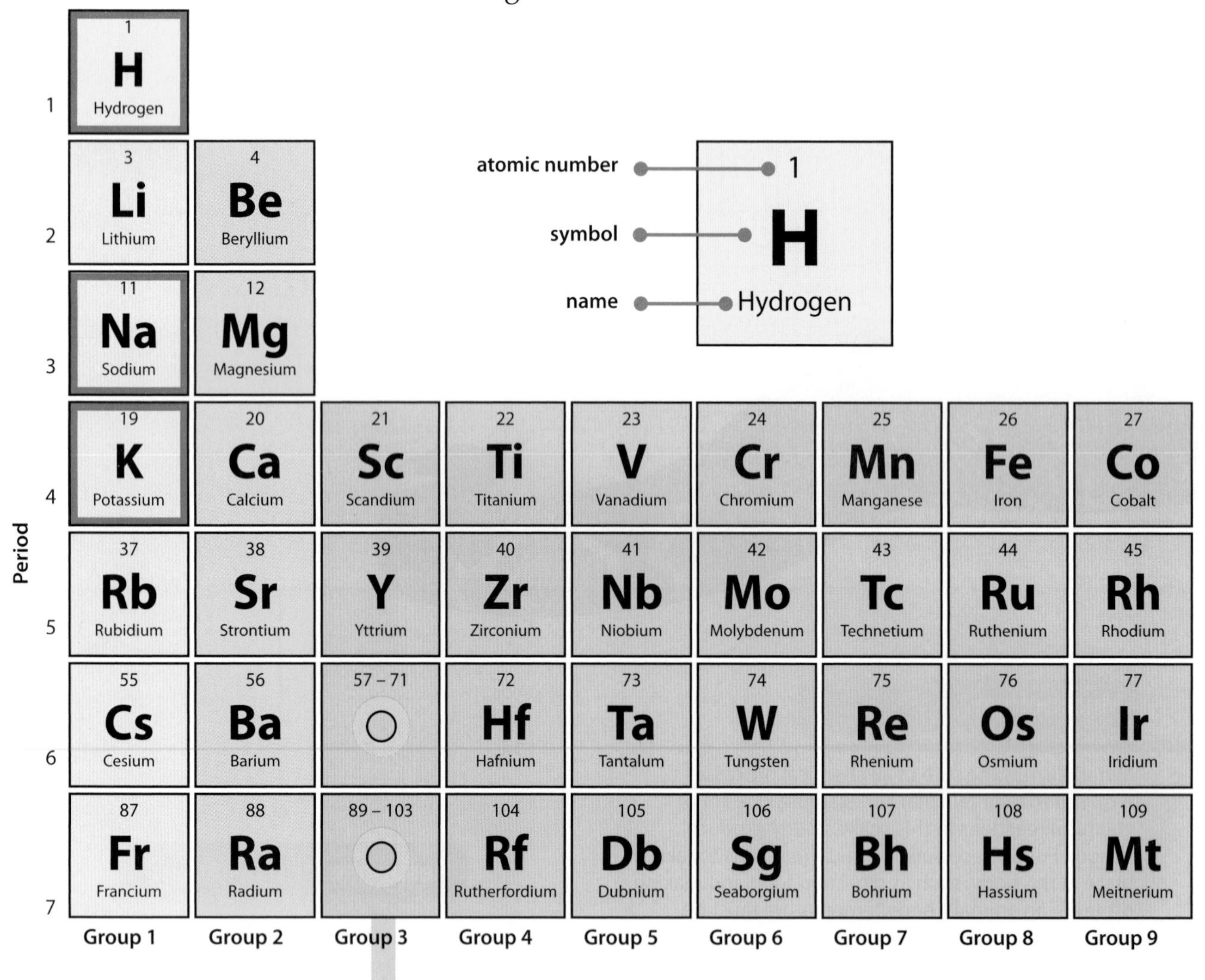

Hydrogen

Semiconductors (also known as metalloids)

Metals

- Alkali metals
- Alkaline-earth metals
- Transition metals
- Other metals

Nonmetals

- Halogens
- Noble gases
- Other nonmetals

Group 10	Group 11	Group 12	Group 13	Group 14	Group 15	Group 16	Group 17	Group 18
								2 **He** Helium
			5 **B** Boron	6 **C** Carbon	7 **N** Nitrogen	8 **O** Oxygen	9 **F** Fluorine	10 **Ne** Neon
			13 **Al** Aluminum	14 **Si** Silicon	15 **P** Phosphorus	16 **S** Sulfur	17 **Cl** Chlorine	18 **Ar** Argon
28 **Ni** Nickel	29 **Cu** Copper	30 **Zn** Zinc	31 **Ga** Gallium	32 **Ge** Germanium	33 **As** Arsenic	34 **Se** Selenium	35 **Br** Bromine	36 **Kr** Krypton
46 **Pd** Palladium	47 **Ag** Silver	48 **Cd** Cadmium	49 **In** Indium	50 **Sn** Tin	51 **Sb** Antimony	52 **Te** Tellurium	53 **I** Iodine	54 **Xe** Xenon
78 **Pt** Platinum	79 **Au** Gold	80 **Hg** Mercury	81 **Tl** Thallium	82 **Pb** Lead	83 **Bi** Bismuth	84 **Po** Polonium	85 **At** Astatine	86 **Rn** Radon
110 **Ds** Darmstadtium								

63 **Eu** Europium	64 **Gd** Gadolinium	65 **Tb** Terbium	66 **Dy** Dysprosium	67 **Ho** Holmium	68 **Er** Erbium	69 **Tm** Thulium	70 **Yb** Ytterbium	71 **Lu** Lutetium
95 **Am** Americium	96 **Cm** Curium	97 **Bk** Berkelium	98 **Cf** Californium	99 **Es** Einsteinium	100 **Fm** Fermium	101 **Md** Mendelevium	102 **No** Nobelium	103 **Lr** Lawrencium

Atoms are the basic building blocks of all matter.

Atoms are made up of three types of smaller particles: protons, neutrons, and electrons. Protons and neutrons form the nucleus of an atom. Electrons move around the nucleus in electron clouds, or *orbitals*. The images on these pages show the atomic structures of some of the most important atoms in living things.

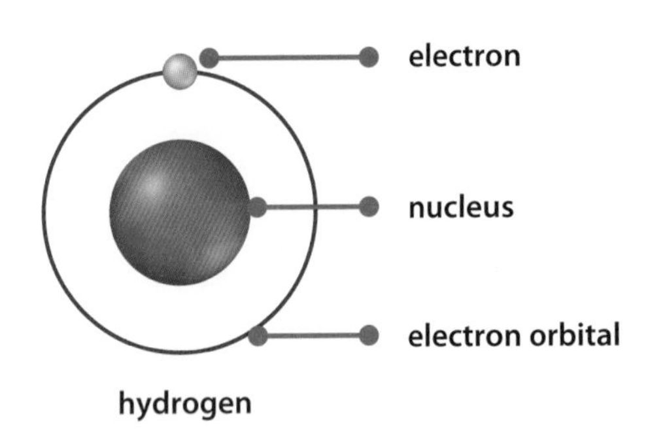

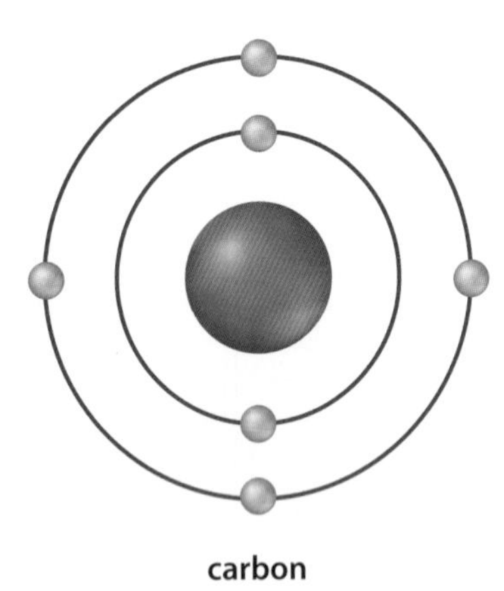

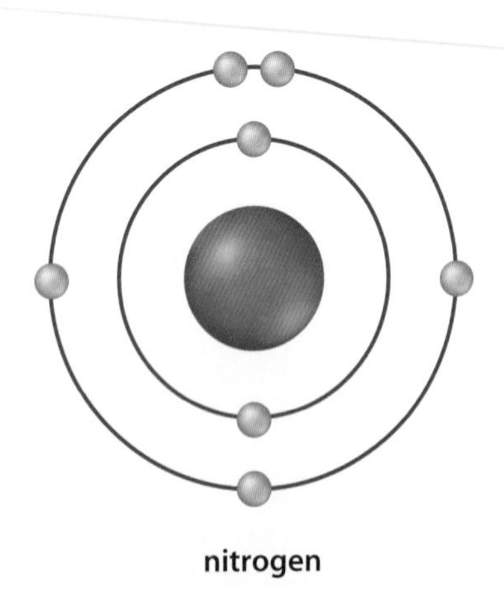

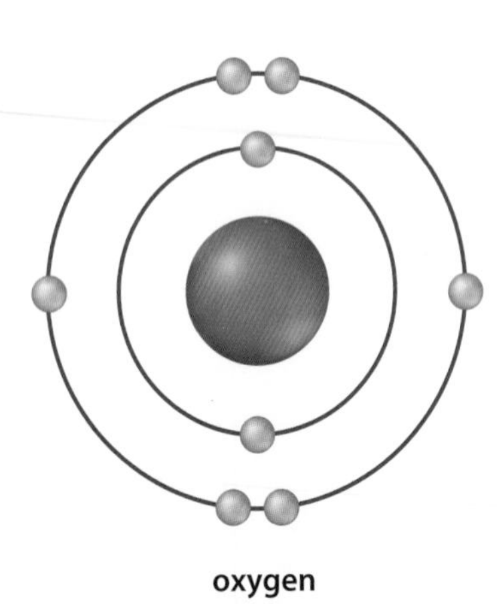

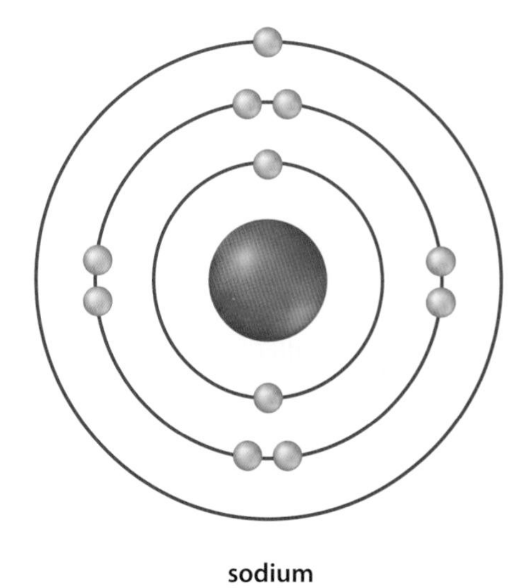
sodium

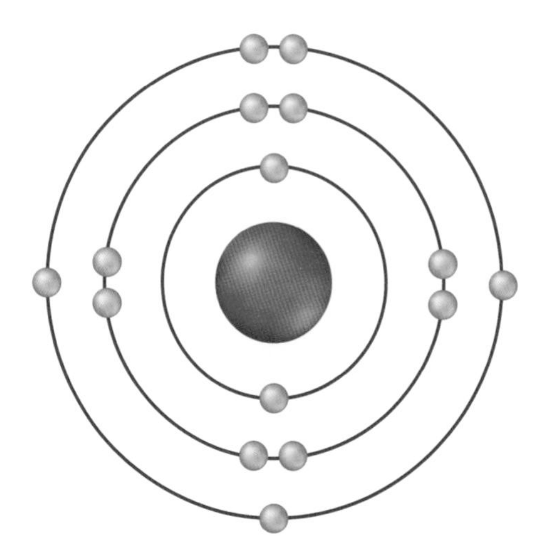
phosphorus

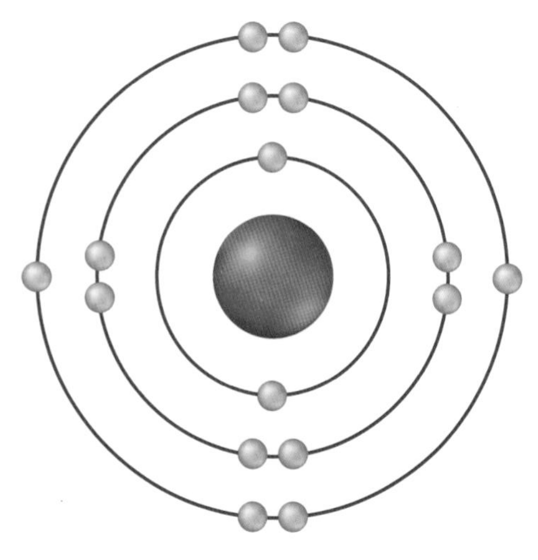
sulfur

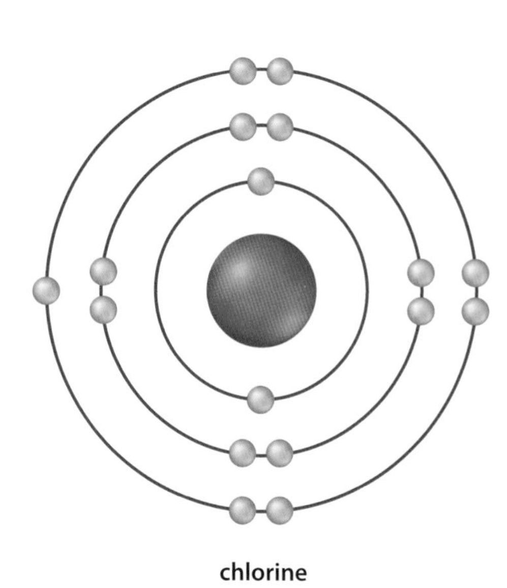
chlorine

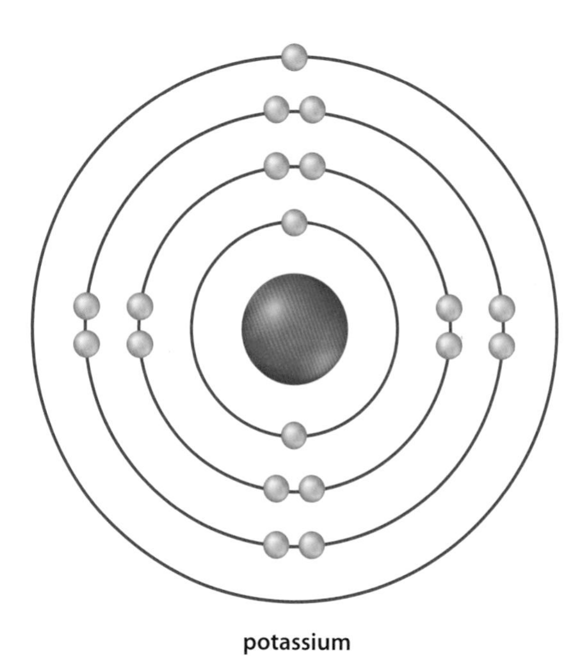
potassium

Chemical bonds form when the outer electrons of atoms or molecules interact.

The types of bonds between atoms or molecules of a substance affect the properties of the substance. There are three main types of chemical bonds: ionic, covalent, and hydrogen. Each type of bond forms because of a different kind of interaction between the outer electrons, which are called *valence electrons*.

Ionic Bond

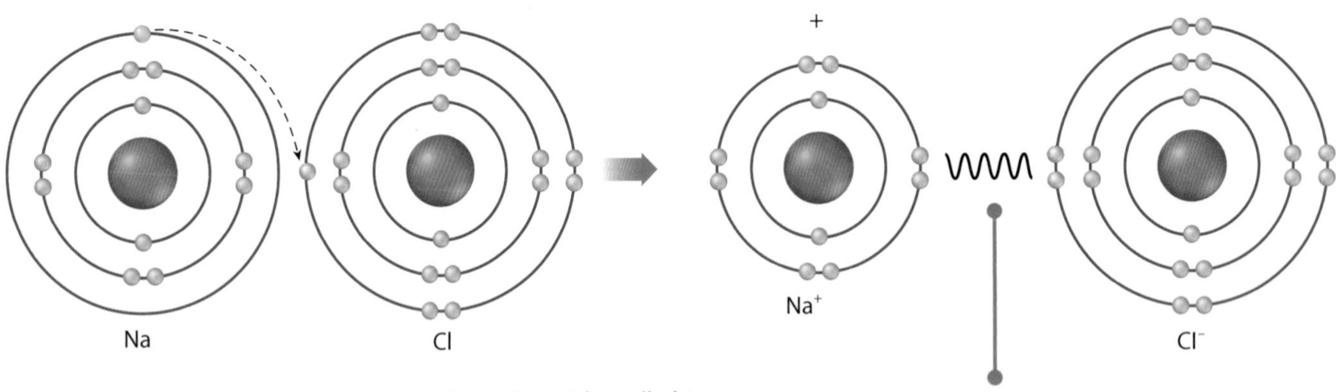

Atoms that gain or lose electrons become charged particles called *ions*. Oppositely charged ions attract each other to form **ionic bonds.** The electrons lost by one atom are gained by another. For example, 1 atom of sodium (Na) can easily lose 1 electron to become the positively charged ion Na^+. Chlorine (Cl) can gain that electron and become the negatively charged chloride ion (Cl^-). The sodium and chloride ions attract each other and form an ionic bond. The resulting compound, sodium chloride (NaCl), is the familiar substance table salt.

Covalent Bond

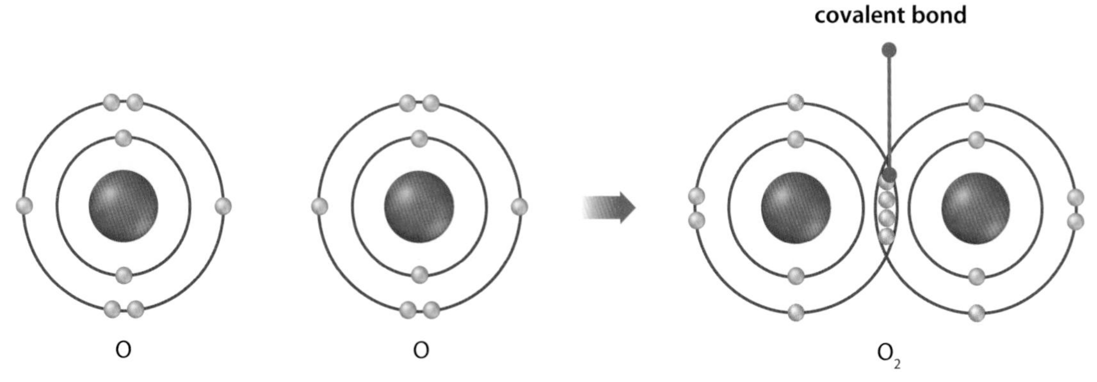

Covalent bonds are the strongest kind of chemical bond. They form when 2 atoms share valence electrons. For example, 2 atoms of oxygen (O) share valence electrons to form the bond in an oxygen molecule. The shared electrons orbit both oxygen atoms in the molecule. Oxygen gas (O_2) is a major component of the air that we breathe.

Hydrogen Bond

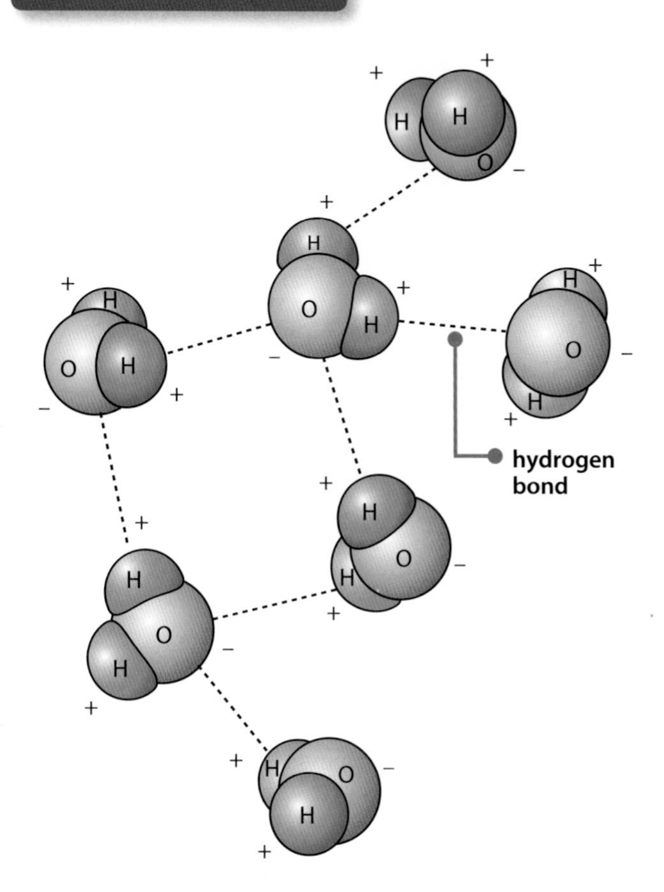

Molecules of water are made of 2 atoms of hydrogen (H) covalently bound to 1 atom of oxygen (O). The oxygen atom attracts electrons more strongly than the hydrogen atoms, so the oxygen atom has a slight negative charge. Each hydrogen atom has a slight positive charge. The negatively charged oxygen in one water molecule attracts the positively charged hydrogen atoms in another water molecule. This attraction is known as a **hydrogen bond.** Hydrogen bonds can form between hydrogen atoms and atoms of oxygen, nitrogen, or fluorine on the same molecule or a different molecule. Hydrogen bonds play a major role in many of the molecules important to life, including water, DNA, and most proteins.

Water makes up about 70 percent of a living human cell. Most of the rest of the material in a cell belongs in one of four main groups of molecules: carbohydrates, lipids, proteins, or nucleic acids.

Five elements—carbon, hydrogen, nitrogen, oxygen, and phosphorus—combine in a variety of ways to make up most of the matter of living cells.

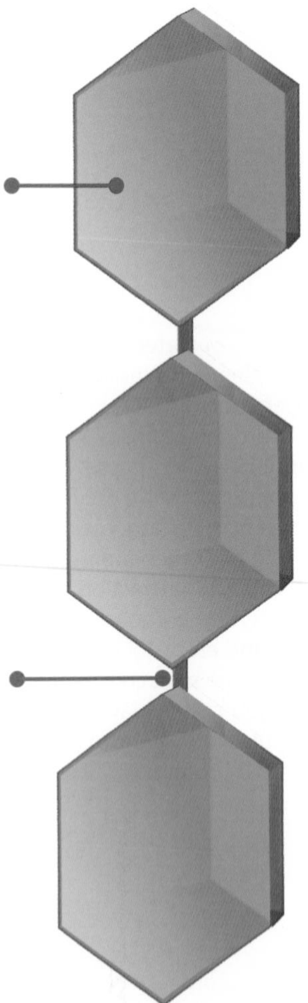

Carbohydrates are the main energy source for most cells. Plant cells also use carbohydrates for structural support. The simplest carbohydrates are ring-shaped structures called *monosaccharides*.

Long carbohydrate molecules form when **monosaccharides** bond with each other. Some carbohydrates, such as maltose, are made of short chains of sugar molecules. Others, such as cellulose, may contain hundreds or thousands of simple sugars.

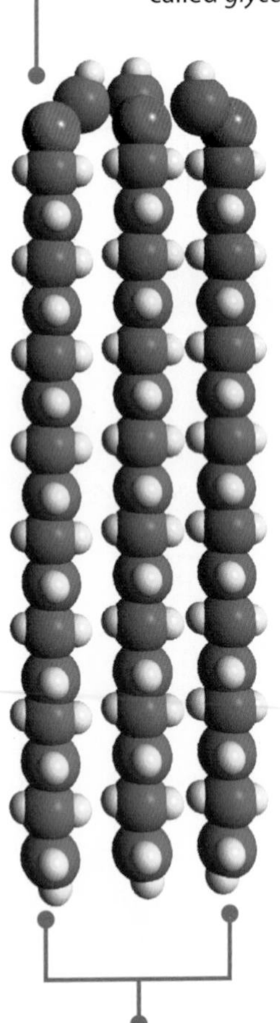

In a **lipid**, fatty acid chains are bonded to a shorter backbone. This backbone is a molecule called *glycerol*.

Most lipids are composed of **fatty acids**—or chains of carbon atoms—bound to a shorter molecule. Cells use lipids to store energy, form membranes, and produce hormones.

Nucleic acids are made of units called *nucleotides*. Each nucleotide contains a sugar, a phosphate group, and another group called a *nitrogenous base*. The sugar and phosphate groups of the nucleotides form the backbone of a nucleic acid. The nitrogenous bases are attached to the backbone.

Proteins are made up of units called *amino acids*. There are 20 known amino acids. Cells produce thousands of different proteins by combining these amino acids in different ways and proportions.

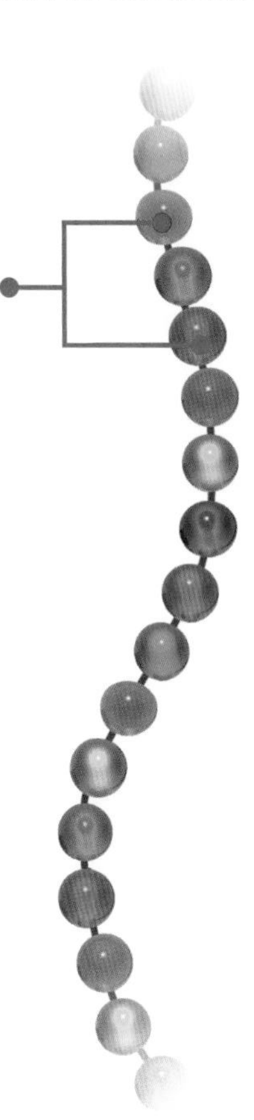

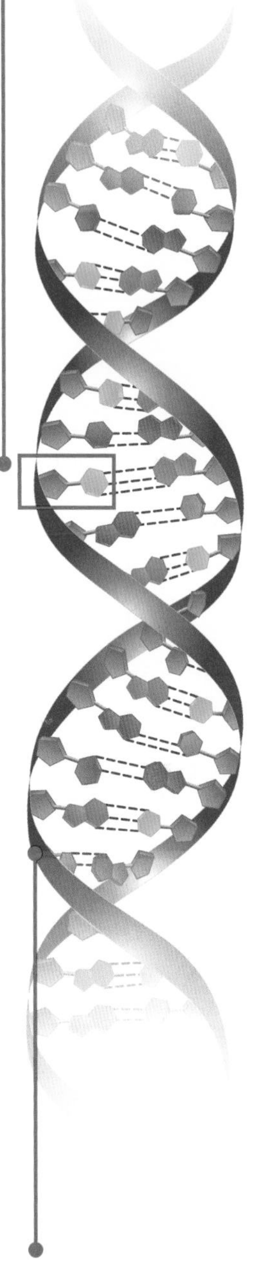

In proteins, amino acids bond with one another to form long chains. These chains can **fold up** to form many differently shaped proteins. The shape of a protein affects its function.

Deoxyribonucleic acid (DNA) and ribonucleic acid (RNA) are the main two kinds of nucleic acids. DNA is composed of two strands of **nucleotides** bound together. All living things and some viruses carry their genetic information in molecules of DNA. RNA contains a single strand of nucleotides. Some viruses carry their genetic information in RNA. The cells of living things use RNA in the production of proteins.

Some of the most important compounds for living things are made up of only three elements: carbon, hydrogen, and oxygen.

Many important biological compounds also contain atoms of phosphorus, nitrogen, and sulfur. Although water is an inorganic compound, it is also critical for life.

IMPORTANT COMPOUNDS

COMPOUND	BASIC SUBUNIT	CATEGORIES	FUNCTIONS	EXAMPLES
Proteins	Amino acids	Polypeptides	Control chemical reactions Support parts of the body Make up muscles Carry oxygen in the blood Regulate blood sugar	Enzymes Collagen Actin and myosin Hemoglobin Insulin
Carbohydrates	Simple sugars	Monosaccharides Polysaccharides	Provide quick energy Store energy Provide structure	Glucose Glycogen (in animals) and starch (in plants) Cellulose (plant cell walls)
Lipids	Fatty acids	Phospholipids Triglycerides Waxes	Regulate passage of materials into and out of cells Store energy Protect tissues and organs	Plasma membranes Fats and oils Cuticle on plants Ear wax
Nucleic acids	Nucleotides	Polymers of nucleotides Nucleotides	Carry genetic material Synthesize proteins Carry water through a cell	DNA RNA ATP
Water	None	None	Transports materials throughout an organism	Liquid water Ice

The cell walls of plant cells are made of a polysaccharide called *cellulose*. This material gives the cell strength and structure. The strings in **celery stalks** are made of cells with extra-thick cell walls.

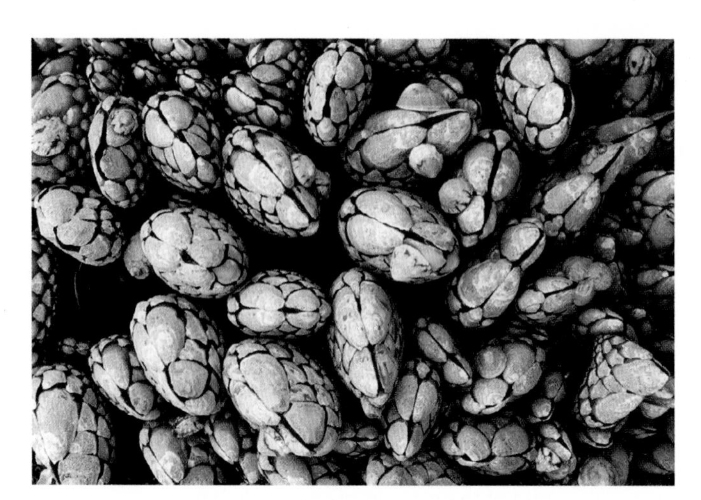

Gooseneck barnacles survive in rough, wave-swept tidal zones by clinging to rocks by a powerful glue. This adhesive, which is made of proteins secreted by a special gland, allows the animals to stay securely in place as waves crash down on them. The protein glue of the gooseneck barnacle is one of the strongest known adhesives.

All organisms need water to survive. Animals such as this **lion** may have to search many miles during the dry season on an African savanna just to find a watering hole. Organisms that cannot migrate, such as plants, have adaptations that help them store water and prevent water loss during dry conditions.

This **baby harp seal** has a thick layer of fat called *blubber* to keep it warm. Like all mammals, the harp seal feeds on its mother's milk. The milk is high in fat, and it helps the baby seal build up a layer of blubber. Fats are also a good source of energy for the growing pup.

Sugarcane is one of the main sources of commercial sugar and grows best in tropical or subtropical environments such as the Caribbean, Central and South America, and parts of Asia. These plants, in the genus *Saccharum*, are members of the grass family.

Monosaccharides are the simplest carbohydrates. When two monosaccharides bond, they form disaccharides.

Monosaccharides and disaccharides are the most common sources of energy used by organisms. Carbohydrates are one of the three types of macronutrients essential to organisms.

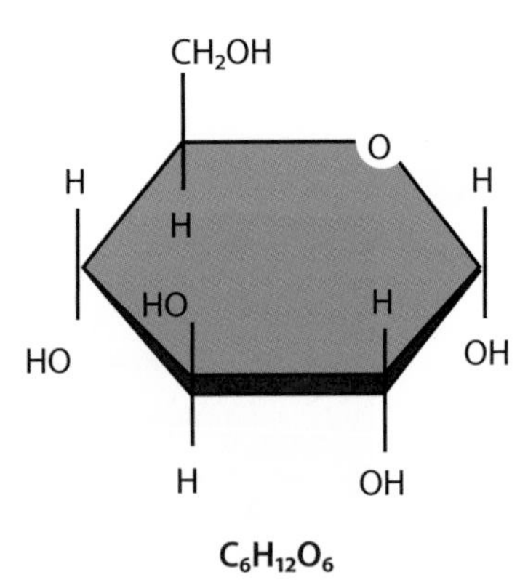

$C_6H_{12}O_6$

Glucose is a common monosaccharide, one of the most important to living things. Cells use glucose for energy and metabolic processes that are essential to life.

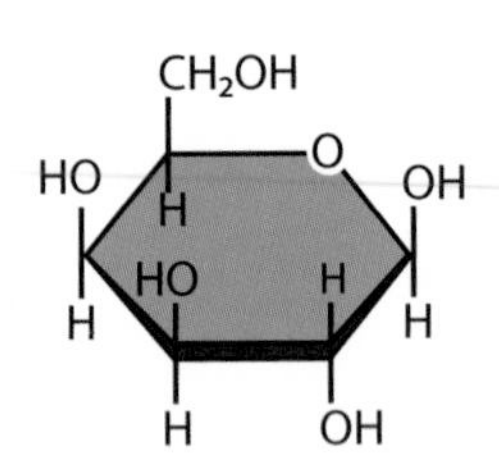

Organisms use **galactose**, a monosaccharide found in milk and other foods, in metabolic processes and the maintenance of tissues.

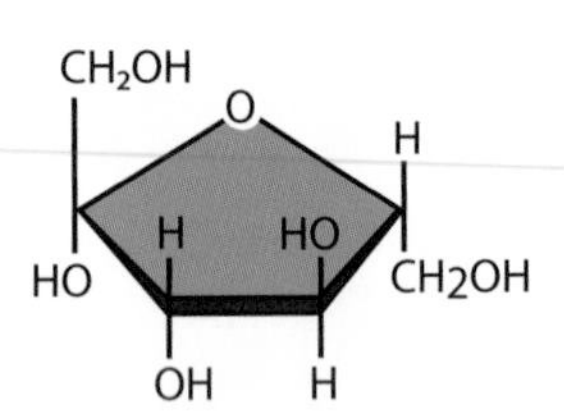

An organism's liver converts **fructose**, a monosaccharide found in fruits, into glucose.

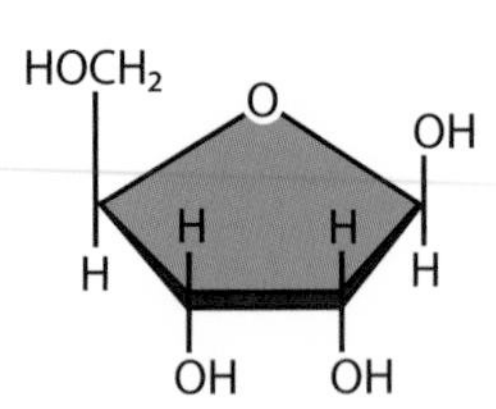

Ribose is a monosaccharide that functions as the sugar component of RNA. It is also a component of adenosine triphosphate (ATP), the molecule that provides the energy to drive chemical reactions within a cell.

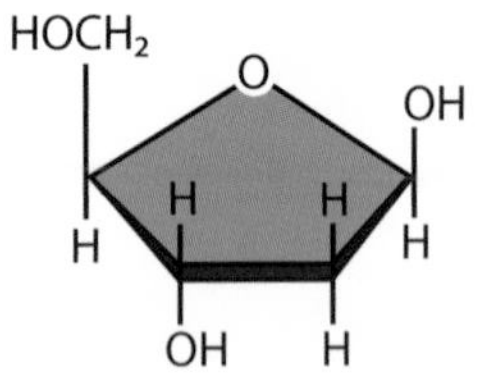

The monosaccharide **deoxyribose** functions as the sugar component of DNA, the molecule that passes on the information for the structure of a cell's proteins.

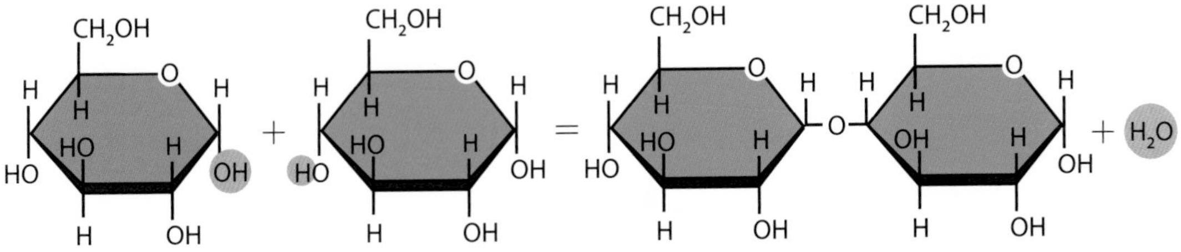

CH$_2$OH O H H H HO H HO H OH OH + HO CH$_2$OH O H H H HO H OH H OH = CH$_2$OH O H H H HO H HO H OH O CH$_2$OH O H H H OH H OH H OH + H_2O

glucose

glucose

Maltose, a disaccharide consisting of two glucose molecules, is one of the main products that results when saliva breaks down glycogen and starch.

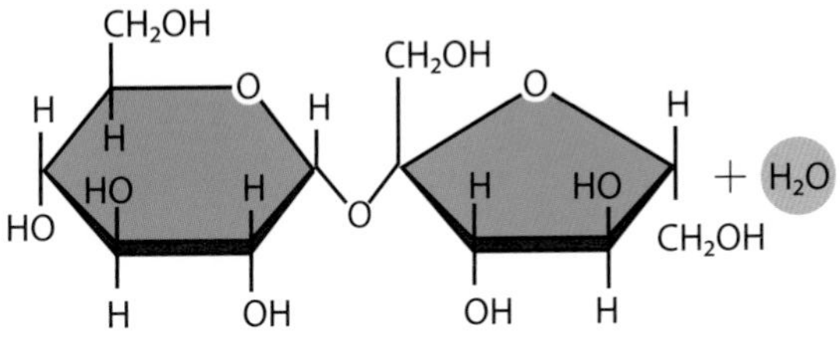

CH$_2$OH O H H H HO H HO H OH O CH$_2$OH O H H HO CH$_2$OH OH H + H_2O

Sucrose is a disaccharide commonly produced by plants.

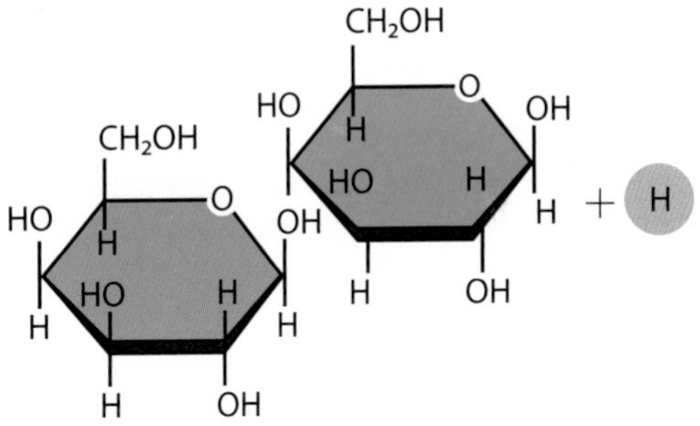

CH$_2$OH O HO OH H HO H H + H OH H CH$_2$OH O HO H HO H H OH H H OH

Lactose is a disaccharide that consists of glucose and galactose. The only natural source of lactose is milk.

Polysaccharides are complex carbohydrates that are vital for energy storage and for cellular structure.

A polysaccharide is a long chain of monosaccharides bound together in a specific way. Three examples of polysaccharides that are important for living things are starch, glycogen, and cellulose.

Starch

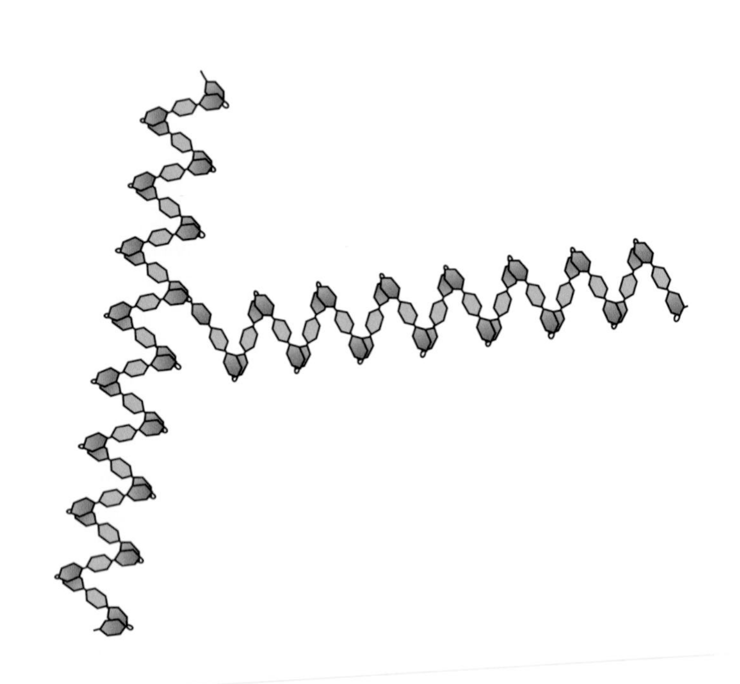

Plants, such as this potato, store energy in the polysaccharide **starch**. Starch is made up of a long chain of glucose molecules. Some kinds of starch have glucose chains that branch into other chains. Other kinds of starch consist of single, long chains of glucose molecules.

Glycogen

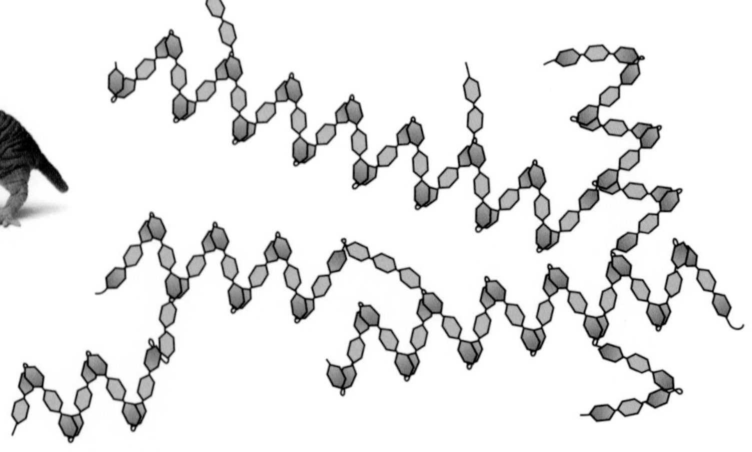

Animals, such as this naked mole rat, store energy in the polysaccharide **glycogen**. Glycogen is a long chain of glucose molecules with many branches. In humans and other vertebrates, glycogen is produced by the liver.

Cellulose

Ancient Egyptians used **papyrus** to make one of the first forms of paper. Although papyrus is generally no longer used in papermaking, the word *paper* is a reminder of the plant's historical significance.

Plants use the polysaccharide **cellulose** for structural support. Cellulose consists of long, unbranched chains of glucose molecules held together by hydrogen bonds. The bonding in cellulose makes it stiff and difficult to break down; therefore, it can provide support for tall plants such as papyrus.

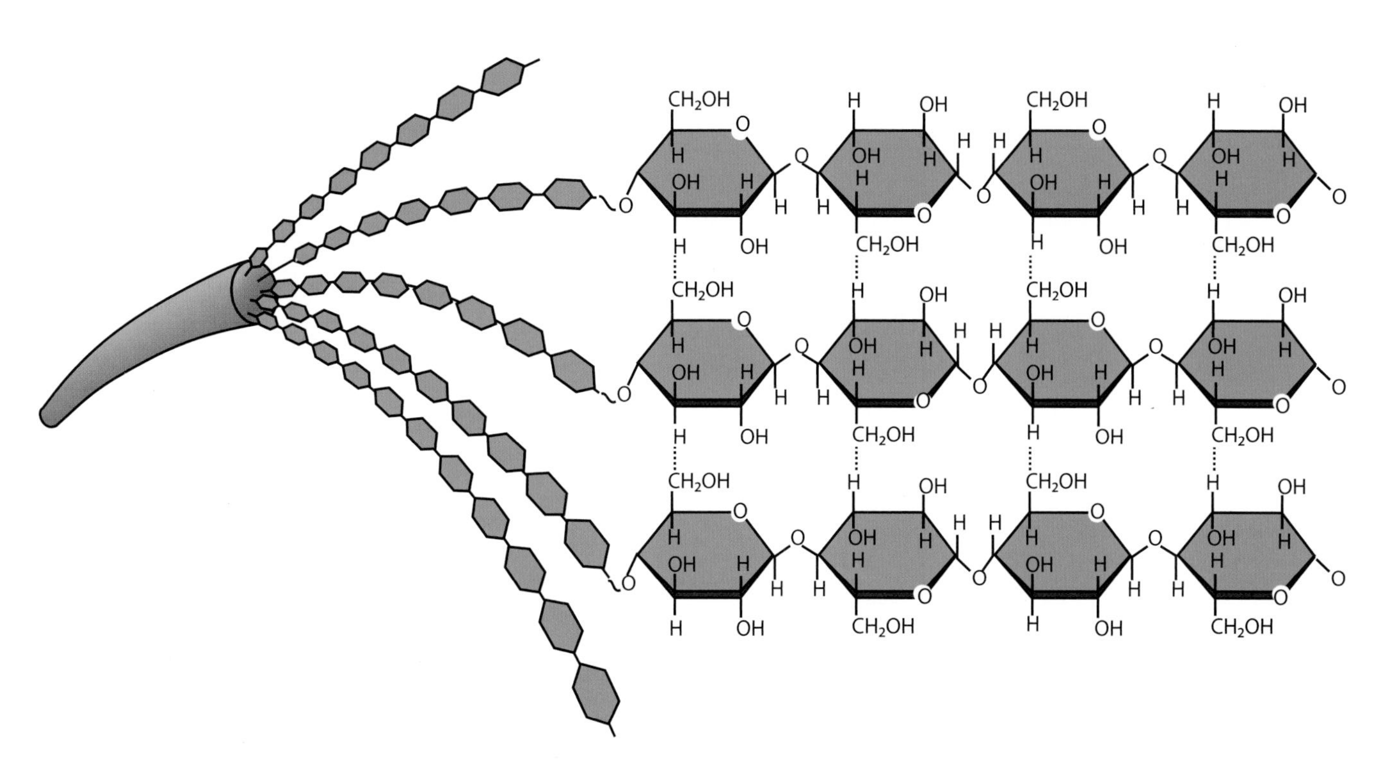

Living things need proteins for almost all of their structures and activities.

Proteins can provide structure and support for the body, speed up chemical reactions, and transport materials throughout the body. Proteins are made up of amino acids strung one after another in a long chain. Cells build thousands of unique proteins using just 20 different amino acids. Proteins make up much of the human body, from muscles to hair.

$$H-N(H)-C(H)(R)-C(=O)-OH$$

All **amino acids** contain a central carbon atom, a hydrogen atom, an amino group, a carboxylic acid group, and an R-group. *R* stands for any one of 20 different additions to the central carbon atom. What sets amino acids apart from each other are the structures of their R-groups.

AMINO ACIDS AND THEIR R-GROUPS

AMINO ACID	R-GROUP	AMINO ACID	R-GROUP	AMINO ACID	R-GROUP
Glycine	H	Tryptophan	H C, CH_2, HC, C, C, CH, HC, C, N H, C H	Serine	H_2C, OH
Alanine	CH_3	Phenylalanine	H C, CH_2, C, C, HC, CH, C H	Aspartic acid	O, CH_2, C, OH
Proline*	H, N, H_2C, C – C, O, OH, H_2C – CH_2	Tyrosine	H C, CH_2, HC, C, C, C, HO, C H	Glutamic acid	CH_2, H_2C, C, HO, O
Valine	CH, H_3C, CH_3	Threonine	CH, HO, CH_3	Lysine	H_2N, $C H_2$, CH_2, $C H_2$, $C H_2$
Isoleucine	H_3C, CH, C H_2, CH_3	Cysteine	H_2C, SH	Arginine	CH_2, H_2C, HN, C – N H, CH_2, H_2N
Leucine	H_3C, CH_2, CH, CH_3	Asparagine	O, CH_2, C, NH_2	Histidine	H C, N, C – CH_2, HC – N
Methionine	CH_2, H_2C, S, H_3C	Glutamine	CH_2, H_2C, H_2N, C, O		

*Because the R-group binds to the NH_2 as well as to the stem, the entire amino acid is shown instead of just the R-group.

Peptide Bond

When two amino acids bond they form a **peptide**. The bond is called a *peptide bond*. Hundreds or even thousands of amino acids link together to form a polypeptide. Some proteins are only a single polypeptide; others are made of more than one polypeptide.

$$\mathrm{H{-}N(H){-}C(R)(H){-}C({=}O){-}OH} \; + \; \mathrm{H{-}N(H){-}C(R)(H){-}C({=}O){-}OH}$$

$$\downarrow$$

$$\mathrm{H{-}N(H){-}C(R)(H){-}C({=}O){-}N(H){-}C(R)(H){-}C({=}O){-}OH} \; + \; H_2O$$

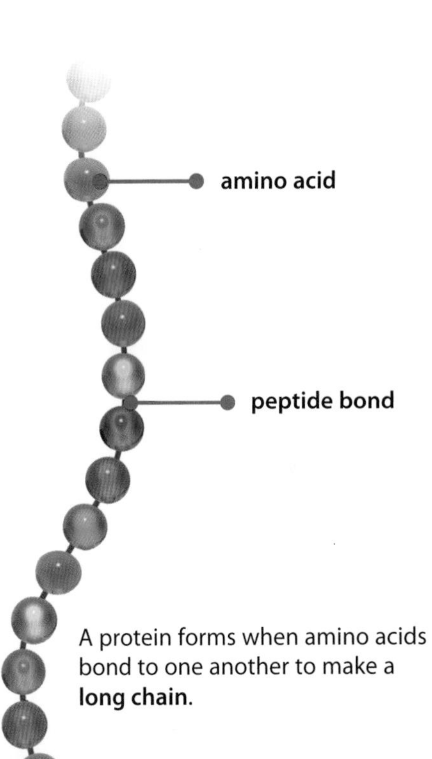

A protein forms when amino acids bond to one another to make a **long chain**.

Keratin is one of the proteins that make up hair. It is also a major component of wool, fingernails and toenails, horns, hooves, and the outer layer of skin.

The structure of a protein allows it to perform its function.

Proteins have three main levels of structure: primary, secondary, and tertiary. Some proteins have a fourth level of structure: quaternary. The venom of a black widow spider (*Lactrodectus mactans*) includes a special kind of protein called *alpha-latrotoxin*. This protein can carry out its particular function in venom because it has a unique structure.

Primary Structure

A protein's **primary structure** is the order or sequence of amino acids in the chain. The primary structure of a protein generally determines its secondary, tertiary, and quaternary structures. The primary structure of alpha-latrotoxin is a chain of 1,041 amino acids.

Secondary Structure

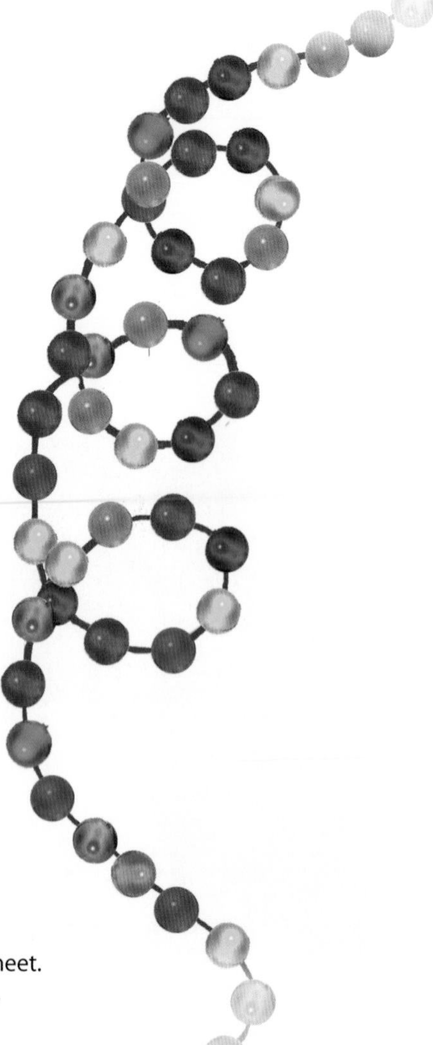

Proteins are coiled or folded into a **secondary structure**. The chain of amino acids folds because of interactions among the atoms that make up the chain's backbone. Two of the most common secondary structures are a helix and a pleated sheet. Alpha-latrotoxin has a helix structure.

Alpha-latrotoxin is the principal component of the black widow spider's venom. This toxin affects the nervous system of the prey, causing the prey's muscles to contract uncontrollably.

Tertiary Structure

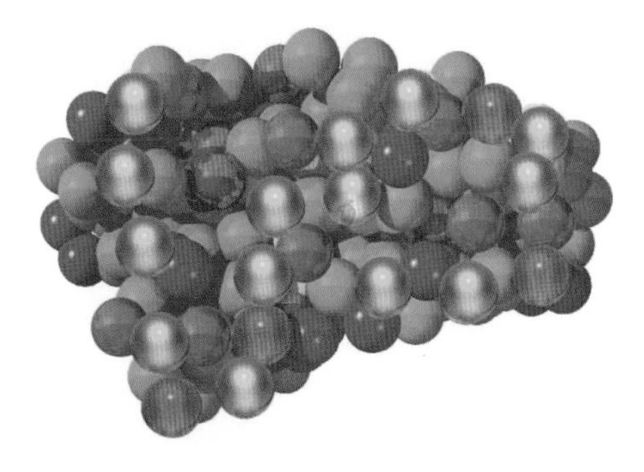

Further folding or coiling of the protein produces the **tertiary structure**. This folding results from interactions among the R-groups of amino acids. The tertiary structure of alpha-latrotoxin is globular or round.

Quaternary Structure

Some proteins are made up of more than one chain of amino acids (polypeptide) functioning as one large molecule. This cluster is known as a **quaternary structure**. Four polypeptides make up alpha-latrotoxin.

Enzymes are proteins that speed up the chemical reactions that make life possible.

An enzyme is a type of catalyst. It speeds up a chemical reaction without being depleted or changed. For example, the enzyme amylase is found in human saliva. This enzyme catalyzes the breakdown of starches, such as those in bread or rice, into simple sugars. Cells can then use these simple sugars for energy. Enzymes control almost all reactions and processes in living things. Without enzymes, many reactions would not proceed or would proceed too slowly, and life would cease to exist.

Without Enzyme

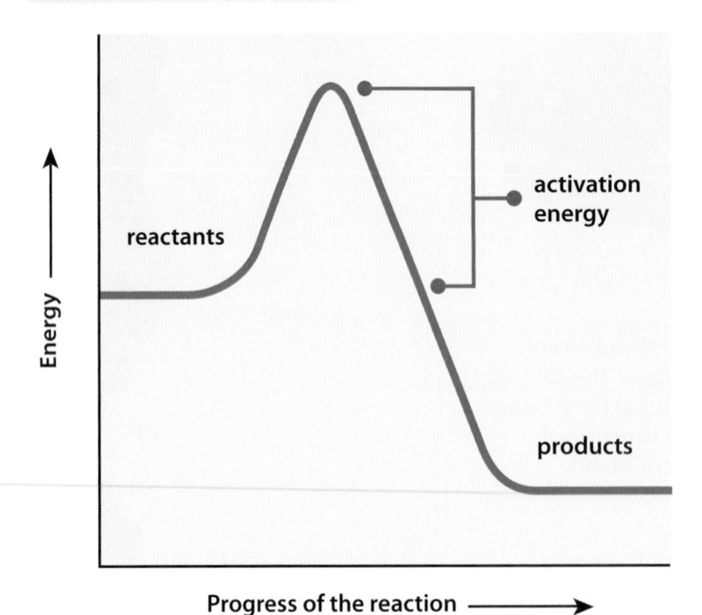

In a spontaneous chemical reaction, the reactants contain more energy than the products. However, most spontaneous reactions must overcome an energy barrier before they can proceed. This energy barrier is called the *activation energy* of the reaction. The higher the activation energy, the less likely it is that the reaction will proceed.

Like humans, **dogs** have enzymes in their saliva that help break down food. These enzymes speed up the reactions that break down food.

With Enzyme

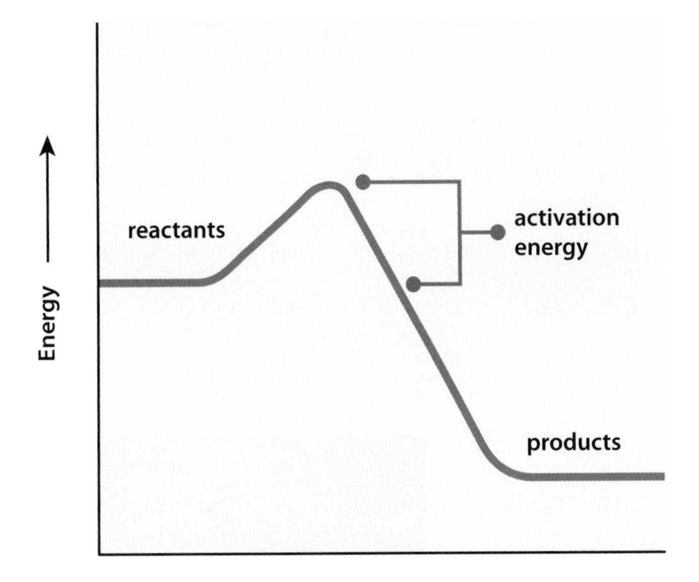

Enzymes, like other catalysts, help reactions happen more easily by decreasing the activation energy. For example, amylase reduces the activation energy of the reaction in which starch is converted to simple sugars. Without amylase, the breakdown of starches into simple sugars has a very high activation energy. Under normal human body conditions, this reaction would take a long time to complete. With amylase, the reaction actually occurs every time a person eats foods with starch.

Lipids, which include fats, oils, waxes, and steroids, are an important class of biological compounds.

Lipids are insoluble in water. They are critical components of membranes in living things. They also play important roles in energy storage and as hormones.

Diagram of a Lipid Molecule

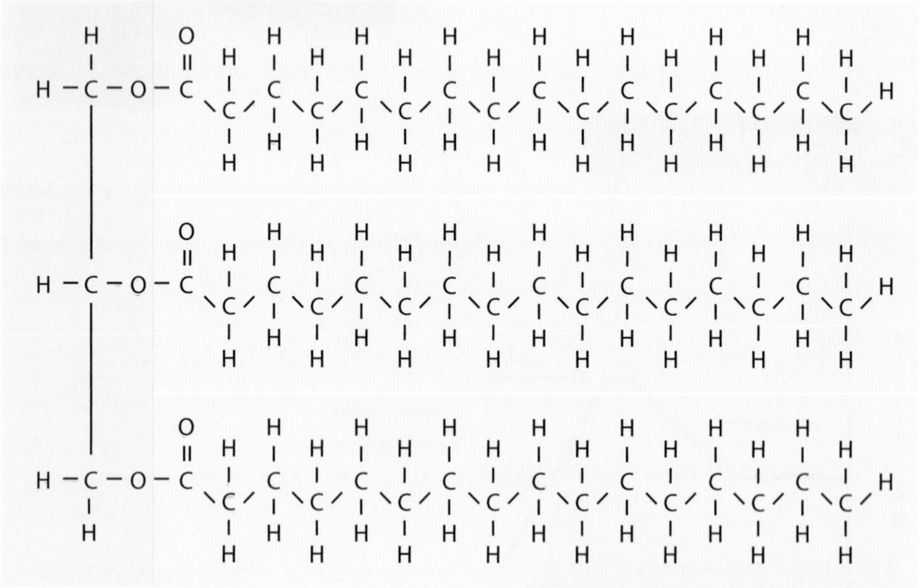

Fats and phospholipids, two major groups of lipids, have two molecular components: glycerol and fatty acids.

Glycerol (in blue) is a three-carbon molecule that forms the backbone of these lipids.

Fatty acids (in tan), the second component of fats and phospholipids, are long chains of hydrocarbons. Like hydrocarbons in general, fatty acids are not soluble in water.

```
    H       O       H       H       H       H       H       H       H
    |       ||  H   |   H   |   H   |   H   |   H   |   H   |   H   |   H
H - C - O - C   |   C   |   C   |   C   |   C   |   C   |   C   |   C   |   H
    |         \ C /  | \ C /  | \ C /  | \ C /  | \ C /  | \ C /  | \ C /  | \ C /
    |           |   H   |   H   |   H   |   H   |   H   |   H   |   H   |
    |           H       H       H       H       H       H       H       H
    |
    |       O       H       H       H       H       H       H       H
    |       ||  H   |   H   |   H   |   H   |   H   |   H   |   H   |   H
H - C - O - C   |   C   |   C   |   C   |   C   |   C   |   C   |   C   |   H
    |         \ C /  | \ C /  | \ C /  | \ C /  | \ C /  | \ C /  | \ C /  | \ C /
    |           |   H   |   H   |   H   |   H   |   H   |   H   |   H   |
    |           H       H       H       H       H       H       H       H
    |
    |       O       H       H       H       H       H       H       H
    |       ||  H   |   H   |   H   |   H   |   H   |   H   |   H   |   H
H - C - O - C   |   C   |   C   |   C   |   C   |   C   |   C   |   C   |   H
    |         \ C /  | \ C /  | \ C /  | \ C /  | \ C /  | \ C /  | \ C /  | \ C /
    H           |   H   |   H   |   H   |   H   |   H   |   H   |   H   |
                H       H       H       H       H       H       H       H
```

Unsaturated fats, which have one or more double bonds between carbon atoms in the fatty acid chains, are called *oils*. **Oils** are liquid at room temperature. Humans use cod oil for medicinal and nutritional purposes. It is a good source of vitamins A and D.

Most **fats** consist of three fatty acid chains attached to a molecule of glycerol. Because of this formation, fats are also known as *triglycerides*. Saturated fats, which have only single bonds between carbon atoms in the fatty acid chains, are solid at room temperature. The blubber of a walrus is a fat used by the animal's body for storing energy and regulating temperature.

Waxes are made up of long chains of fatty acids bonded to long chains of alcohols. These lipids are solid at room temperature. Many plants produce waxes that coat their leaves, protecting the leaves from excessive water loss. Some animals produce waxes to help maintain fur or feathers. Some animal waxes, such as the wax produced by honeybees to make their honeycomb cells, have antibacterial properties.

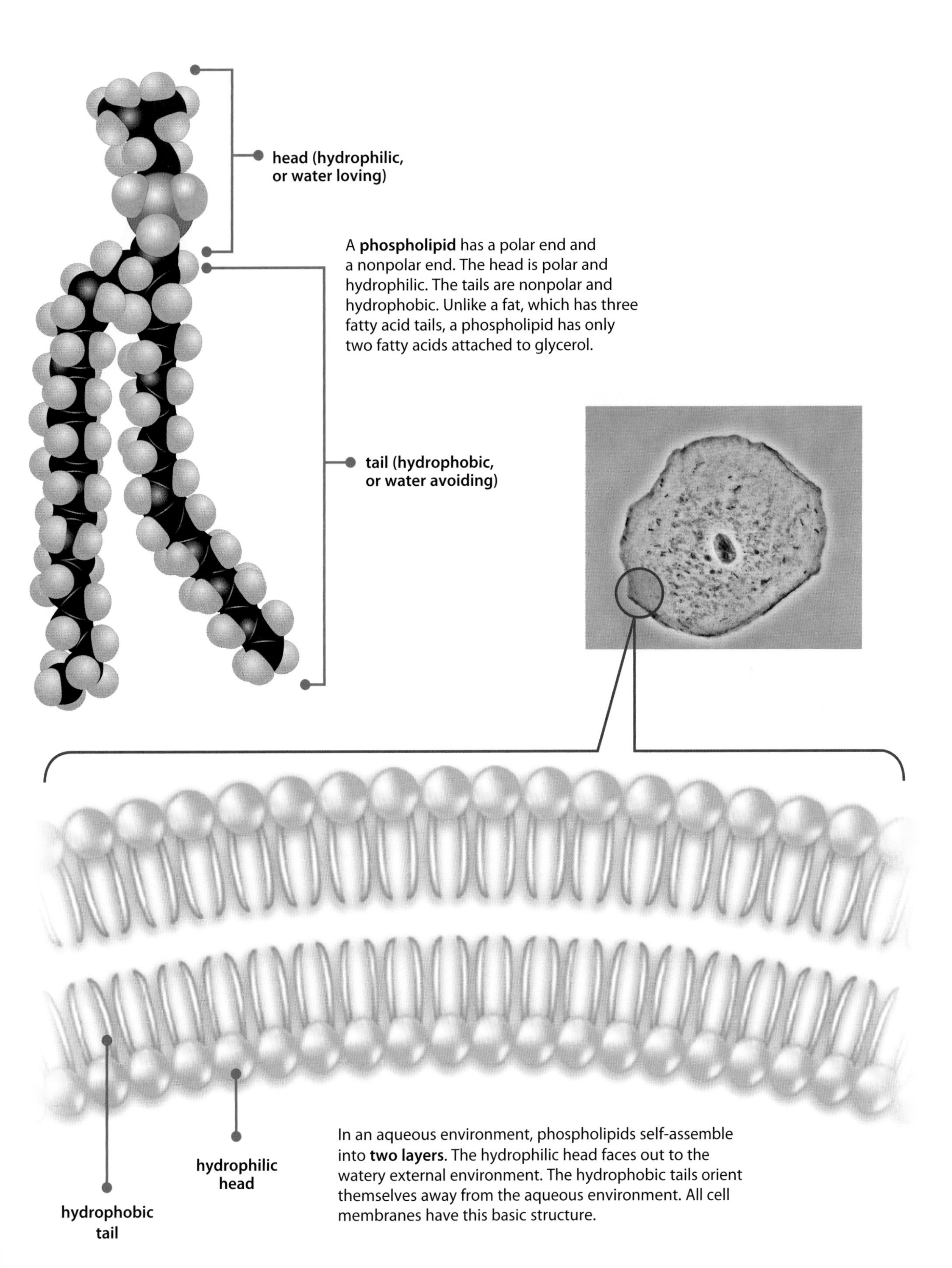

A **phospholipid** has a polar end and a nonpolar end. The head is polar and hydrophilic. The tails are nonpolar and hydrophobic. Unlike a fat, which has three fatty acid tails, a phospholipid has only two fatty acids attached to glycerol.

In an aqueous environment, phospholipids self-assemble into **two layers**. The hydrophilic head faces out to the watery external environment. The hydrophobic tails orient themselves away from the aqueous environment. All cell membranes have this basic structure.

Each cell in the branch and leaves of a **redwood** has exactly the same amount and kind of DNA.

Nucleic acids are large molecules that are responsible for storing and translating genetic information.

There are two kinds of nucleic acids—DNA and RNA. DNA contains an organism's genetic information. RNA uses the instructions stored in DNA to build proteins. Nucleic acids are made up of subunits called *nucleotides*. Each nucleotide consists of a phosphate group, a five-carbon sugar, and a nitrogenous base.

DNA

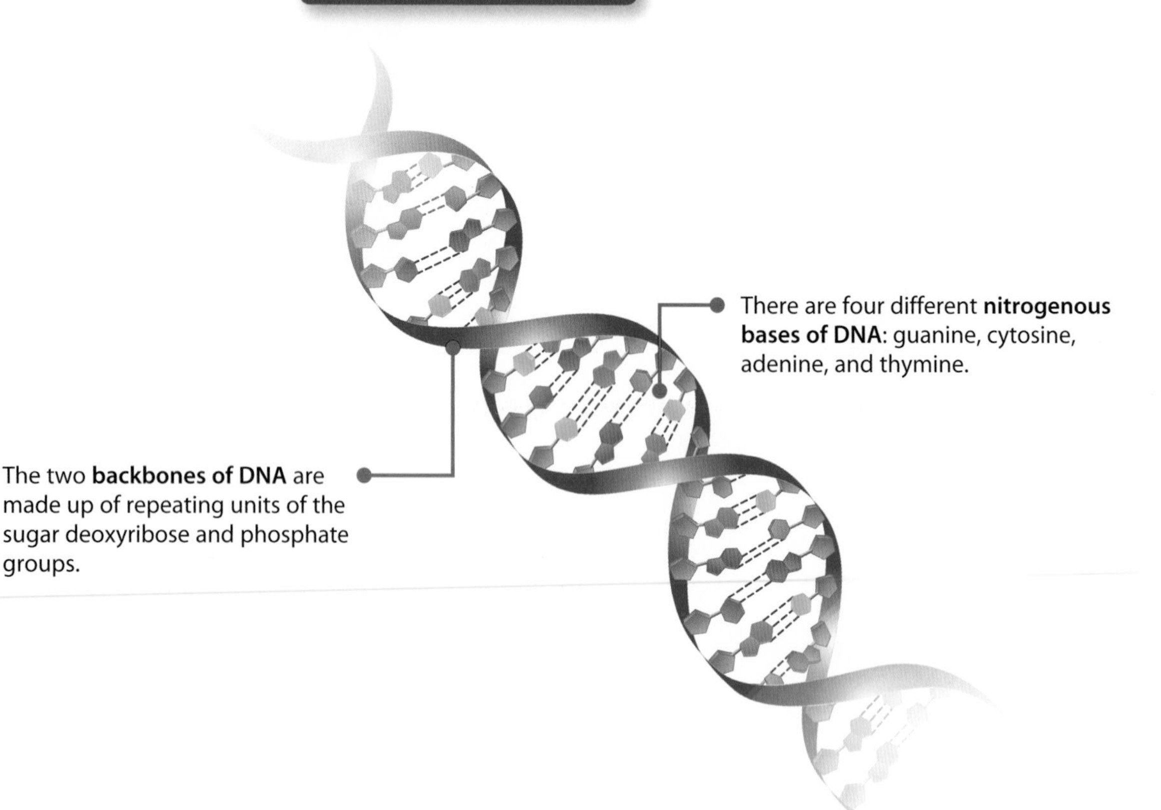
There are four different **nitrogenous bases of DNA**: guanine, cytosine, adenine, and thymine.
The two **backbones of DNA** are made up of repeating units of the sugar deoxyribose and phosphate groups.

SIMILARITIES BETWEEN DNA AND RNA
Are made of chains of nucleotides
Contain the same three basic subunits: a phosphate group, a five-carbon sugar, and a nitrogenous base
Have three of the same nitrogenous bases: guanine, cytosine, and adenine

RNA

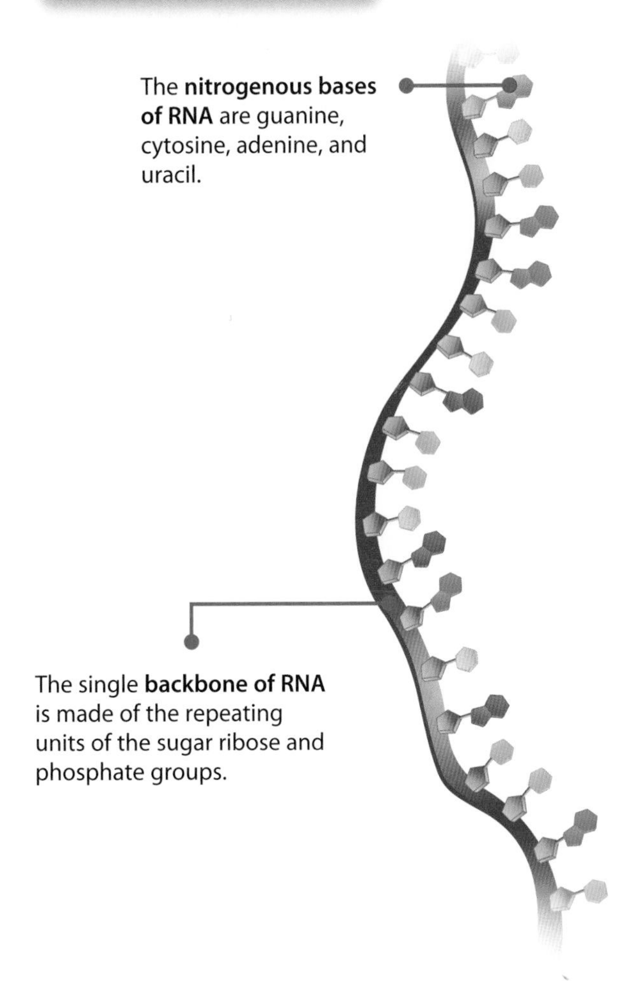

The nitrogenous bases of RNA are guanine, cytosine, adenine, and uracil.
The single backbone of RNA is made of the repeating units of the sugar ribose and phosphate groups.

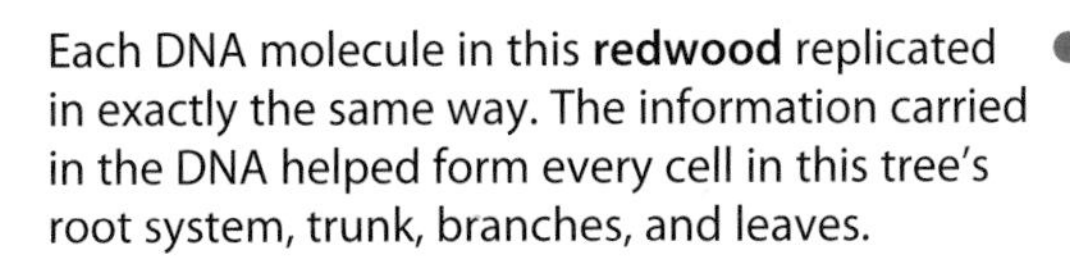
Each DNA molecule in this **redwood** replicated in exactly the same way. The information carried in the DNA helped form every cell in this tree's root system, trunk, branches, and leaves.

DIFFERENCES BETWEEN DNA AND RNA	
DNA	*RNA*
Is double stranded	Is single stranded
Contains the nitrogenous base thymine	Contains the nitrogenous base uracil
Is generally very long and contains hundreds or thousands of genes	Is shorter than DNA
Has the sugar deoxyribose in backbones	Has the sugar ribose in backbone

Water makes life on earth possible.

Water allows chemical reactions to take place in cells. It is a habitat for many living things and has been since life originated. All the important functions of water depend on its chemical properties.

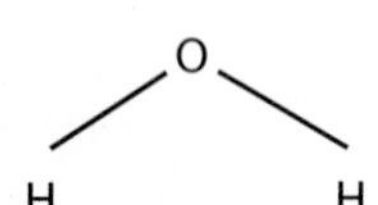

A **water molecule** consists of one oxygen atom bound to two hydrogen atoms. The atoms are arranged at an angle of 104.45°.

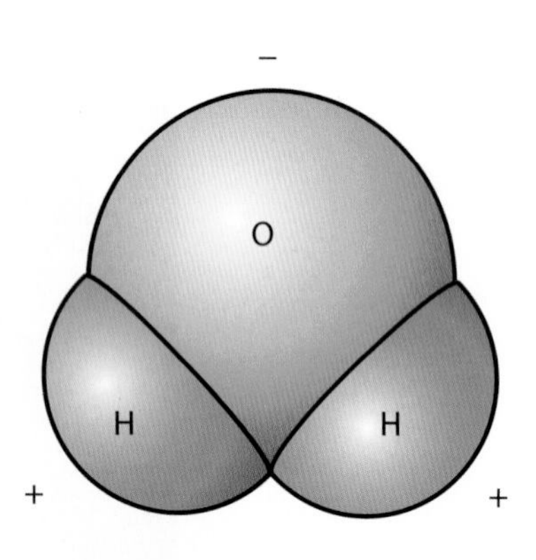

This **space-filling model** shows the 3-D structure of a water molecule. The spherical, color-coded atoms help you visualize a water molecule and the relative size of each atom.

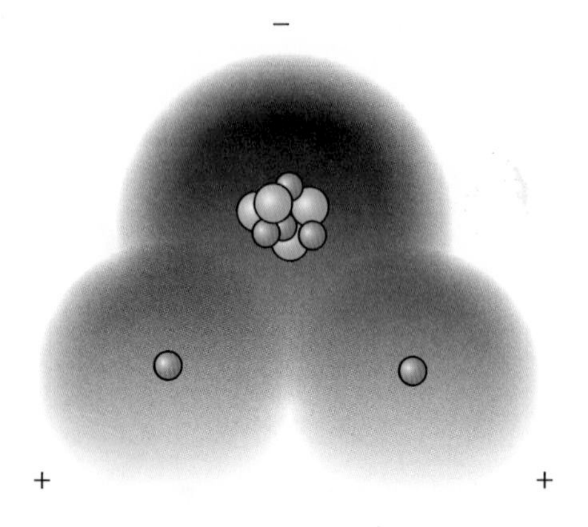

This **electron-cloud diagram** shows where the electrons are most likely to be located in a water molecule. You can see that the cloud is denser around the oxygen atom.

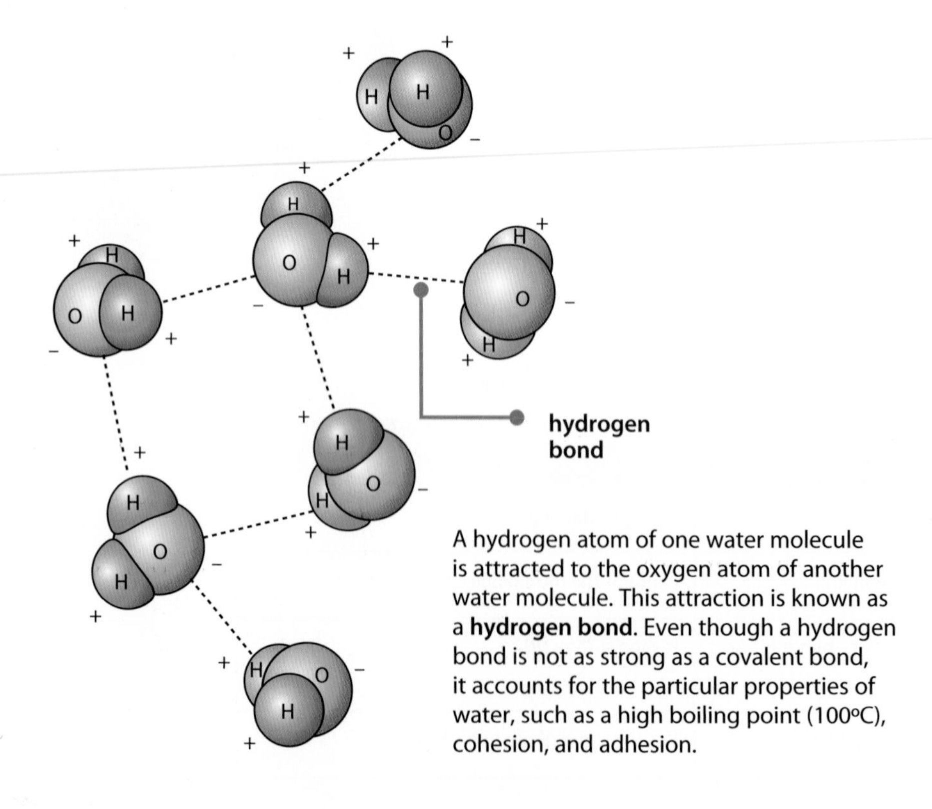

A hydrogen atom of one water molecule is attracted to the oxygen atom of another water molecule. This attraction is known as a **hydrogen bond**. Even though a hydrogen bond is not as strong as a covalent bond, it accounts for the particular properties of water, such as a high boiling point (100°C), cohesion, and adhesion.

Cohesion is the attraction of similar molecules. Water has high cohesion because its molecules interact with each other through hydrogen bonds. When one molecule moves in one direction, other molecules follow it.

hydrogen bonds

adhesion

cohesion

A molecule of water that is surrounded by other water molecules is equally attracted in all directions. The molecules on the surface of water, however, are attracted only in the direction of the water molecules underneath them. The molecules on the surface form a thin layer that acts like an elastic sheet. This **surface tension** is the reason water striders can glide on the water's surface.

Adhesion is the ability of the molecules of one substance to be attracted to the molecules of other substances. Water can be considered sticky because it can adhere to many surfaces. If you dipped a very thin tube into a cup of water, the water molecules would adhere to the tube and pull along all of the other water molecules bonded to them by cohesion. This process is called *capillary action*. Thus, water moving up from the roots to the leaves of a plant by capillary action do so through adhesion and cohesion.

ATP is the source of energy for almost all processes that a cell must undergo to survive.

Cells produce ATP by breaking down food molecules. Together, the cells of your body use about 100,000,000,000,000,000,000 (10^{20}) molecules of ATP every second.

ATP Structure

An ATP molecule has 3 phosphate groups, 1 adenine group, and 1 ribose group.

adenine

phosphate groups

ribose

ATP–ADP Reaction

When 1 phosphate group is removed, adenosine diphosphate (ADP) and 1 free phosphate (P) are produced and energy is released. A cell uses this energy to drive many of its chemical reactions.

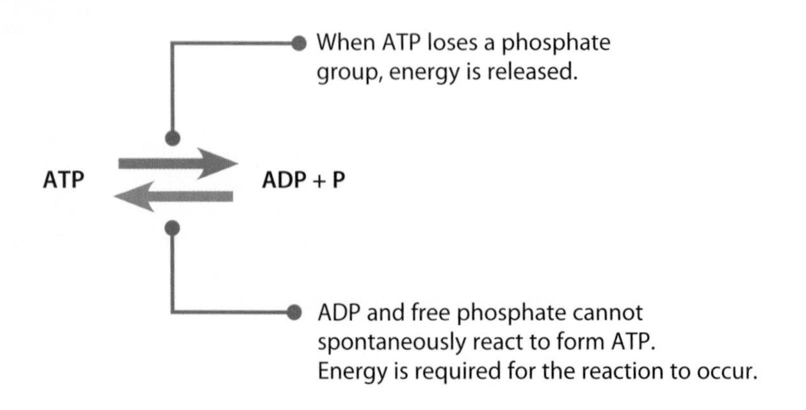

When ATP loses a phosphate group, energy is released.
ATP
ADP + P
ADP and free phosphate cannot spontaneously react to form ATP. Energy is required for the reaction to occur.

How ATP Works in a Cell: An Example

Glutamine is the most abundant amino acid in the human body. It is an important component of skeletal muscles. Glutamine forms when glutamic acid reacts with ammonia. Glutamic acid and ammonia can react only when energy is supplied. This energy comes from ATP.

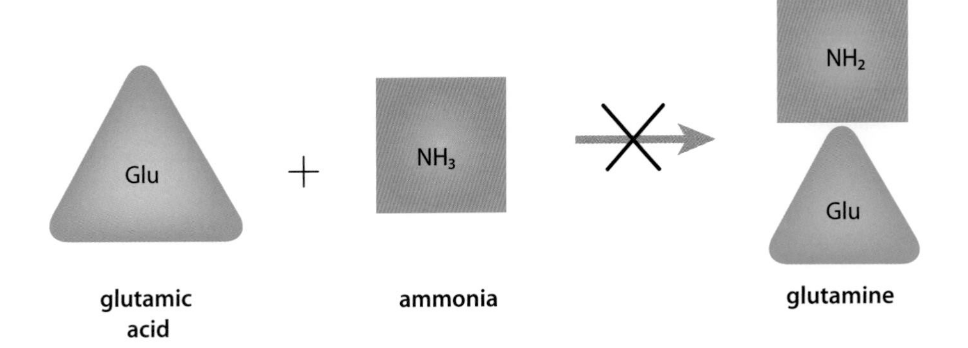

Glutamine forms when glutamic acid reacts with ammonia, but the reaction cannot occur spontaneously in a cell. It requires the energy of ATP.

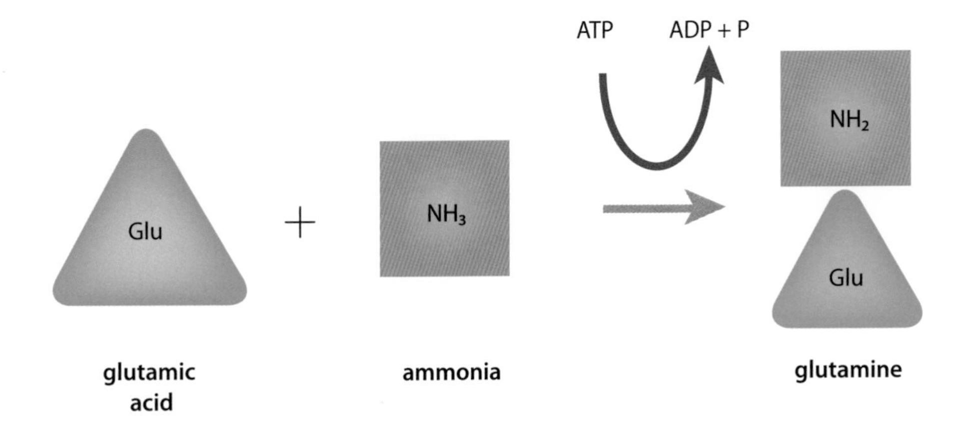

The cells of a **sea star** are many and varied, often modified to perform specific functions. However, all the cells are eukaryotic and share many of the same structural characteristics as the typical eukaryotic cell shown below.

From plants to sea stars, the cells of all eukaryotes share many characteristics, including the presence of a cell membrane.

The cell membrane encloses the cell, controlling the substances that pass into and out of the cell. This ability—called *selective permeability*—makes life possible.

Eukaryotic Cell

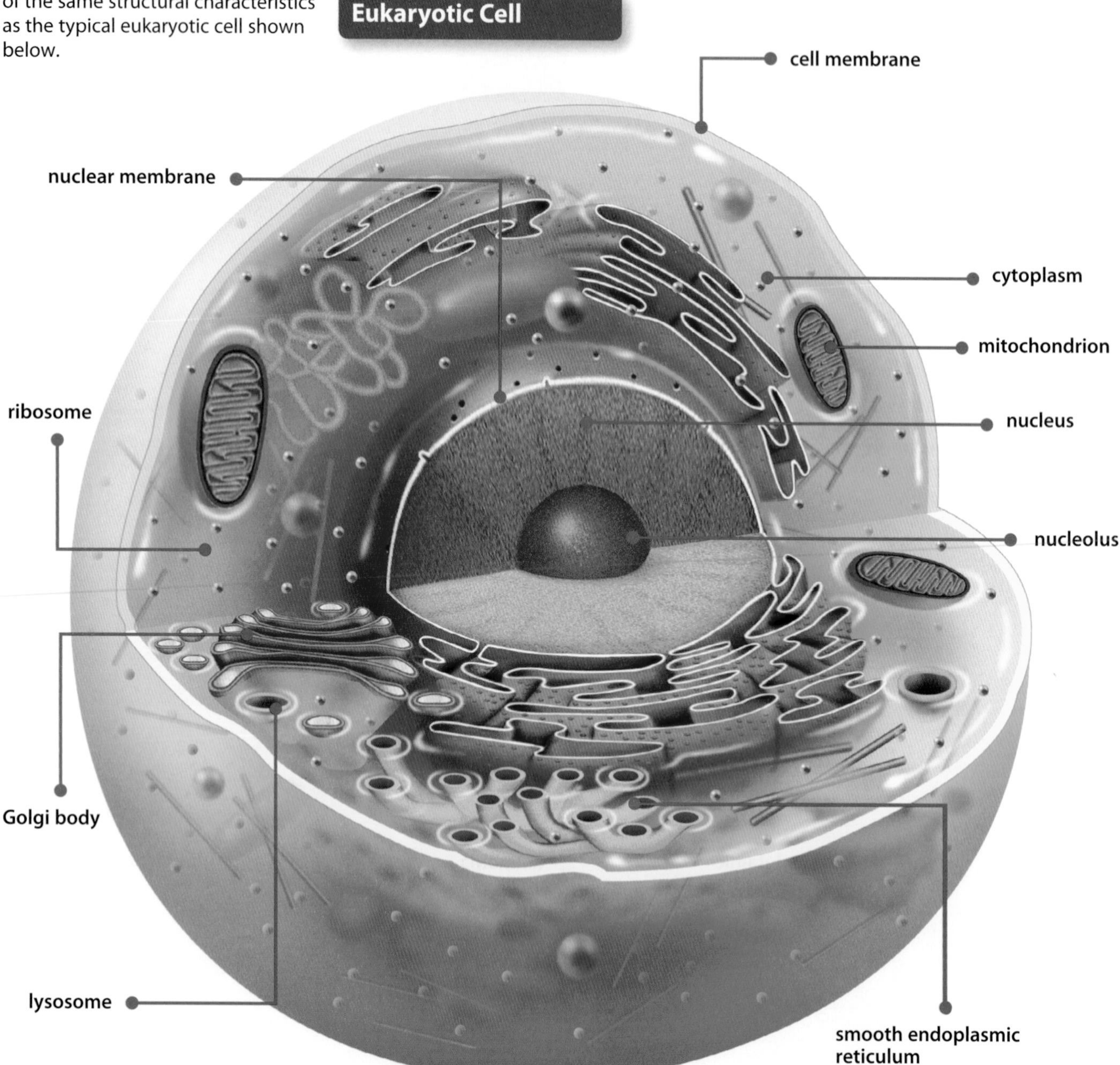

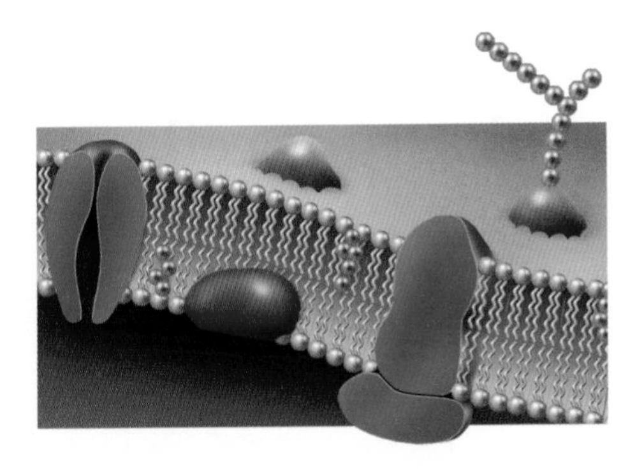

Cell membranes are made primarily of phospholipids. They also contain some proteins and carbohydrates. Proteins in the cell membrane have various functions, including the movement of materials across the membrane.

Cytoplasm is everything that is contained within the cell membrane except the nucleus. It consists of a jelly-like fluid, fibers that aid cell movement and structure, and the cell's organelles.

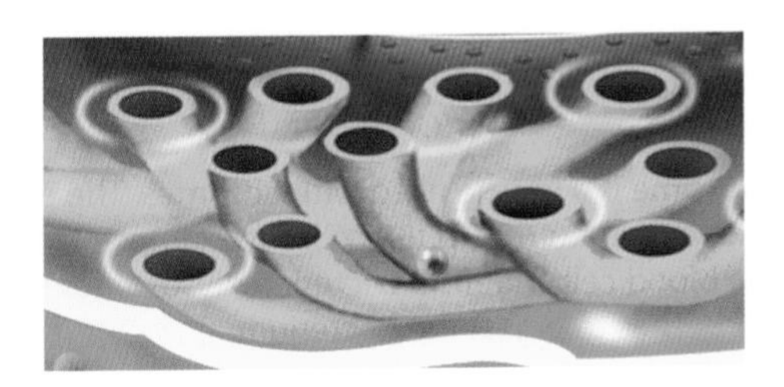

The **endoplasmic reticulum (ER)** is a series of interconnected flattened sacs, tubes, and channels within the cell. ER is where fats are made, drugs are detoxified, and calcium is stored.

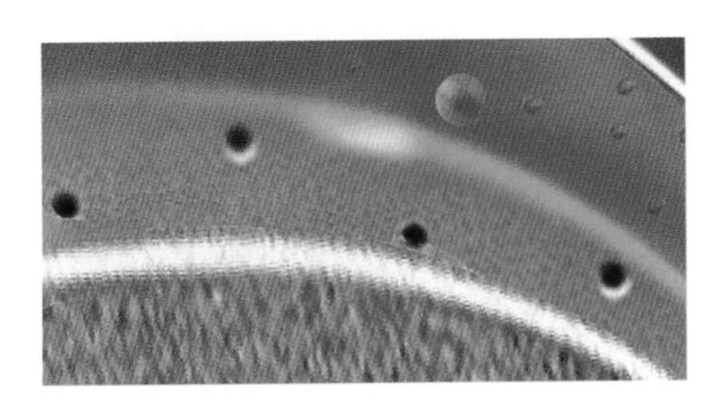

The envelope surrounding the nucleus, called the **nuclear membrane**, is made up of two membranes. Each membrane is a lipid bilayer with many pores that allow the passage of molecules such as RNA from the nucleus to the cytoplasm.

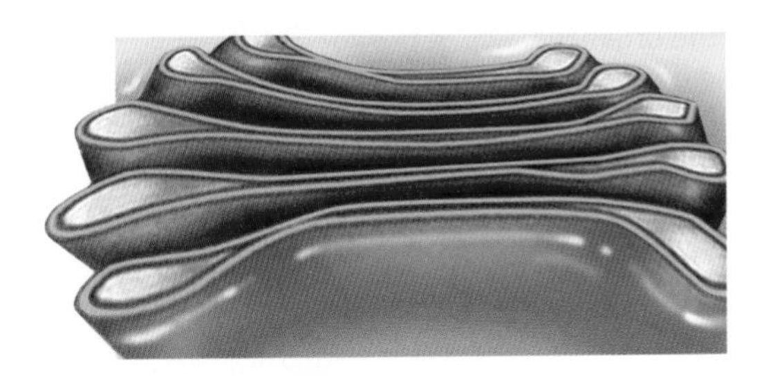

The **Golgi body** is a network of flattened membrane sacs stacked together. It receives the products of the ER (mostly proteins), sorts their contents, modifies them, and distributes them throughout the cell.

Organelles are membrane-bound structures within a eukaryotic cell.

Without properly functioning organelles, the organism's cells—and the organism as a whole—would be unable to survive. Each organelle has a specific set of chemical and physical tasks.

Each cell of this **sea star** has organelles that keep the organism functioning. Sea star larvae drift and feed in ocean currents for several weeks. They then attach temporarily to a solid surface, where they become adults through extremely rapid cell division.

Each kind of **organelle** performs a specific and necessary function within the cell. Different cells may have different numbers and arrangements of organelles based on their particular functions.

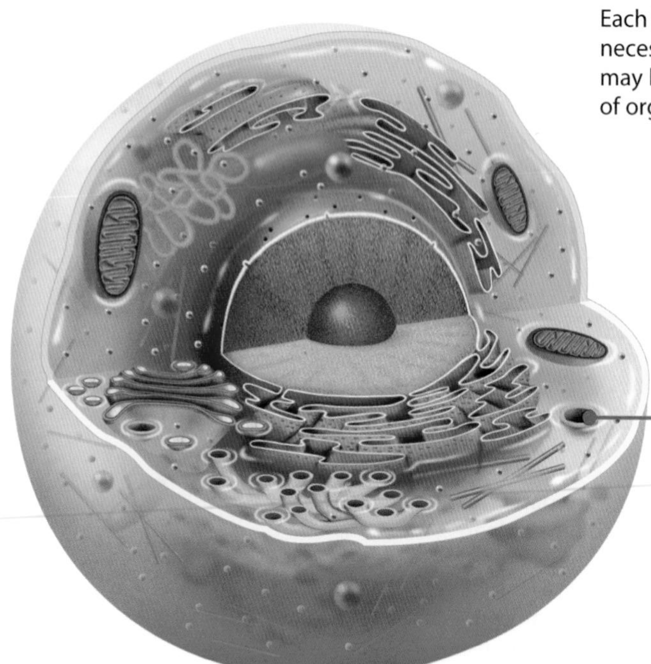

A **lysosome** is a vesicle filled with enzymes. The enzymes break down materials in the cell. For example, when a white blood cell engulfs a bacterium, lysosomes provide the enzymes to digest the bacterium.

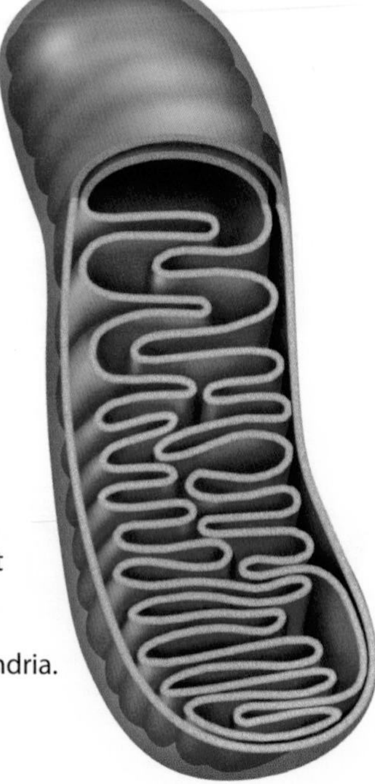

A **mitochondrion** is the organelle that generates usable energy from glucose. Depending on how much energy a certain cell needs, it will have different numbers of mitochondria. Muscle cells, for example, are stuffed with mitochondria.

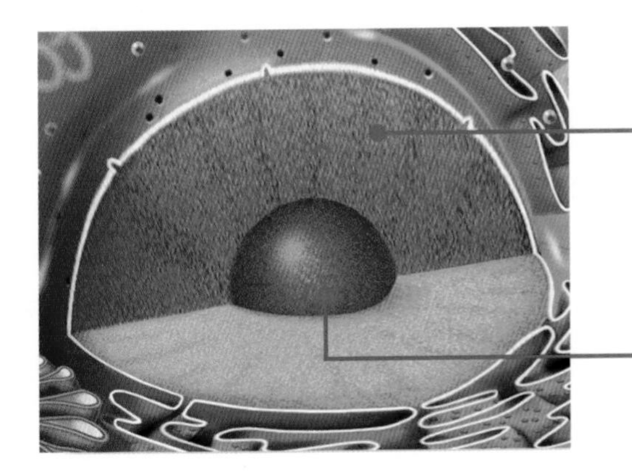

The **nucleus** of the cell contains DNA, which carries the genetic information passed from parent to offspring. It uses the continuous influence of that DNA to control all functions of the cell, both inside and outside the nucleus.

Biologists often do not consider the nucleus to be a true organelle.

A **nucleolus** is a region of the nucleus where one type of RNA, called *ribosomal RNA (rRNA)*, is produced.

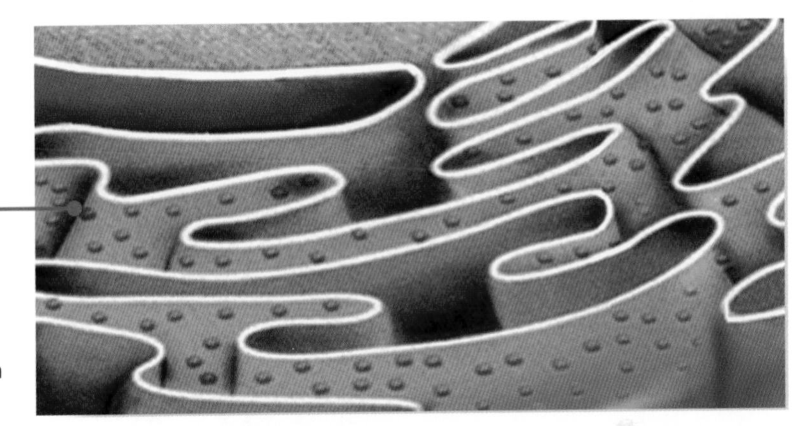

Ribosomes are the site of protein synthesis. These structures may be attached to the ER or suspended in the cytosol.

The **ER** is a series of interconnected flattened membrane sacs, tubes, and channels. There are two kinds of ER: Rough ER has ribosomes attached to it, and smooth ER does not. Rough ER plays an important role in protein synthesis. After proteins are made, they are exported to the Golgi body in vesicles.

SOME ORGANELLES AND THEIR FUNCTIONS

ORGANELLE	*FUNCTION*
Lysosome	Contains enzymes to break down materials in a cell
Mitochondrion	Provides energy to a cell
Rough ER	Synthesizes proteins
Smooth ER	Aids in transport of molecules within a cell

Underlying the amazing diversity of life are only two fundamental cell types: prokaryotic and eukaryotic.

From single-cell yeasts and bacteria to giant redwoods and whales, the diversity of life on the planet is vast. For all living things, the cell is the basic unit of life.

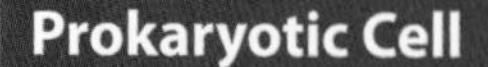

Prokaryotic Cell

An organism made up of a prokaryotic cell is called a *prokaryote*. All prokaryotes are single-cell organisms. Bacteria and archaeans are prokaryotes.

The **cell membrane** of a prokaryotic cell regulates the movement of materials into and out of the cell, and keeps the cell's internal chemical reactions separate from the outside environment. The membrane consists of two layers of phospholipids and is described as a *phospholipid bilayer*. A cell wall surrounds the cell membrane of most prokaryotic cells.

cell wall

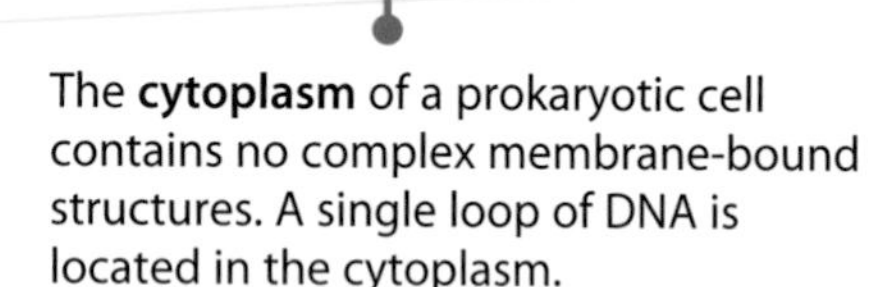

The **cytoplasm** of a prokaryotic cell contains no complex membrane-bound structures. A single loop of DNA is located in the cytoplasm.

SIMILARITIES BETWEEN PROKARYOTIC AND EUKARYOTIC CELLS
Both have DNA as their genetic material
Both have a cell membrane made of two layers of phospholipids
Both contain cytoplasm

Eukaryotic Cell

Organisms made up of eukaryotic cells are called *eukaryotes*. Earthworms, eagles, honeysuckles, and humans are all eukaryotes. Although all prokaryotes are unicellular, eukaryotes may be unicellular or multicellular.

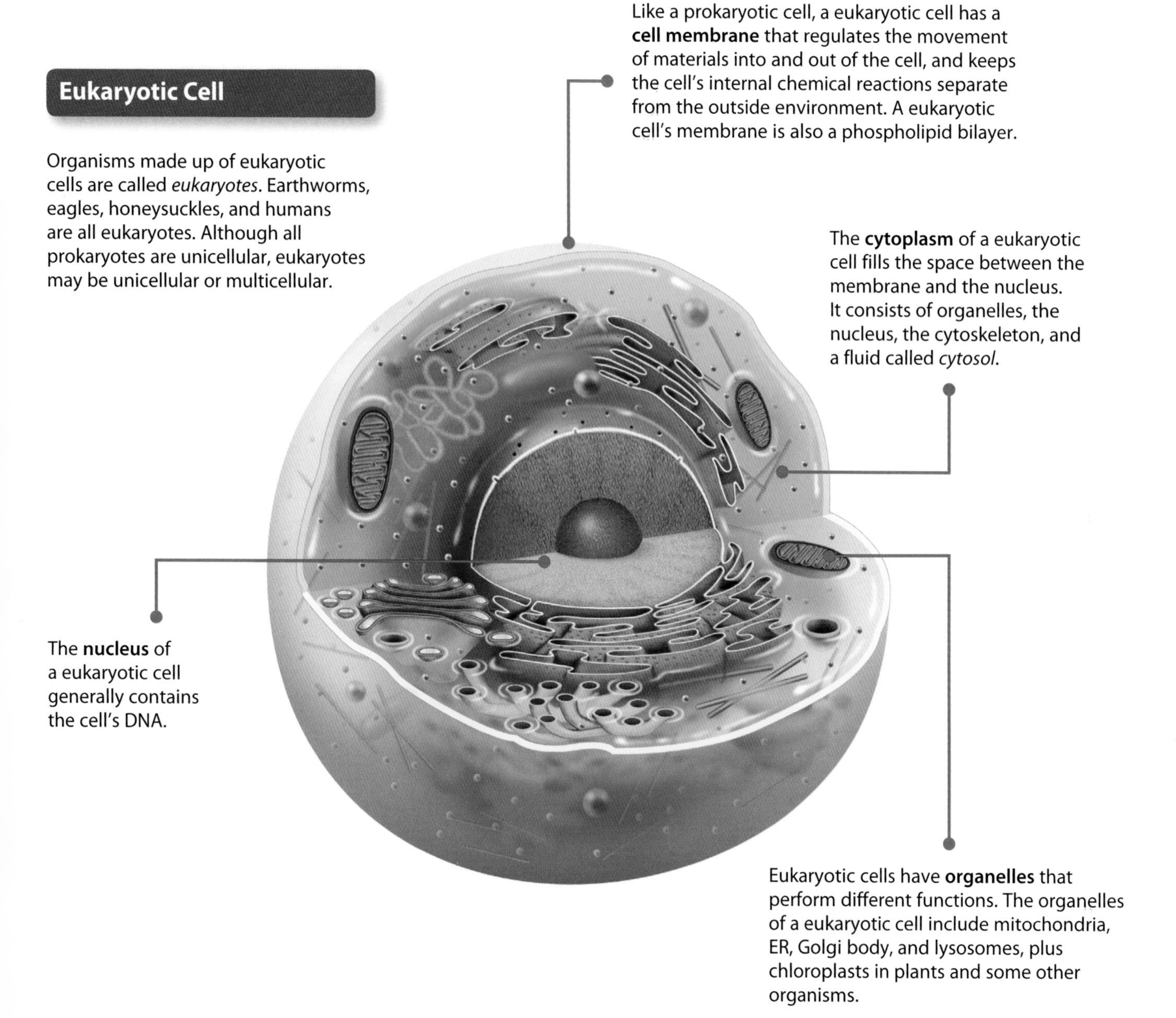

Like a prokaryotic cell, a eukaryotic cell has a **cell membrane** that regulates the movement of materials into and out of the cell, and keeps the cell's internal chemical reactions separate from the outside environment. A eukaryotic cell's membrane is also a phospholipid bilayer.

The **cytoplasm** of a eukaryotic cell fills the space between the membrane and the nucleus. It consists of organelles, the nucleus, the cytoskeleton, and a fluid called *cytosol*.

The **nucleus** of a eukaryotic cell generally contains the cell's DNA.

Eukaryotic cells have **organelles** that perform different functions. The organelles of a eukaryotic cell include mitochondria, ER, Golgi body, and lysosomes, plus chloroplasts in plants and some other organisms.

DIFFERENCES BETWEEN PROKARYOTIC AND EUKARYOTIC CELLS

PROKARYOTIC CELLS	*EUKARYOTIC CELLS*
Are generally simple and small	Are generally larger and more complex than prokaryotic cells
Have no nucleus	Have a nucleus
Have DNA as one circular chromosome	Have DNA contained in more than one linear chromosome
Have no true organelles	Have membrane-bound organelles

To survive, a cell must be able to take in nutrients and expel wastes.

A cell needs to move materials across its cell membrane to maintain homeostasis. The movement of many materials is passive—that is, it does not require energy from the cell. Diffusion and osmosis are both passive mechanisms of movement of materials into and out of a cell.

Diffusion

In **diffusion**, particles such as atoms and molecules move from an area where they are more concentrated to an area where they are less concentrated.

When iodine is first dropped into water, all the iodine molecules are **concentrated** in one small area. Like all particles, however, iodine molecules are in constant motion, moving randomly in all directions.

As time passes, the movement of both the water and the iodine molecules causes the iodine molecules to **spread out** or diffuse through the water.

The iodine molecules continue to move randomly in all directions. Eventually they will be **evenly distributed** among the water molecules.

Osmosis

Osmosis is the diffusion of water across a membrane. Most organisms have mechanisms to control osmosis. Without this ability, an organism's cells could not maintain their water balance and would either burst or shrivel up.

When the concentration of water inside the cell is **higher** than the concentration outside the cell, water flows out of the cell, and the cell begins to shrink.

If the concentration of water inside the cell is **lower** than the concentration outside the cell, water flows into the cell, and the cell begins to swell.

When the concentration of water inside and outside the cell is **balanced**, water moves into a cell at the same rate that it moves out. In this case, there is no net movement of water across the cell membrane.

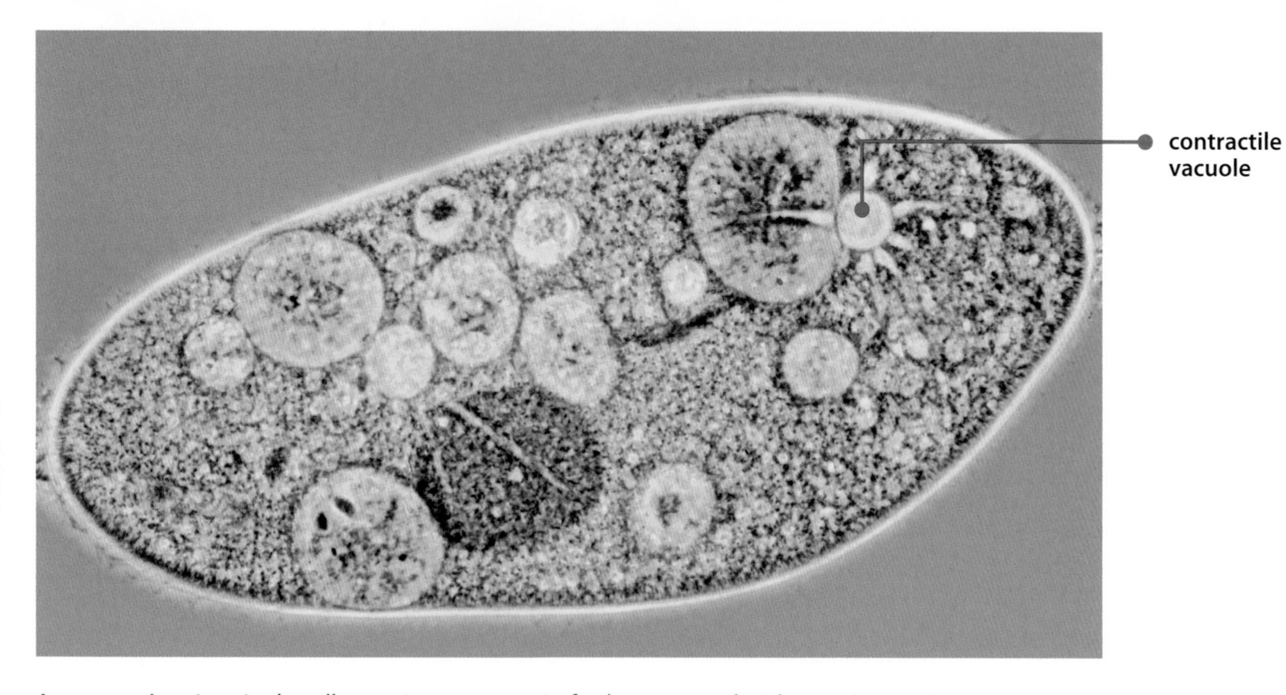

A **paramecium** is a single-cell organism common in freshwater ponds. Like most organisms, a paramecium must be able to control the amount of water inside its cell membrane to keep the shape above. To pump out excess water, it uses a structure called a *contractile vacuole.* Without this structure, the paramecium would swell and eventually burst.

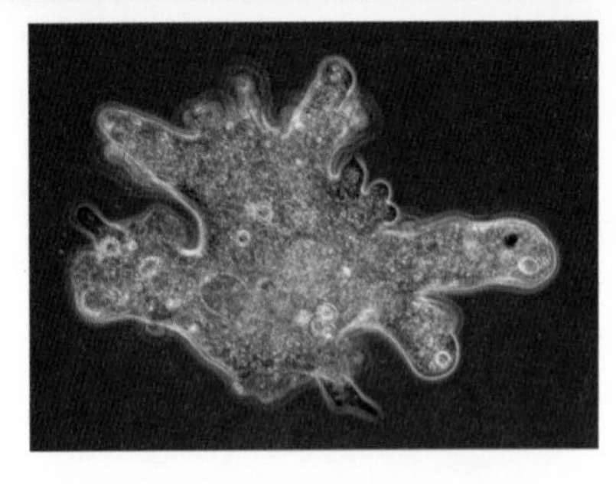

There are two types of passive transport—simple diffusion and facilitated diffusion. This **single-cell amoeba** takes in and gets rid of many materials by both simple diffusion and facilitated diffusion.

Some large materials can pass through the cell membrane without additional energy from the cell.

The movement across a membrane that does not require energy from the cell is called *passive transport*. Osmosis and diffusion are types of passive transport involving small atoms or molecules. Some larger materials move passively with the use of carrier proteins.

Many small molecules, such as carbon dioxide and oxygen, can pass directly through the membrane at any point. This process is **simple diffusion**, a kind of passive transport.

Molecules that are too large to pass through a cell's membrane must enter or leave via carrier proteins in the membrane, which is known as **facilitated diffusion**. The numbered illustration shows facilitated diffusion.

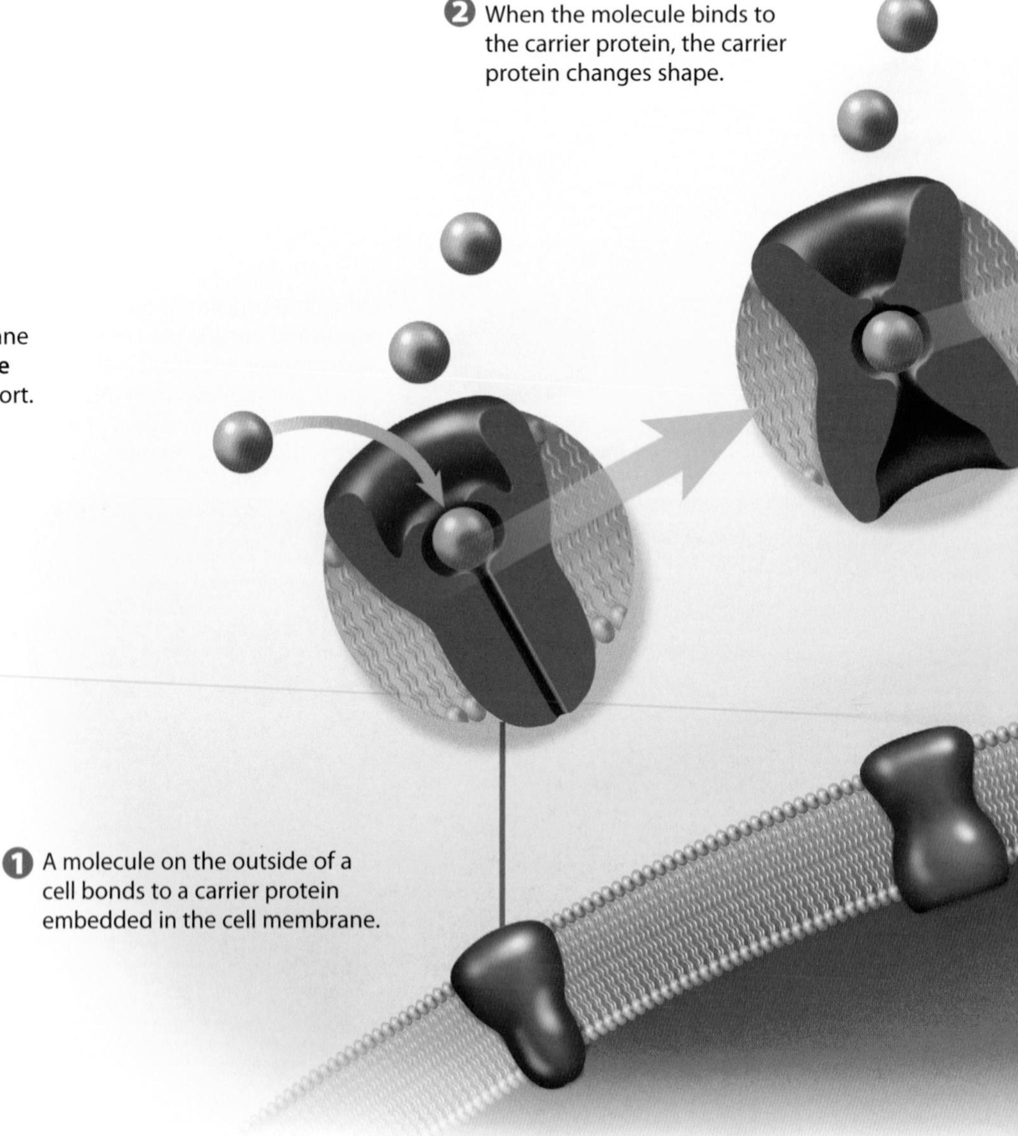

1. A molecule on the outside of a cell bonds to a carrier protein embedded in the cell membrane.
2. When the molecule binds to the carrier protein, the carrier protein changes shape.

❸ When the carrier protein changes shape, it exposes the molecule to the inside of the cell. The protein then releases the molecule on the other side of the cell membrane.

❹ Once the molecule is inside the cell, the carrier protein returns to its original shape and is ready to bind to another molecule.

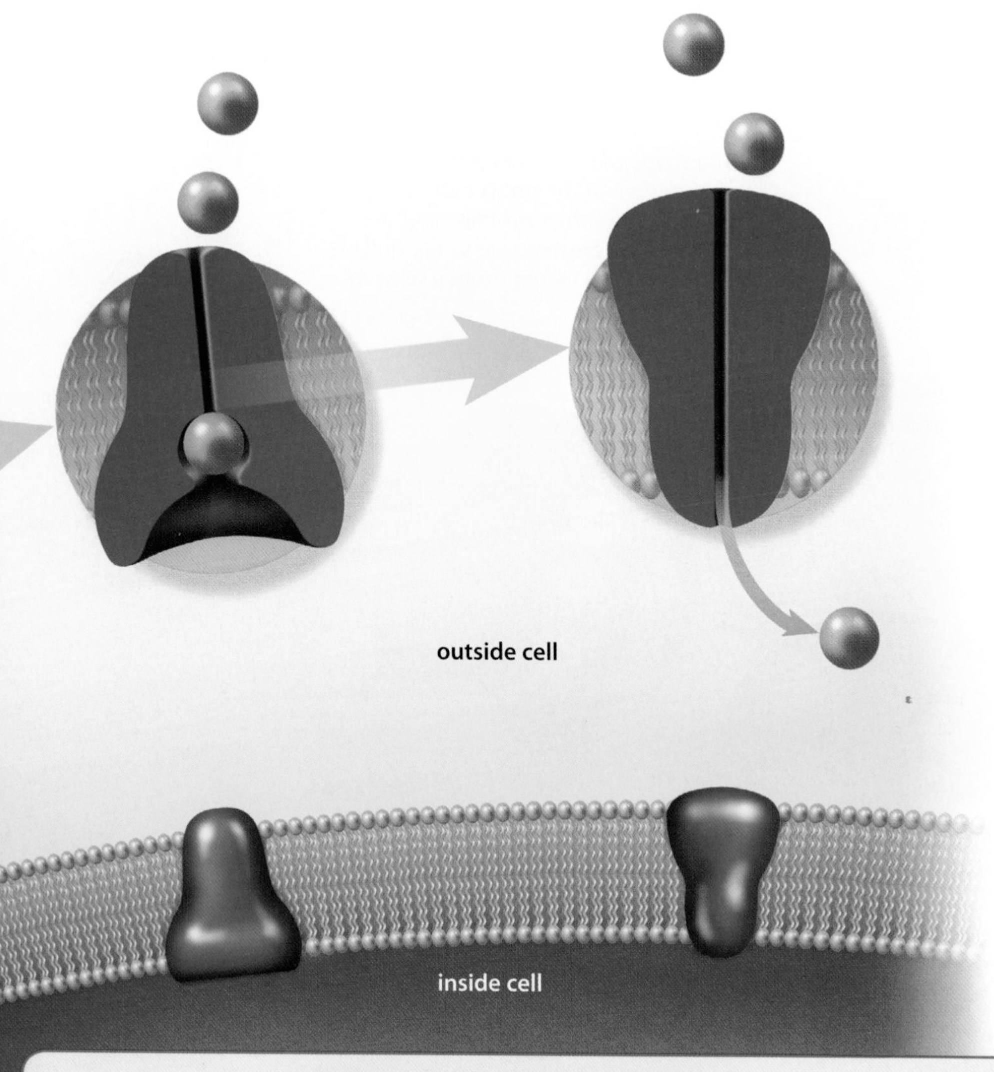

FORMS OF PASSIVE TRANSPORT

TYPE OF TRANSPORT	*DESCRIPTION*
Osmosis	Osmosis is the diffusion of water through a semipermeable membrane, such as the cell membrane. This process requires no input of energy from the cell.
Simple diffusion	Small molecules that are soluble in lipids can pass through the phospholipid bilayer. This process requires no input of energy from the cell.
Facilitated diffusion	Molecules move across the cell membrane with the aid of carrier proteins.

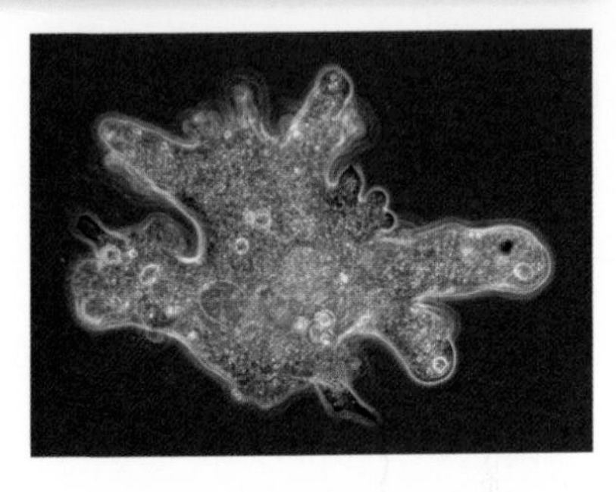

A **single-cell amoeba** can take in and get rid of some materials by diffusion, but it must expend energy to move other materials across its cell membrane.

Sometimes a cell requires chemical energy to move materials across the cell membrane.

This process is called *active transport*. Some types of active transport involve proteins in the cell membrane. Others require the movement of membrane-bound sacs across the cell membrane.

The numbered illustration is an example of **active transport** involving proteins embedded in the cell membrane. These proteins are called *sodium–potassium pumps*.

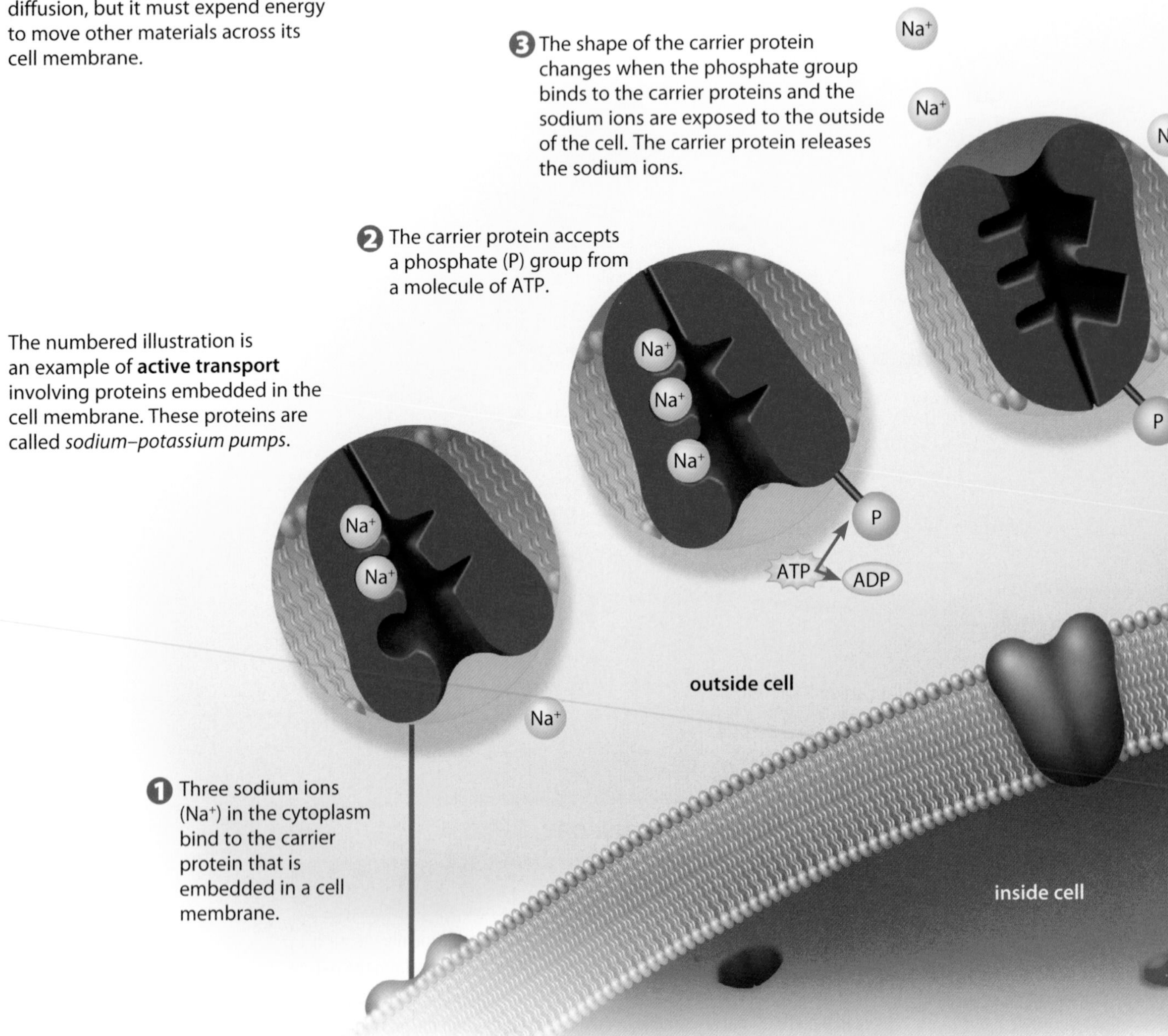

3 The shape of the carrier protein changes when the phosphate group binds to the carrier proteins and the sodium ions are exposed to the outside of the cell. The carrier protein releases the sodium ions.
2 The carrier protein accepts a phosphate (P) group from a molecule of ATP.
1 Three sodium ions (Na^+) in the cytoplasm bind to the carrier protein that is embedded in a cell membrane.
Na^+
P
ATP
ADP
outside cell
inside cell

Sodium-Potassium Pump

Sometimes cells must move materials across the cell membrane from areas of lower concentration to areas of higher concentration. In this type of active transport, materials must pass through the cell membrane via carrier proteins. Because materials are moving to areas where they are already more concentrated, these carrier protein pumps need energy to function. The diagram below shows the active transport of two substances that cells must keep in balance to remain healthy. This carrier protein pump moves sodium ions (Na^+) out of the cell and moves potassium ions (K^+) into the cell.

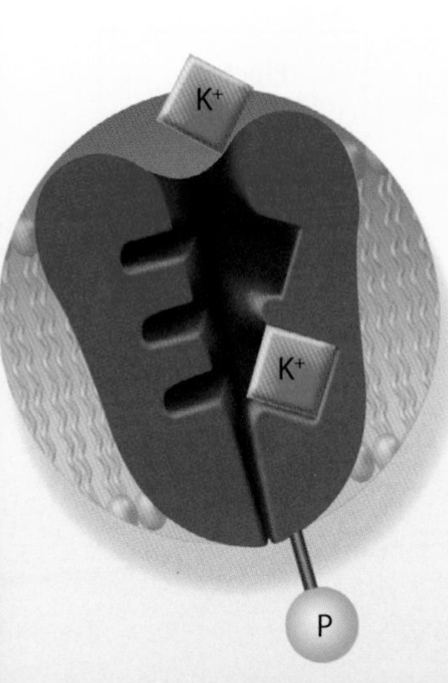

4 The carrier protein pump accepts 2 potassium ions (K^+) from outside the cell.

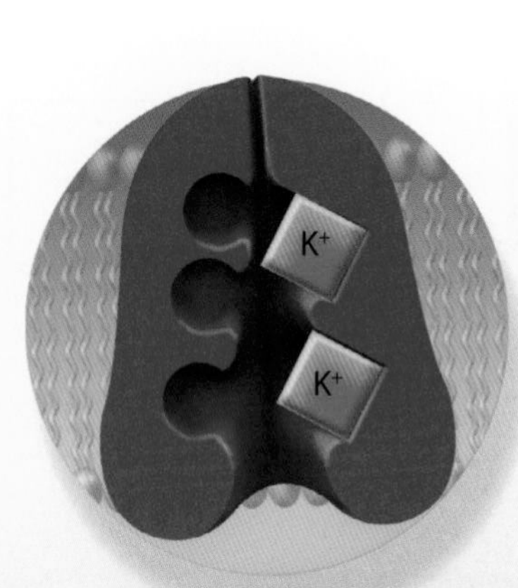

5 The pump releases the phosphate group. The protein returns to its original shape, exposing the potassium ions to the interior of the cell.

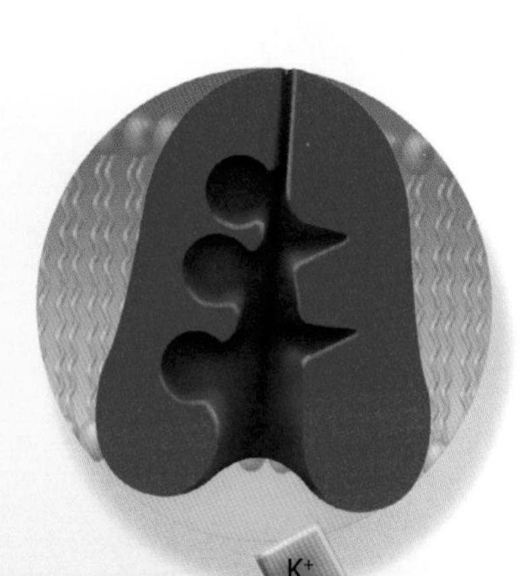

6 The carrier protein releases the 2 potassium ions inside the cell.

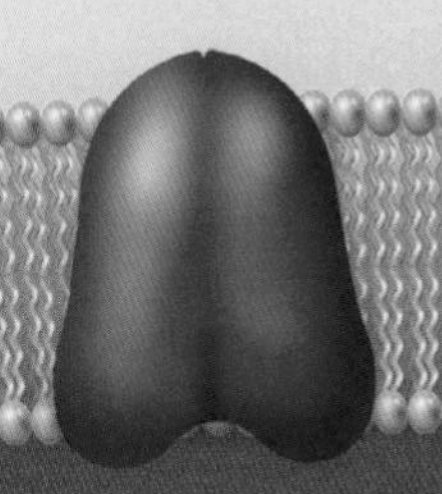

FORMS OF ACTIVE TRANSPORT	
TYPE OF TRANSPORT	*DESCRIPTION*
Direct active transport	Carrier proteins transport molecules or ions across the cell membrane. The molecules and ions move from areas where they are less concentrated to areas where they are more concentrated. This process requires energy in the form of ATP.
Endocytosis	Molecules that are too large to enter the cell through carrier proteins can be enclosed in vesicles formed from the cell membrane. The vesicles pinch off into the cell.
Exocytosis	Vesicles carrying waste materials fuse with the cell membrane and release their contents outside the cell.

Cells use the sugar glucose as fuel to produce energy. The word *glycolysis* means sugar splitting. **Glycolysis** takes place in the cytosol of both prokaryotic and eukaryotic cells.

Organisms use the food they eat by converting it into energy that their cells can use.

The cells of most organisms break down molecules of glucose into usable energy. Although cells can release this energy in several ways, each begins with the process of glycolysis.

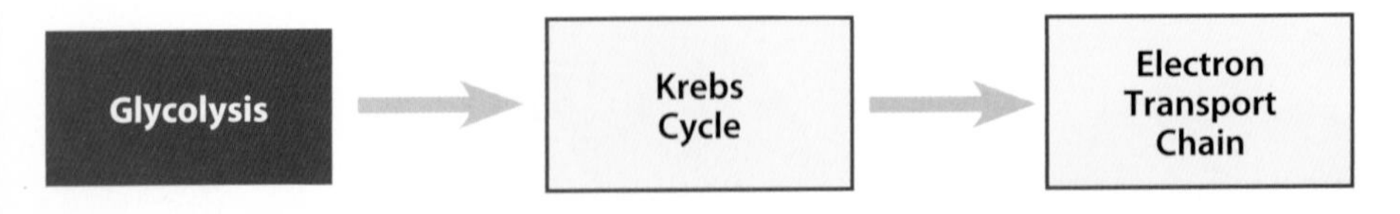

Glycolysis

Glycolysis can be divided into two stages. The **first stage** requires energy. Two ATP molecules are needed to rearrange the glucose molecule into a new 6-carbon compound.

The **second stage** of glycolysis produces energy. This stage produces 4 ATP molecules. Because 2 ATP molecules are needed during the first stage of glycolysis, the net product of the second stage is 2 ATP molecules for every 1 glucose molecule.

The **main products** of glycolysis are 2 molecules of pyruvic acid.

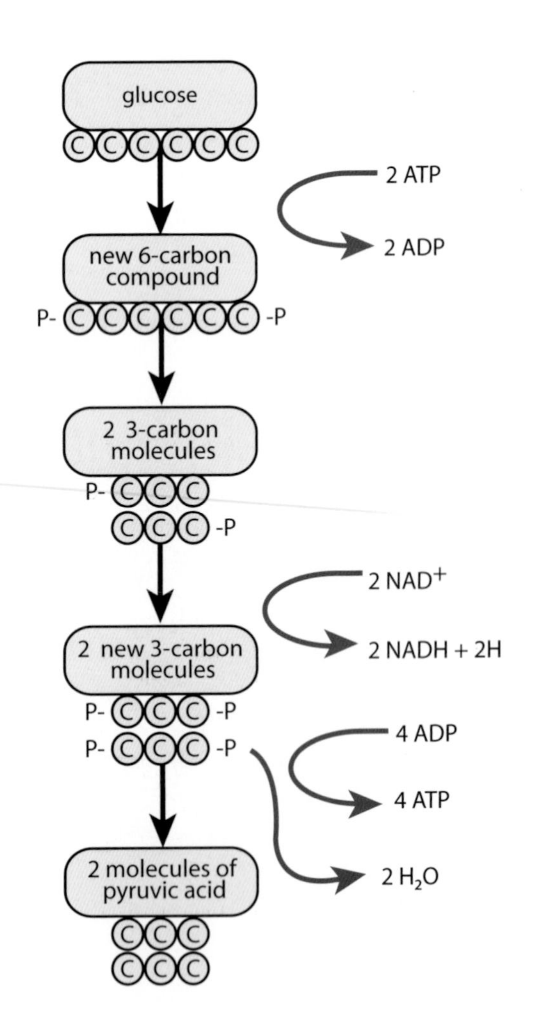

For every glucose molecule that goes through glycolysis, 2 molecules of pyruvic acid are also produced. These molecules may enter one of several **energy-producing pathways**.

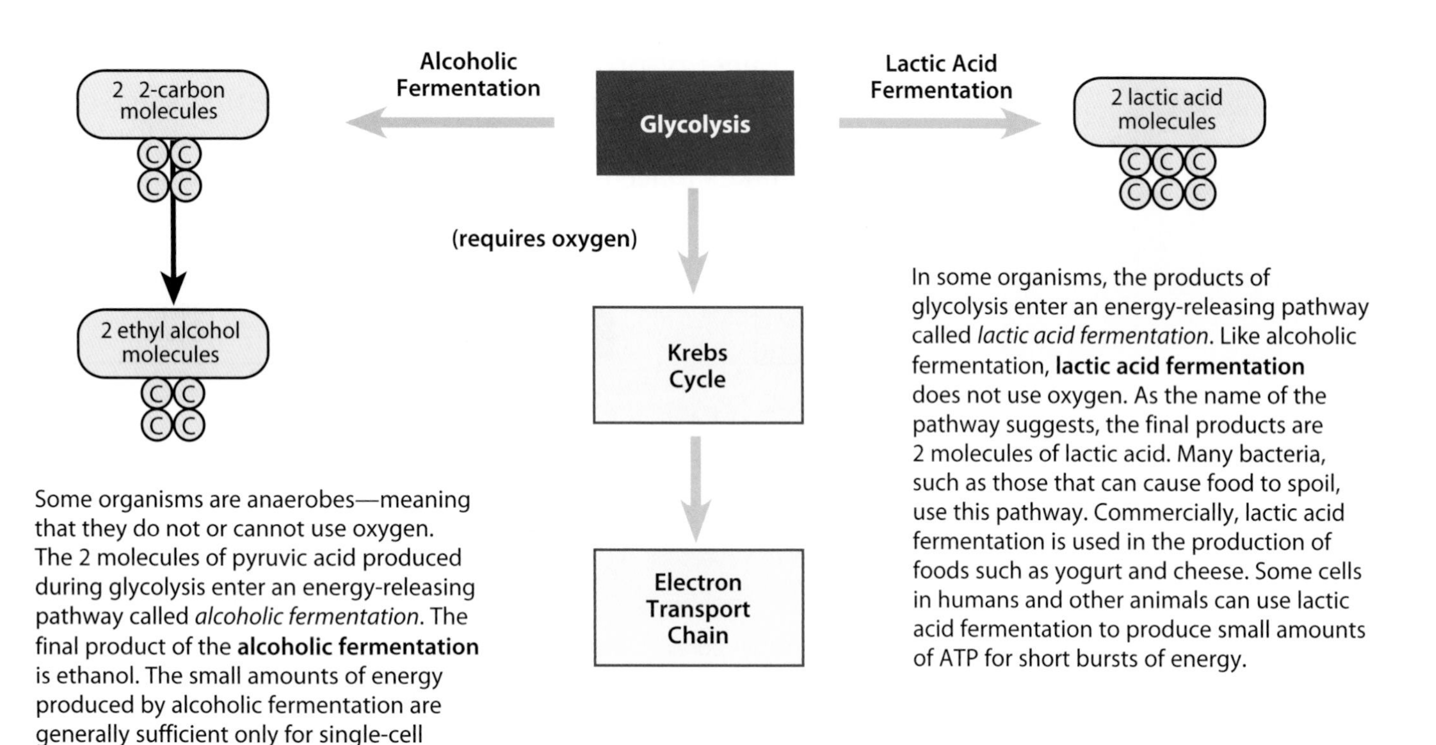

Some organisms are anaerobes—meaning that they do not or cannot use oxygen. The 2 molecules of pyruvic acid produced during glycolysis enter an energy-releasing pathway called *alcoholic fermentation*. The final product of the **alcoholic fermentation** is ethanol. The small amounts of energy produced by alcoholic fermentation are generally sufficient only for single-cell organisms such as bacteria or yeast. This fermentation does not produce enough energy for large, multicell organisms.

In some organisms, the products of glycolysis enter an energy-releasing pathway called *lactic acid fermentation*. Like alcoholic fermentation, **lactic acid fermentation** does not use oxygen. As the name of the pathway suggests, the final products are 2 molecules of lactic acid. Many bacteria, such as those that can cause food to spoil, use this pathway. Commercially, lactic acid fermentation is used in the production of foods such as yogurt and cheese. Some cells in humans and other animals can use lactic acid fermentation to produce small amounts of ATP for short bursts of energy.

Like this **runner**, you may have experienced fatigue and muscle cramps after strenuous exercise. When your muscle cells demand a lot of energy, they can rely on lactic acid fermentation for short periods of time. However, the muscles will tire quickly and may begin to ache. These cramps are caused by the buildup of lactic acid in the muscle cells.

Following glycolysis, the cells of most organisms use pyruvic acid in an energy-producing pathway that requires oxygen.

Like all major energy-producing pathways, including lactic acid fermentation and alcoholic fermentation, the first stage of aerobic respiration is glycolysis. The second stage is the Krebs cycle, which takes place in the matrix of a mitochondrion.

Mitochondrion

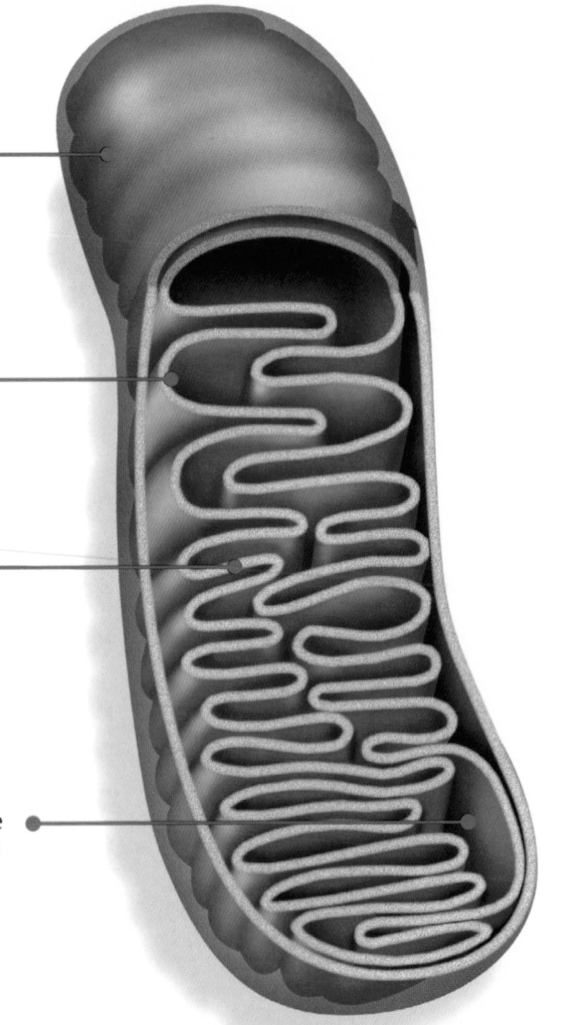

The **outer membrane** of a mitochondrion has pores. These pores allow ions, small proteins, and other small molecules to move between the cytoplasm and the area outside the mitochondrion.

The **inner membrane** of the mitochondrion contains proteins required for cellular respiration, including the enzyme that makes ATP.

The inner membrane of the mitochondrion has many folds called *cristae*. **Cristae** extend the surface area of the inner membrane, increasing the amount of space available for chemical reactions to take place at the membrane.

The **matrix** of the mitochondrion is the area inside the inner membrane. It contains enzymes, ribosomes, and the mitochondrial DNA. The Krebs cycle takes place in the matrix.

The Krebs Cycle

For every glucose molecule that undergoes glycolysis, 2 pyruvic acid molecules are produced. When each pyruvic acid molecule moves into the matrix of the mitochondrion, it reacts with an enzyme to produce a molecule of acetyl-coenzyme A (acetyl-CoA). Acetyl-CoA is the starting material for the **Krebs cycle**. Two molecules of acetyl-CoA pass through the Krebs cycle for each original molecule of glucose.

During each pass of the Krebs cycle, 1 molecule of acetyl-CoA is converted into 2 molecules of carbon dioxide (CO_2) through a series of reactions. The energy released during these reactions is stored in molecules of NADH, $FADH_2$, and ATP. Two passes through the Krebs cycle are required to completely break down 1 molecule of glucose into CO_2. Therefore, each molecule of glucose results in the production of 2 molecules of $FADH_2$, 2 molecules of ATP, and 6 molecules of NADH.

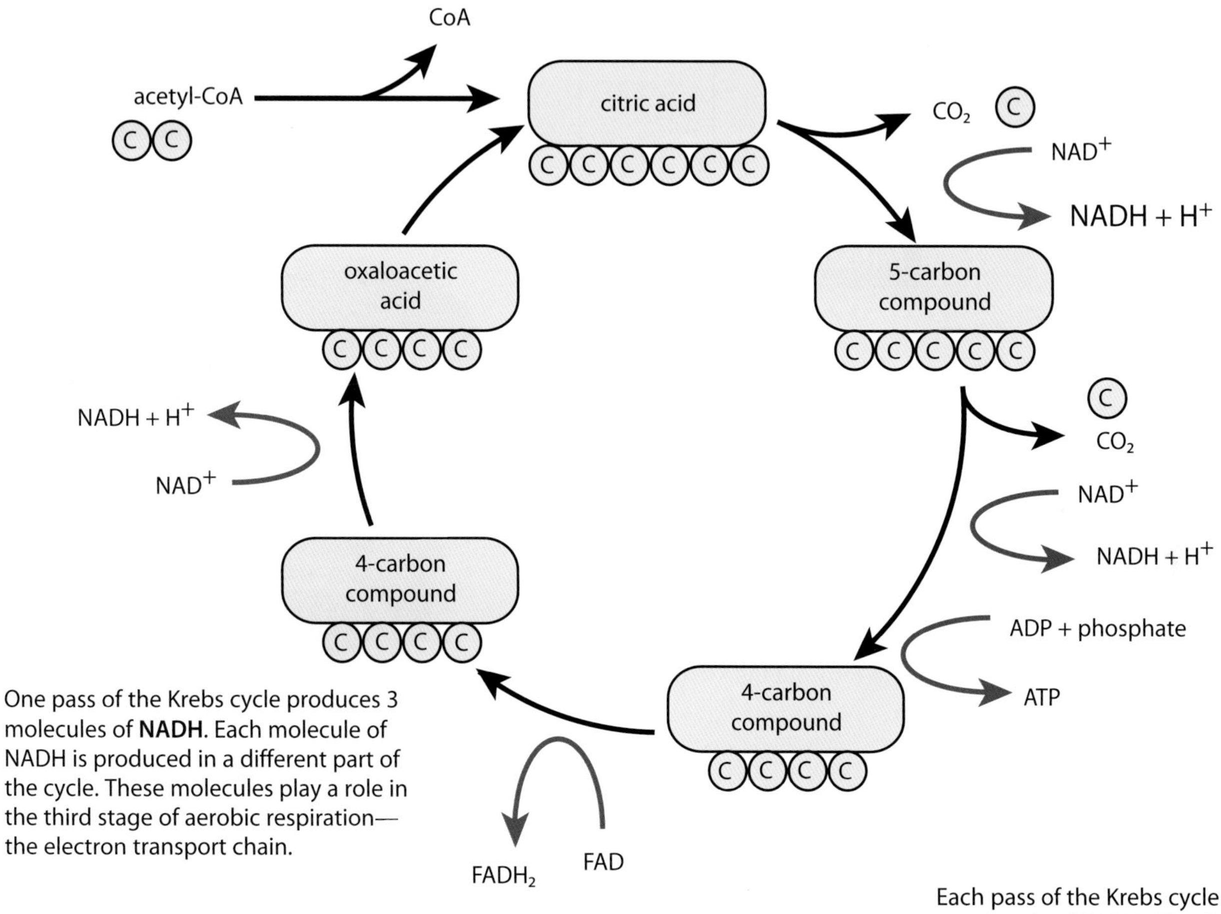

One pass of the Krebs cycle produces 3 molecules of **NADH**. Each molecule of NADH is produced in a different part of the cycle. These molecules play a role in the third stage of aerobic respiration—the electron transport chain.

Each pass of the Krebs cycle produces 1 molecule of **$FADH_2$**. The $FADH_2$ acts as an electron donor during the electron transport chain, which is the third stage in aerobic respiration.

STAGE IN THE AEROBIC ENERGY-PRODUCING PATHWAY	*ATP MOLECULES PRODUCED PER MOLECULE OF GLUCOSE*
Glycolysis	2
Krebs cycle	2 (1 molecule per pass through the cycle)

The major product of the electron transport chain is ATP. How important is ATP? Each cell in your body uses about 1 million molecules of ATP per second.

Most ATP produced during aerobic respiration forms during the third stage—the electron transport chain. This process uses the oxygen that you breathe in.

Glycolysis → Krebs Cycle → **Electron Transport Chain**

Mitochondrion

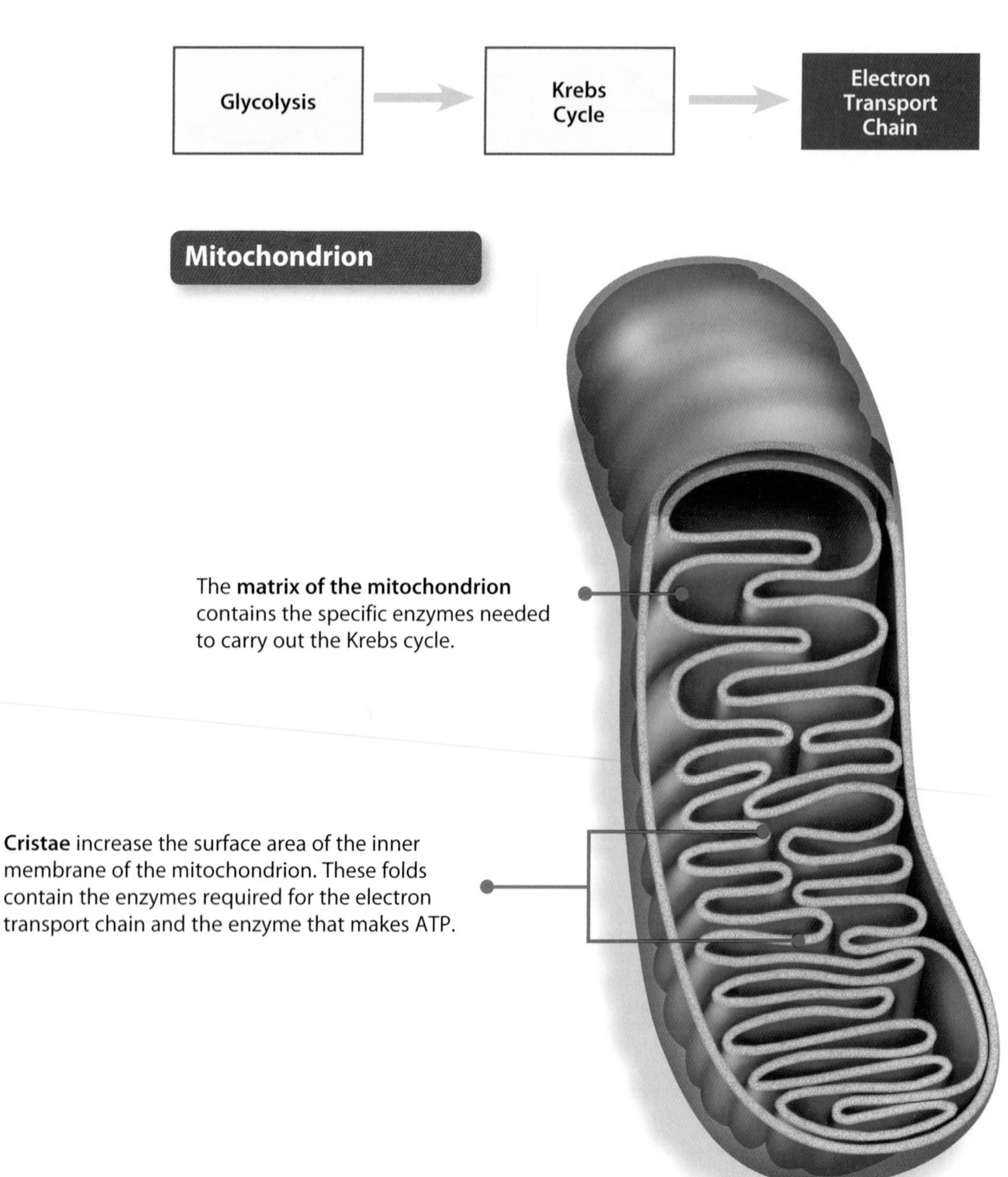

The **matrix of the mitochondrion** contains the specific enzymes needed to carry out the Krebs cycle.

Cristae increase the surface area of the inner membrane of the mitochondrion. These folds contain the enzymes required for the electron transport chain and the enzyme that makes ATP.

The Electron Transport Chain

The third stage of aerobic respiration begins in the matrix of the mitochondrion. NADH and $FADH_2$ produced during the Krebs cycle give up electrons to the **electron transport chain**. As these electrons pass from molecule to molecule in the chain, they pump protons (H^+) through the inner membrane and out of the matrix. When NADH and $FADH_2$ release hydrogen, they regenerate the NAD^+ and FAD used in the Krebs cycle.

At the end of the chain, 1 molecule of oxygen (O_2) accepts 4 electrons and 4 hydrogen ions (H^+), which produces 2 molecules of water (H_2O).

Proteins embedded in the inner membrane act as ion pumps. Protons flowing back into the matrix through these proteins drive the formation of ATP from ADP and a phosphate group (P).

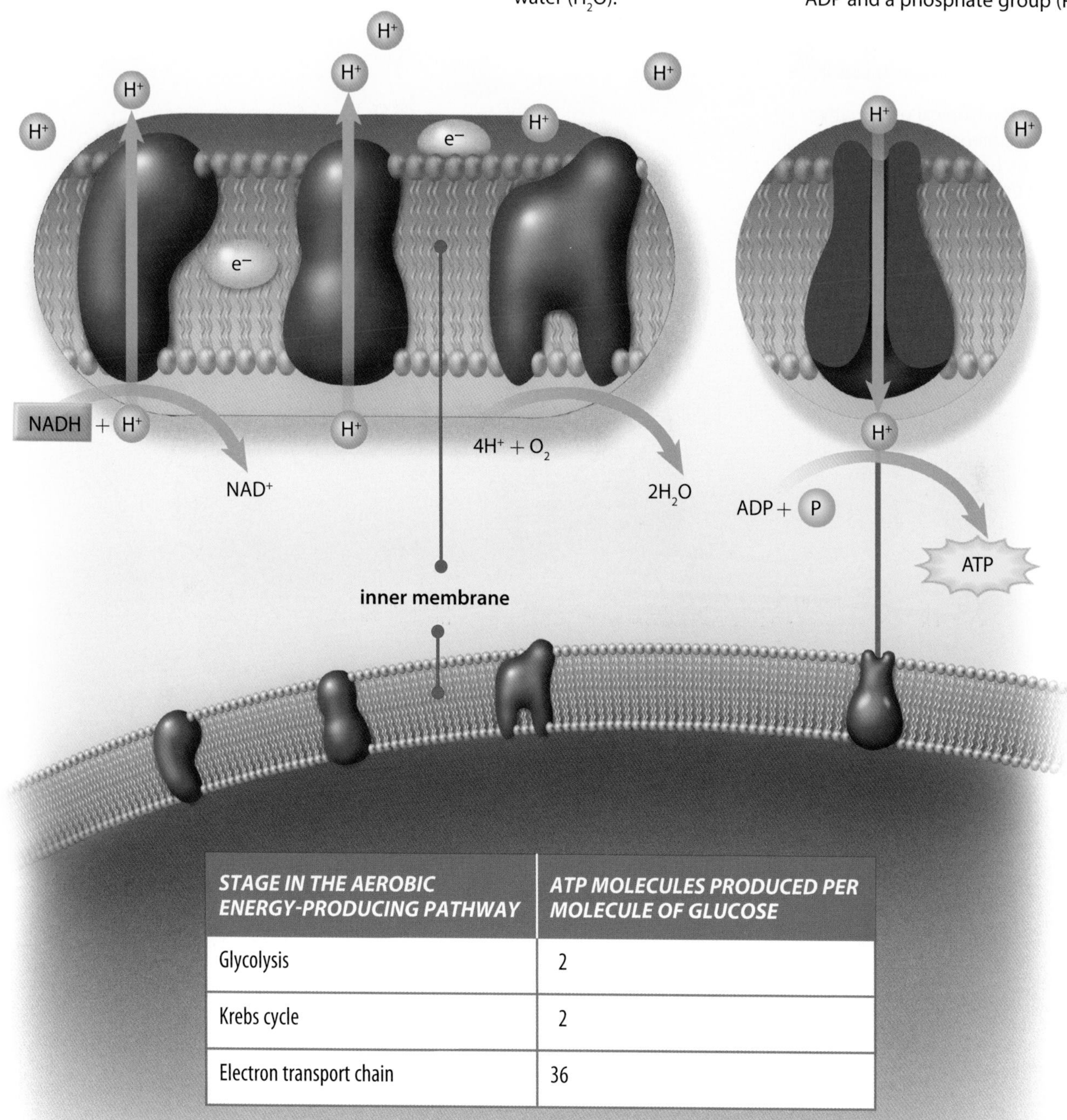

STAGE IN THE AEROBIC ENERGY-PRODUCING PATHWAY	ATP MOLECULES PRODUCED PER MOLECULE OF GLUCOSE
Glycolysis	2
Krebs cycle	2
Electron transport chain	36

Monstera is a tropical plant native to Central America. It has large, perforated, heart-shaped leaves. The dark green color is produced by the chlorophyll in the plant's cells. Favorable growing conditions in *Monstera*'s native habitat allow the plant to photosynthesize year-round.

The sun provides the energy that drives almost all biological processes on earth.

Organisms cannot use light energy directly, however. They must convert it into chemical energy. In all photosynthetic organisms, the structures responsible for capturing light energy are called *chloroplasts*.

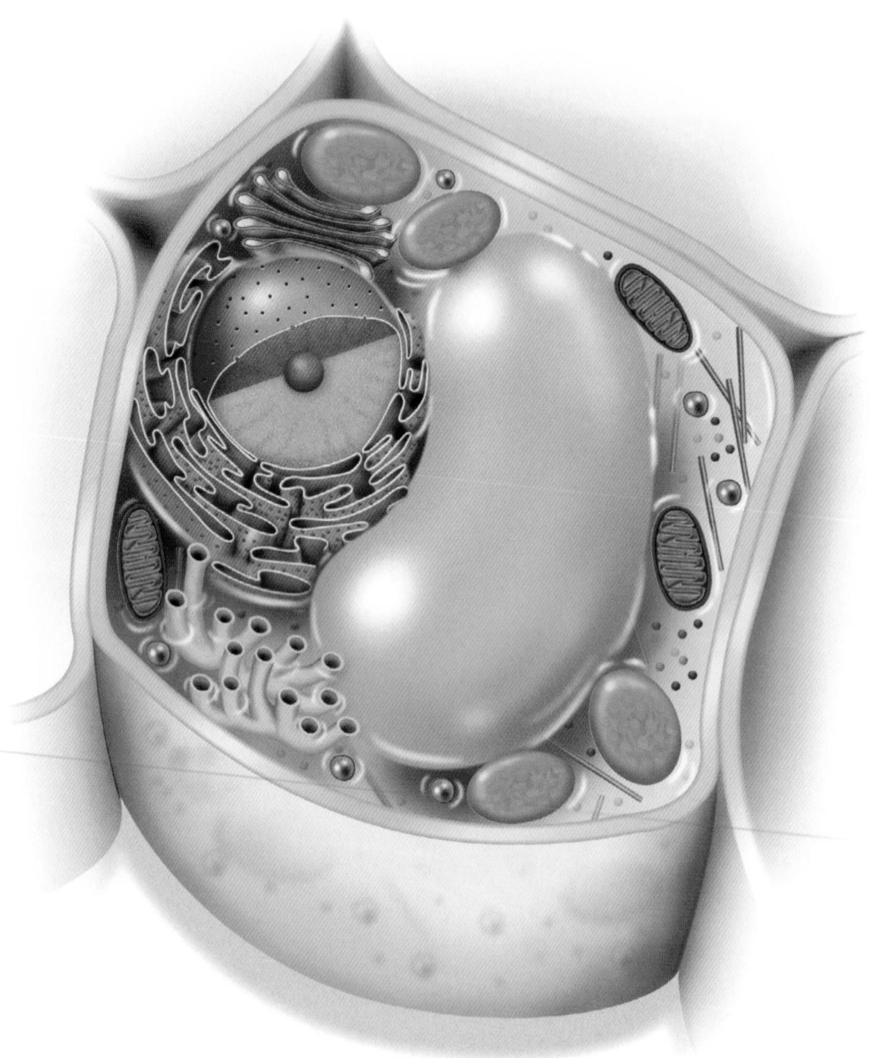

Plant and animal cells have many common features, but **plant cells** have several structures that animal cells do not. A plant cell has a cell wall outside the cell membrane, a large central vacuole, and chloroplasts. Chloroplasts allow plants to produce their own food by photosynthesis.

Chloroplast

A **chloroplast** contains all the chemicals necessary for photosynthesis, as long as it gets carbon dioxide from the air. The pigment chlorophyll is a key molecule in photosynthesis. Chlorophyll absorbs sunlight and transforms light energy to chemical energy that is used to generate NADPH. Chlorophyll absorbs violet, blue, and red wavelengths of light. Plants look green because chlorophyll reflects green light.

The fluid part of the chloroplast is called the **stroma**. It contains DNA, ribosomes, and all the enzymes needed during certain stages of photosynthesis.

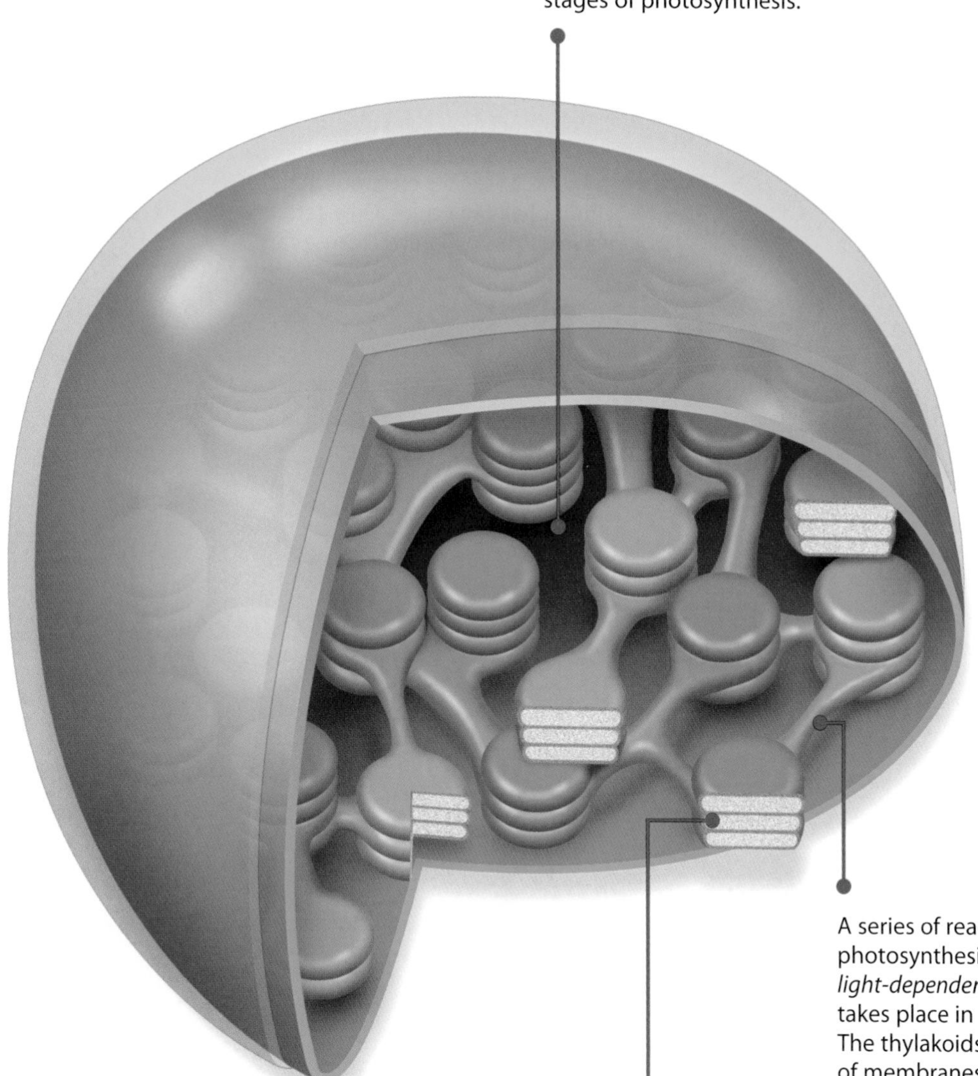

A series of reactions during photosynthesis called *light-dependent reactions* takes place in the **thylakoids**. The thylakoids are a system of membranes within the chloroplast. These interconnected membranes are arranged in flat stacks and contain proteins used in the formation of ATP.

The thylakoids form layered stacks called **grana** (singular, *granum*). Each thylakoid consists of a membrane surrounding an open space.

Photosynthetic organisms use water, carbon dioxide, and energy from the sun to produce oxygen and glucose.

In the first stage of photosynthesis, chlorophyll captures light energy from the sun, which allows a number of chemical reactions to occur. The Calvin cycle is a later stage of photosynthesis in which carbon dioxide from the atmosphere is converted into sugars.

Chlorophyll molecules absorb certain wavelengths of sunlight. The energy in this light excites electrons in the chlorophyll molecules. Only certain wavelengths of light will cause this excitation.

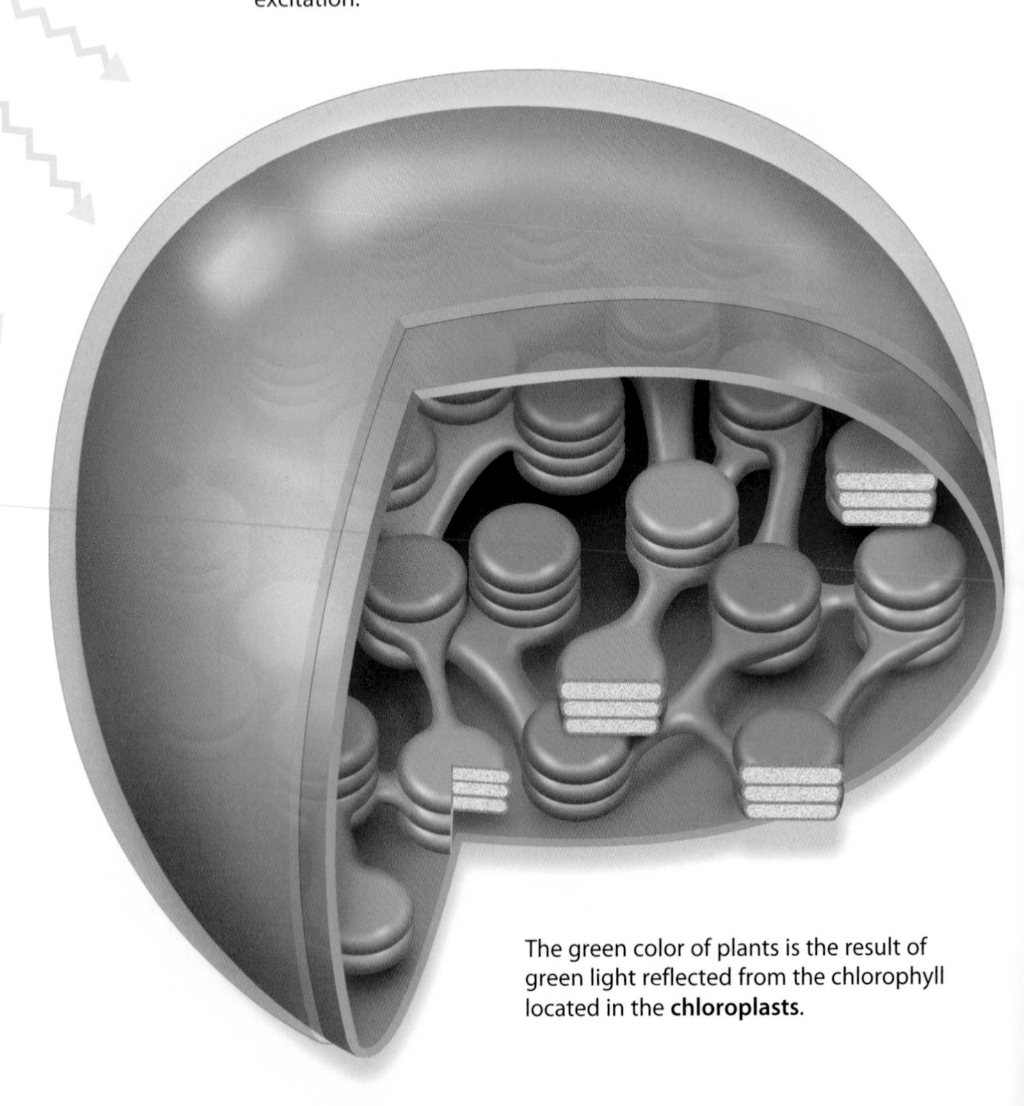

The green color of plants is the result of green light reflected from the chlorophyll located in the **chloroplasts**.

The Calvin Cycle

1 In the **first step** of the Calvin cycle, 1 carbon dioxide molecule enters the stroma. There, it binds with 1 molecule of ribulose bisphosphate or RuBP. This reaction produces 1 6-carbon molecule, which immediately splits into 2 molecules of a 3-carbon compound called *3-PGA (3-phosphoglycerate)*.

4 In the **fourth step** of the Calvin cycle, the remaining 5 G3P molecules combine with phosphate ions from ATP. This process produces 3 molecules of RuBP, which can then be used to start the cycle again.

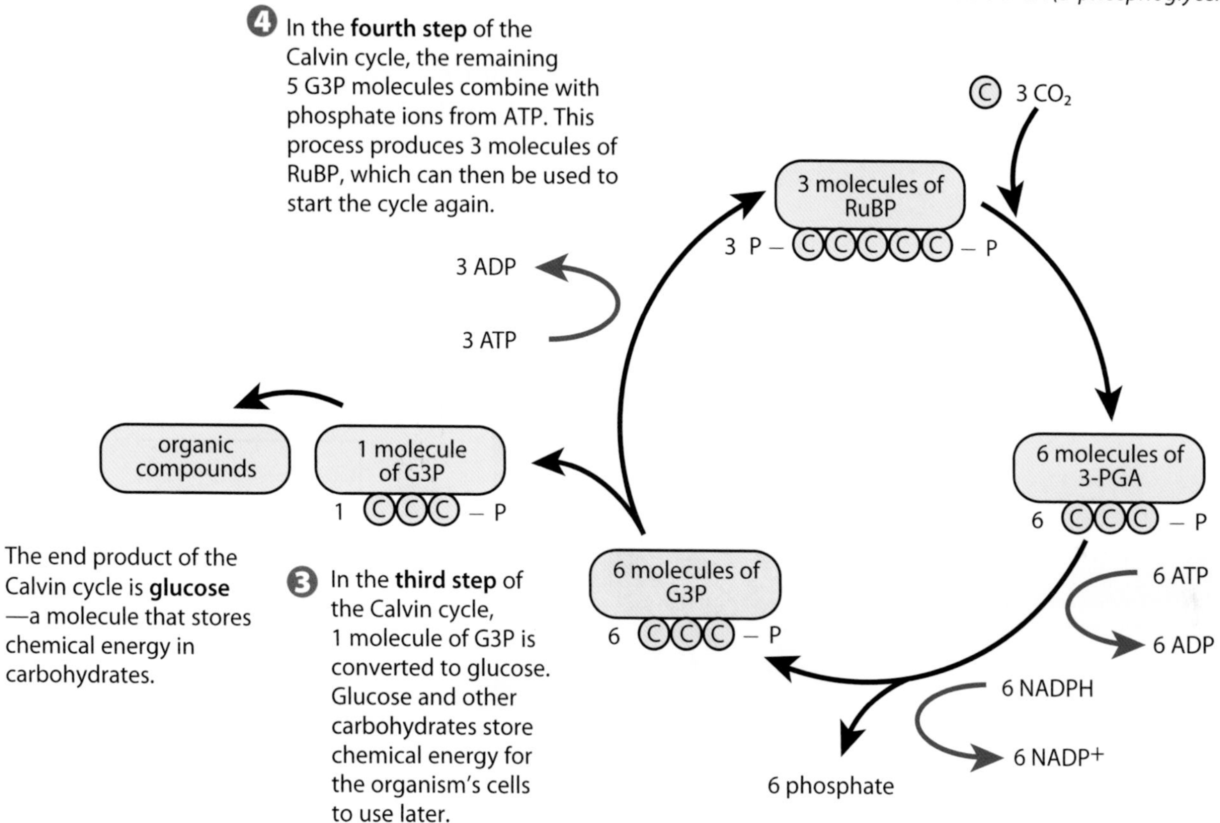

The end product of the Calvin cycle is **glucose**—a molecule that stores chemical energy in carbohydrates.

3 In the **third step** of the Calvin cycle, 1 molecule of G3P is converted to glucose. Glucose and other carbohydrates store chemical energy for the organism's cells to use later.

2 In the **second step** of the Calvin cycle, 6 molecules of 3-PGA are converted into 6 molecules of G3P (glyceraldehyde-3-phosphate). These reactions require energy, which comes from the conversion of ATP to ADP and of NADPH to $NADP^+$.

The sun is the source of energy for most living things on earth, but organisms cannot use the sun's energy directly.

Plants convert the sun's energy to chemical energy through a process called *photosynthesis*. They store the energy in glucose molecules. Organisms that cannot photosynthesize, such as animals, get some of this energy when they eat plants. To use the energy, however, cells of most organisms carry out cellular respiration, which requires oxygen. Photosynthesis and cellular respiration are complementary processes: The products of one process are the reactants of the other.

The **sun** provides the energy for most life on earth.

Photosynthetic organisms, such as grasses and other plants, have a pigment called *chlorophyll* in their cells. Chlorophyll captures energy from the sun.

Photosynthesis

solar energy + $6CO_2$ + $6H_2O$ +

$C_6H_{12}O_6$ (glucose) + $6O_2$

Photosynthesis is the process in which organisms use water, carbon dioxide, and energy from the sun to produce sugars.

Many **organisms** rely on the sugars that photosynthetic organisms produce. Although plants make their own food and animals eat food, both plants and animals use a process called *cellular respiration* to get energy from their food.

Cellular Respiration

$C_6H_{12}O_6$ (glucose) + $6O_2 \rightarrow 6CO_2 + 6H_2O$ + energy

In **cellular respiration**, an organism's cells use oxygen to break down glucose. Cellular respiration produces water, carbon dioxide, and chemical energy in the form of molecules of ATP.

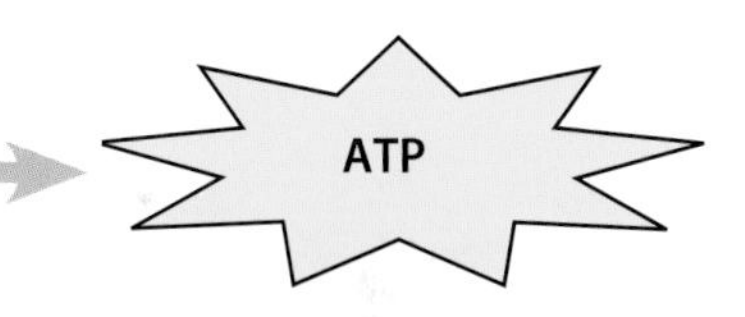

DNA is packaged in the cell as chromosomes, which consist of DNA and proteins wound into tight, compact coils.

Each onion cell contains DNA divided among 16 chromosomes. Each cell contains about a meter of DNA. How does so much material fit into something as tiny as the nucleus of a single cell?

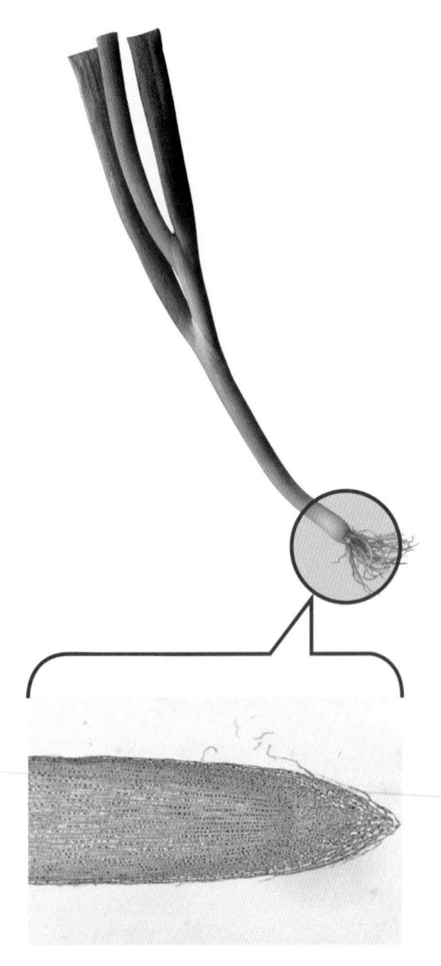

Each cell of an **onion** has a nucleus containing 16 chromosomes. Cells in the root tip of an onion divide very rapidly. Every time a root tip cell divides, both resulting cells inherit a copy of each chromosome.

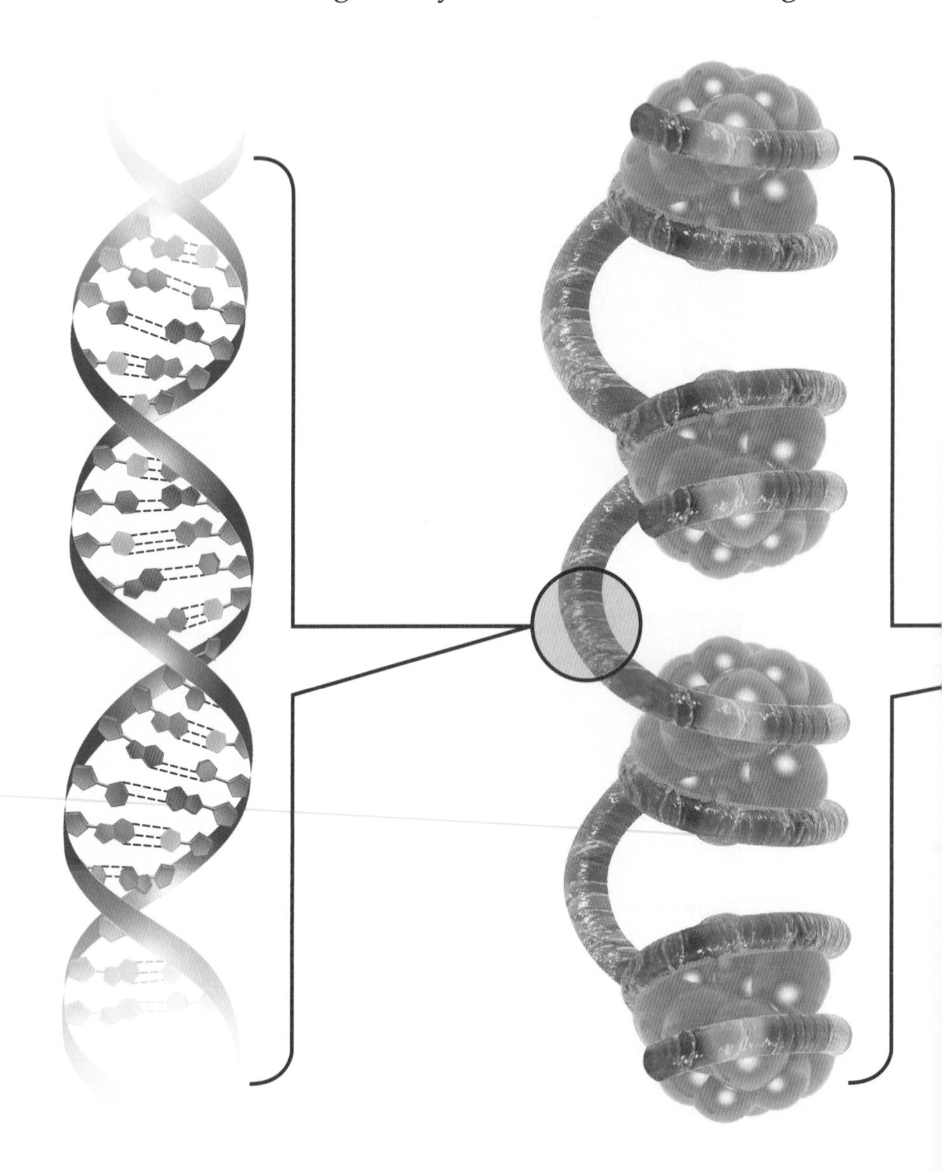

A **DNA molecule** is a double helix consisting of two sugar–phosphate backbones. Hydrogen bonds between pairs of nitrogenous bases hold the two backbones together.

A **chromosome** is a single, long molecule of DNA wound around proteins called *histones*.

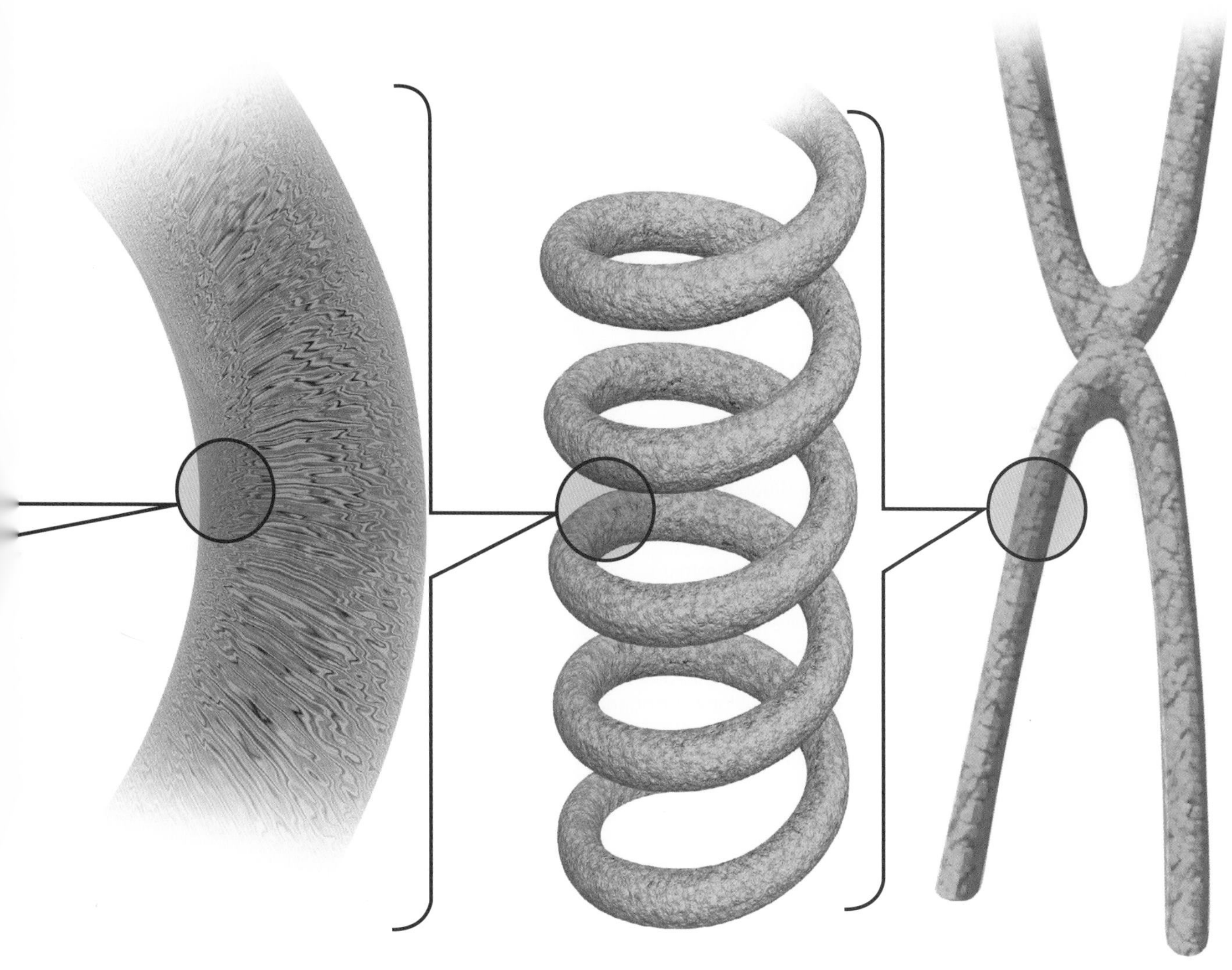

To fit inside the tiny cell nucleus, the DNA and proteins must form tightly **compacted coils**.

The tightly coiled complex winds into **larger coils**.

When a cell is preparing to divide, the cell's DNA and proteins wind together in thick, rod-shaped **chromosomes**, which can be seen with a microscope. The chromosomes consist of two identical halves called *chromatids*, and they are joined at a point called the *centromere*.

Tadpoles undergo metamorphosis to become adult frogs. While some tadpoles have to fend for themselves in a pool or pond as they grow, others, such as poison dart frogs, cling to the backs of their parents until they are ready to survive on their own. During metamorphosis, tadpoles lose their tails and grow legs. These changes occur as cells divide by mitosis and differentiate.

For a multicell organism to grow and develop, its cells must reproduce.

During mitosis, the nucleus of a cell divides to form two nuclei. This process is generally followed by cytokinesis, the division of the cell cytoplasm that produces two separate cells.

Mitosis

Prophase When mitosis begins, the cell has already duplicated its DNA. Each chromosome is made up of 2 identical chromatids connected at the centromere. The chromosomes, which are normally not visible, coil into thick rods that can be seen with a microscope. The nuclear envelope surrounding the chromosomes breaks down, and the spindle starts to form.

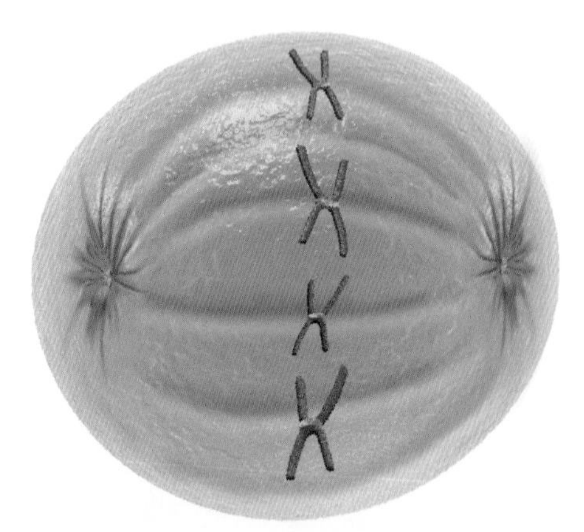

Metaphase The chromosomes line up at the cell equator. They attach to spindle fibers that extend from the two poles of the cell.

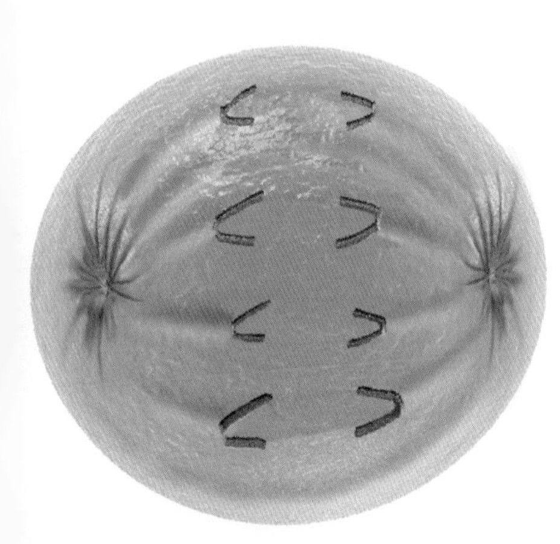

Anaphase The spindle fibers begin to shorten, causing the chromatids to separate and move away from each other toward separate poles. Each chromatid is now a separate chromosome.

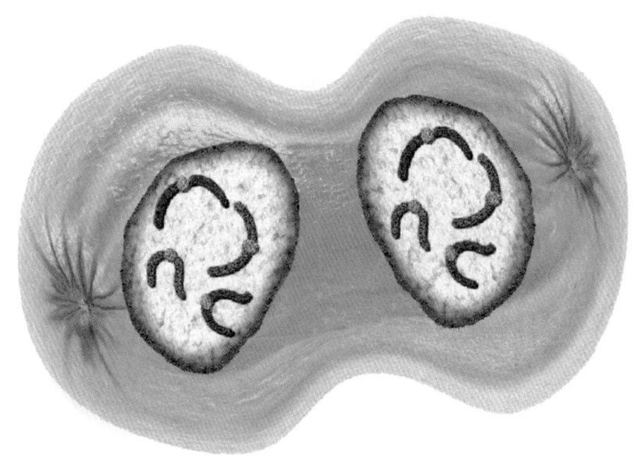

Telophase The spindle fibers break down, and nuclear envelopes form around the 2 separate sets of chromosomes.

Cytokinesis

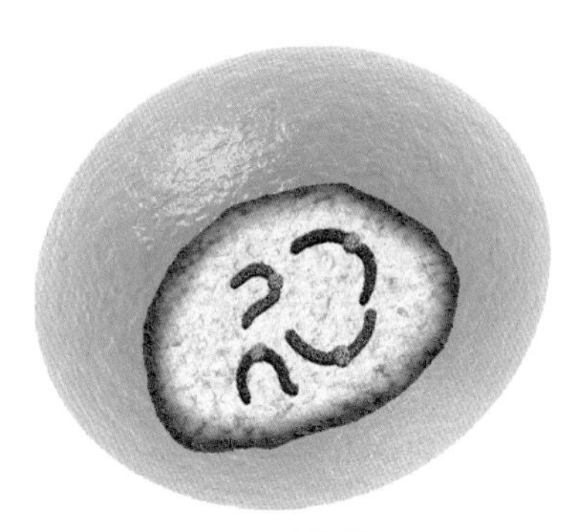

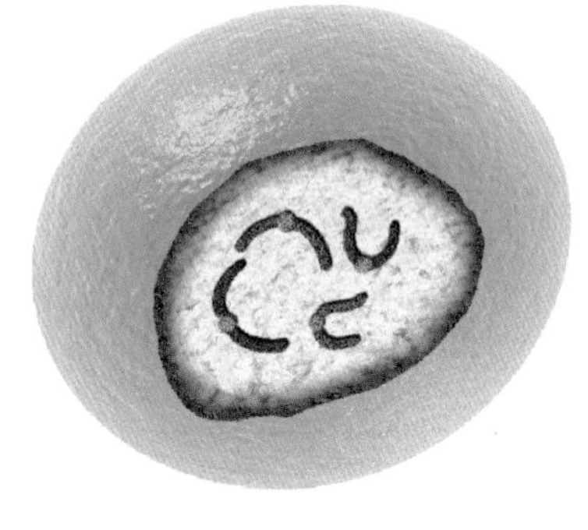

The cytoplasm divides, and the cell membrane grows around each new cell. In place of 1 body cell, there are now 2 body cells. The 2 cells are genetically identical. Plant cells do not undergo cytokinesis, but they form a new cell wall between the resulting cells.

Specialized cells help an organism do its many jobs.

All an organism's cells contain the same genetic information, but they don't all look the same or perform the same functions. Cells that make up skin, muscles, and bones are specialized to give each type of tissue its unique characteristics. For an organism's body to function correctly, all its cells need to work together.

Red blood cells carry a protein called *hemoglobin*. Hemoglobin brings oxygen from the lungs to the cells so the cells can carry out cellular respiration.

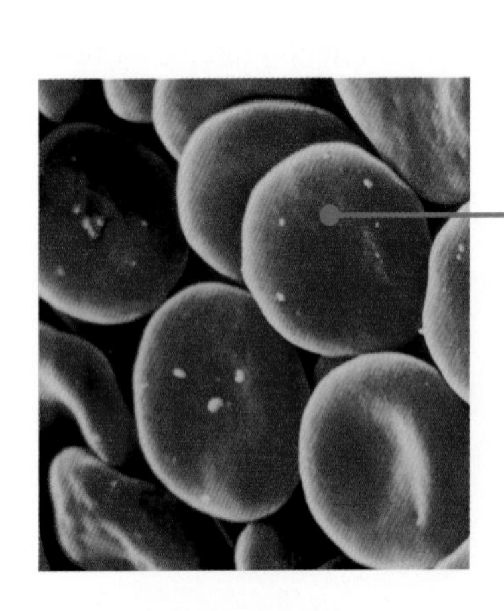

Hair cells produce a protein called *keratin*. Keratin's helical structure makes it very strong. It forms filament-like structures that line up to form hairs.

Bone cells help support the body. They use calcium and phosphate to produce a mineral that makes them hard.

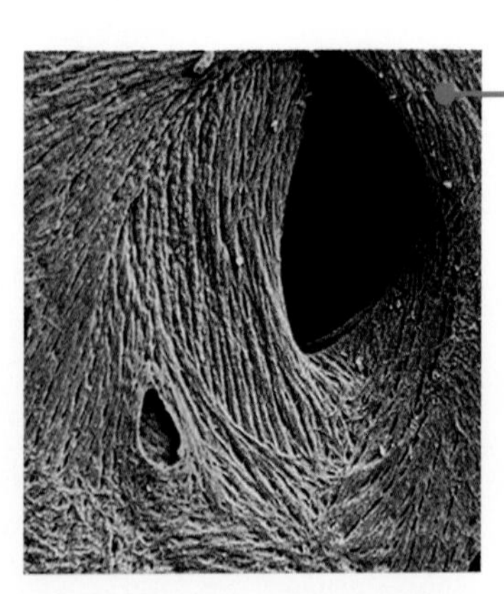

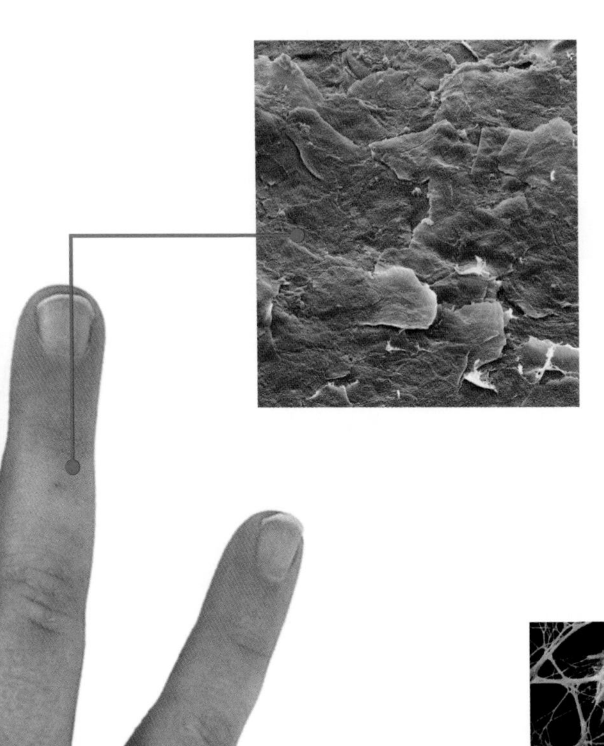

Skin cells produce a protein called *melanin*, which gives skin its color. The amount of melanin that cells produce depends on genetic information and on sun exposure: The more melanin skin cells produce, the darker the skin. Skin cells also help protect the body by blocking pathogens. When dead skin cells slough off, the pathogens go with them.

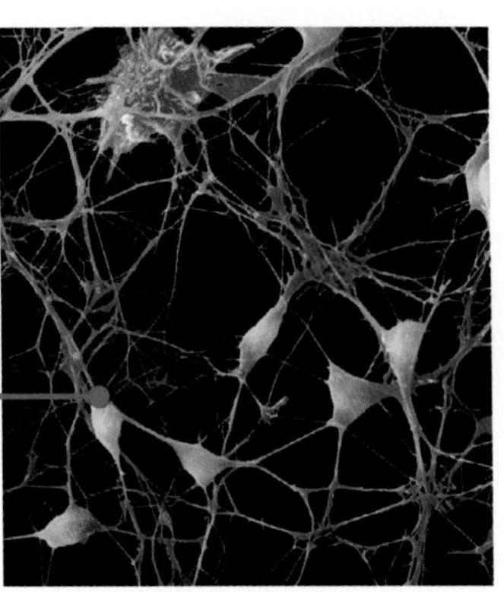

Nerve cells have long extensions called *axons* and *dendrites* that carry electrical impulses. Messages from the brain pass along these axons and dendrites to tell the muscles how and when to move.

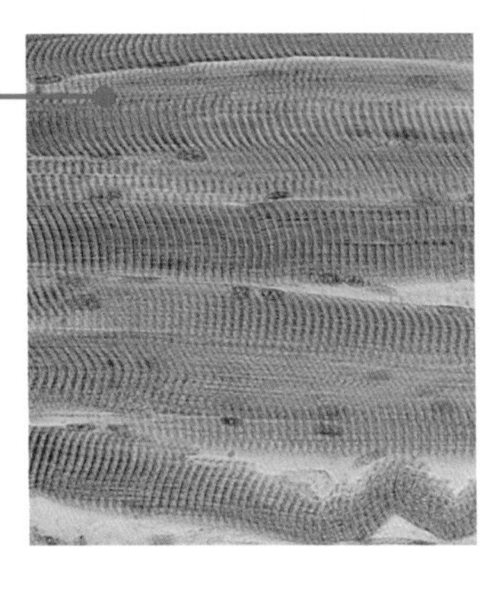

Muscle cells are responsible for movement. They contract when they receive impulses from nerve cells. Muscle cells make protein fibers called *myosin* and *actin*. When they move, they allow a muscle to contract.

Animals that reproduce sexually produce sex cells that contain half the number of chromosomes as a body cell.

Sex cells form during a type of chromosome division called *meiosis*. Meiosis occurs in two distinct parts.

Meiosis I

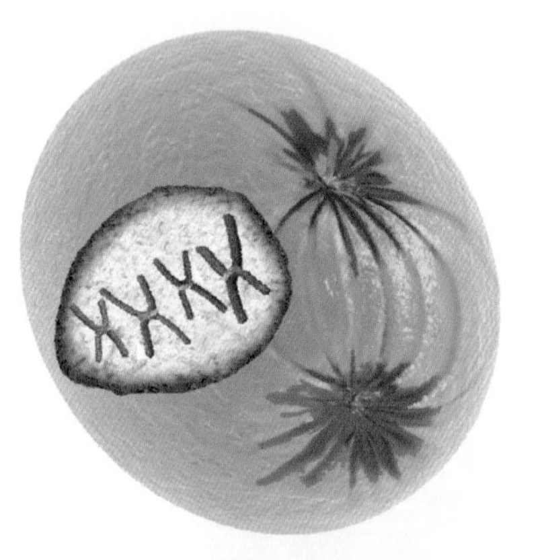

Prophase I This body cell contains 4 chromosomes. Prior to meiosis, the amount of DNA doubles, so each chromosome consists of 2 chromatids joined at the centromere. Each chromosome has a companion chromosome of the same size and shape. Two such chromosomes are called *homologous chromosomes.*

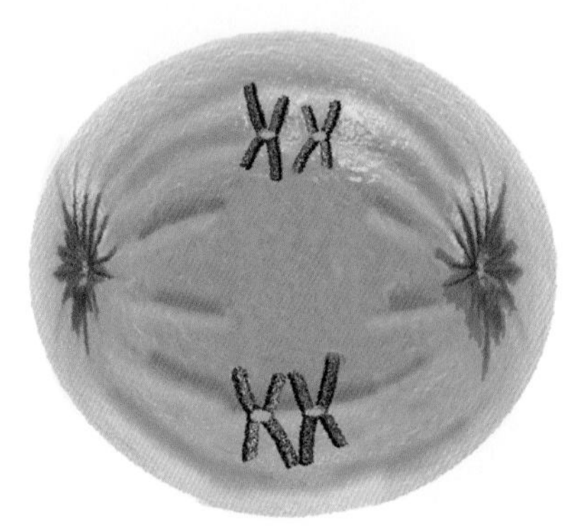

Metaphase I The pairs of homologous chromosomes line up together at the cell equator.

This **stallion** can pass on his genetic information to his offspring. The offspring, however, will receive only half of their DNA from the male. The other half of their DNA will come from the female.

Cytokinesis

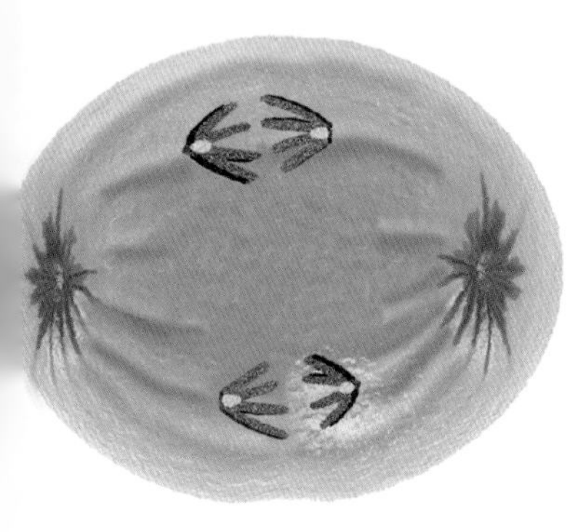

Anaphase I As the cell's spindle fibers contract, they pull the two members of a homologous pair to opposite poles of the cell.

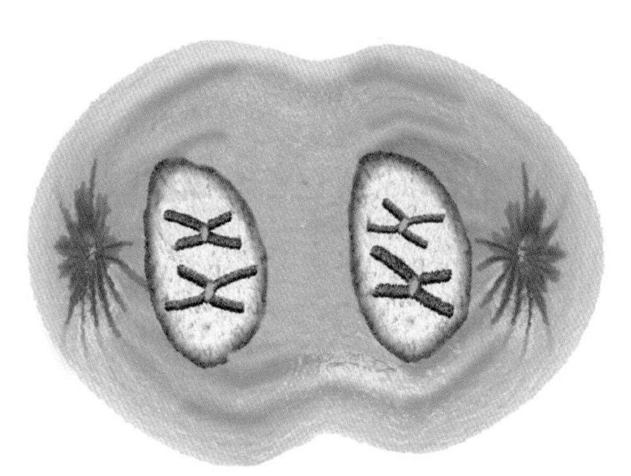

Telophase I Once the pairs of homologous chromosomes have moved to opposite poles, nuclear envelopes form around the 2 new sets of chromosomes.

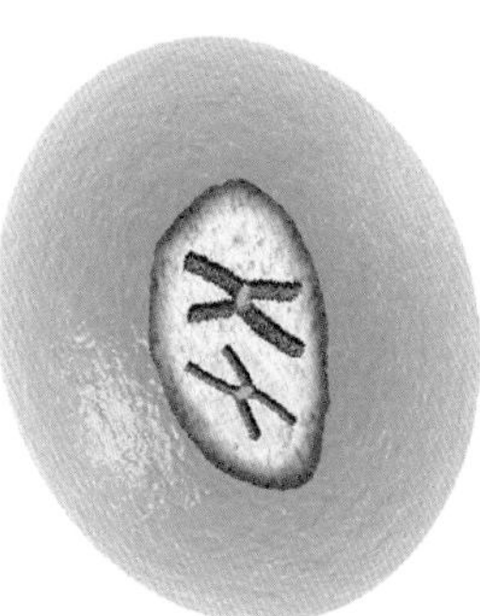

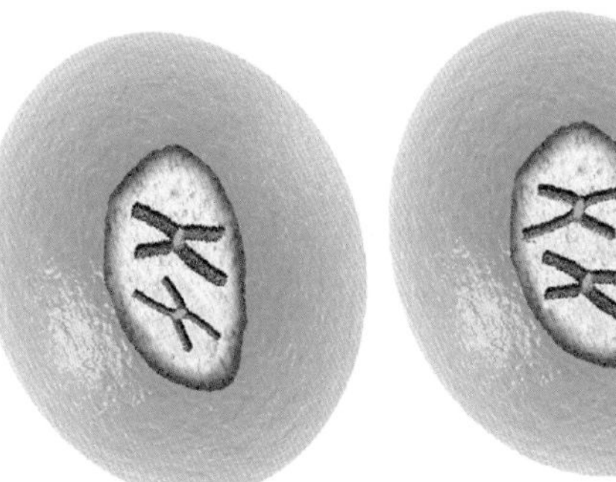

The single cell now divides into 2 cells. Each cell contains half the number of chromosomes of the body cell. However, since each cell has doubled its DNA to start with, a second division—meiosis II—must take place.

During the second part of meiosis, the amount of DNA in each cell is reduced by half.

Without this reduction, gametes would contain twice the DNA as body cells. The fusion of such gametes at fertilization would cause the amount of DNA in an organism's cells to double every generation.

Meiosis II

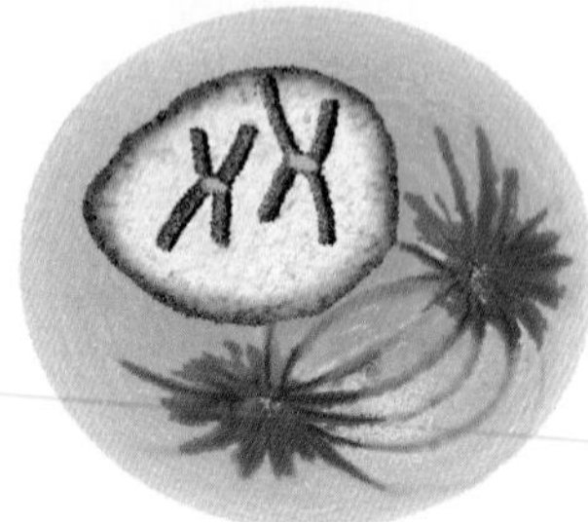

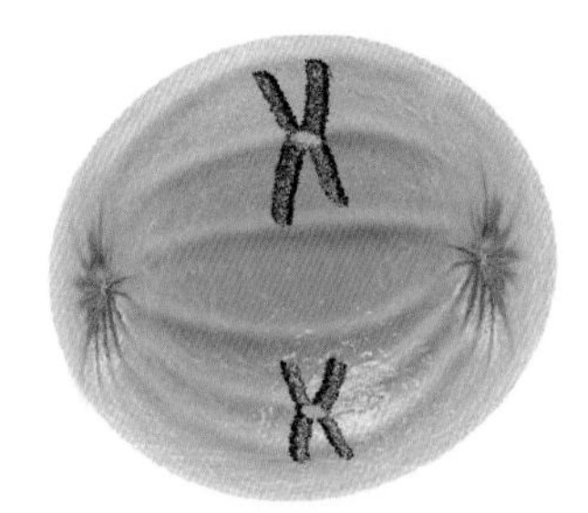

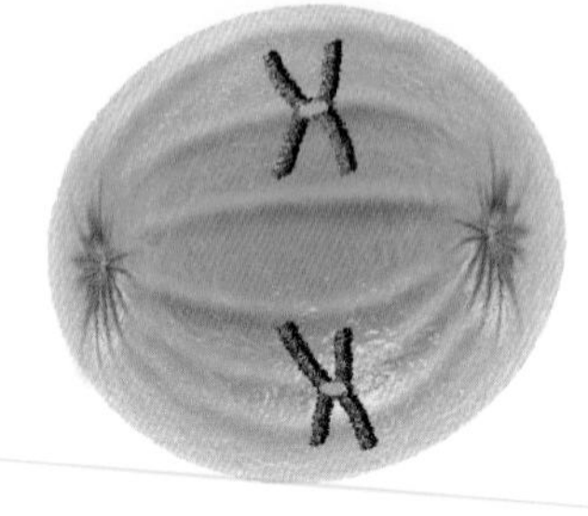

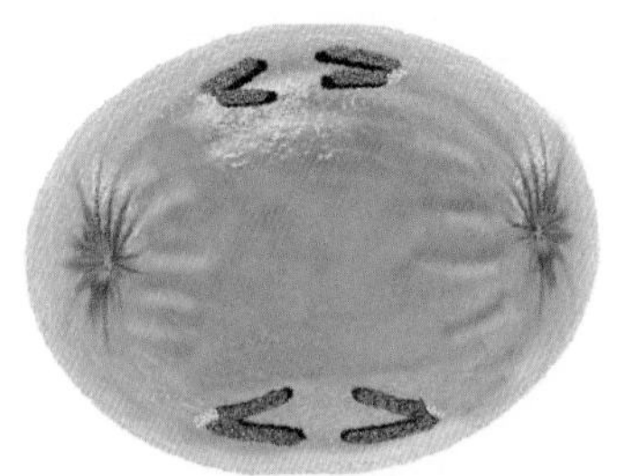

Prophase II The nuclear envelopes break down, and spindles form.

Metaphase II The chromosomes line up at the equator of the cell and attach by the centromeres to spindle fibers.

Anaphase II As the spindle fibers contract, they pull the chromatids to opposite poles.

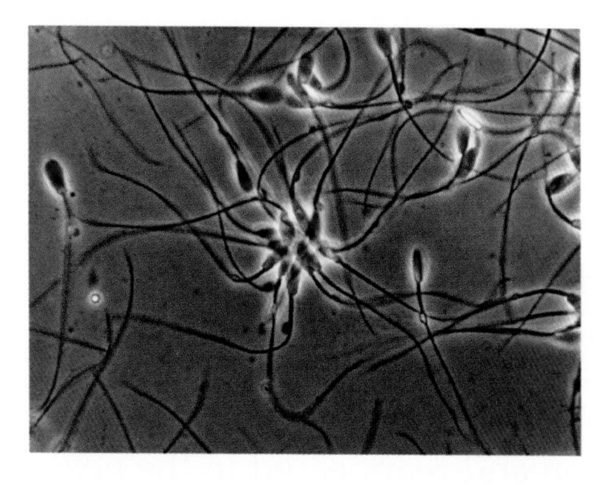

Like all sex cells, these **sperm** are haploid (1*n*)—meaning they contain only half the number of chromosomes that other body cells contain. When a sperm and an egg fuse at fertilization, they form a diploid (2*n*) zygote—the zygote contains two sets of chromosomes.

Cytokinesis

Differentiation

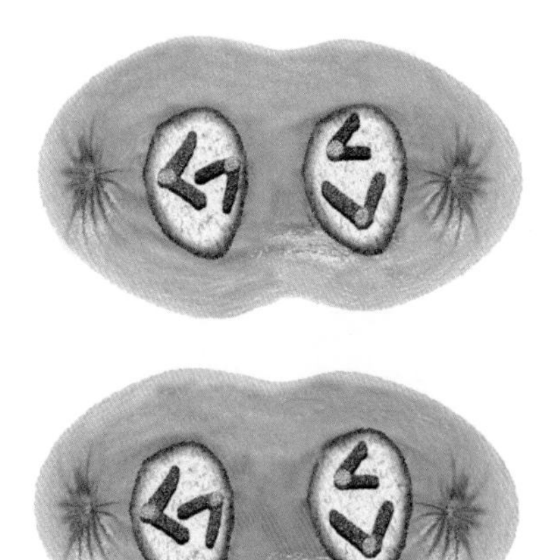

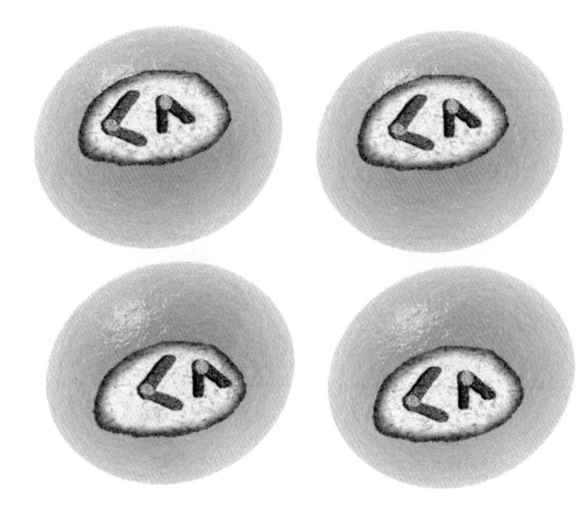

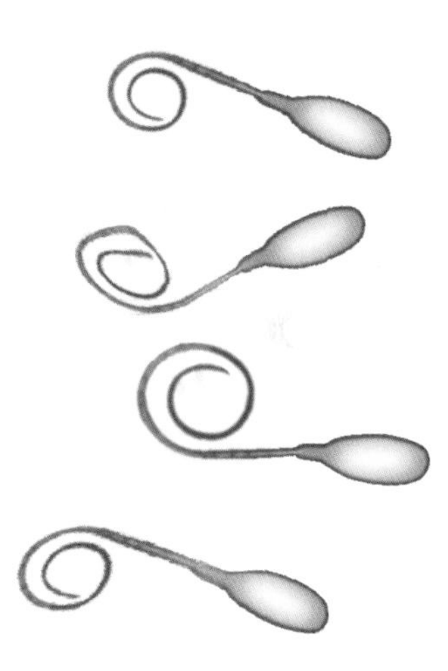

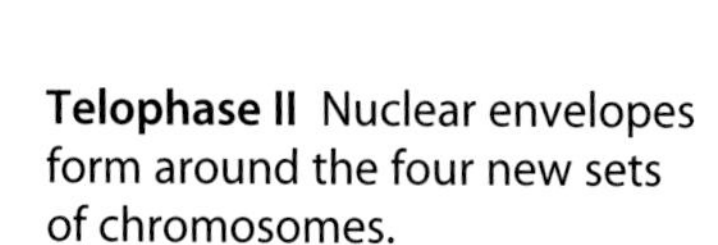

Telophase II Nuclear envelopes form around the four new sets of chromosomes.

The cytoplasm divides, and a cell membrane forms around each new cell. Each cell has half the number of chromosomes of the body cell.

In a male horse, each cell then differentiates to become a sperm cell. The process has produced four sperm cells. Each sperm is haploid—it has half the usual chromosome number for the species.

Gregor Mendel's scientific studies of heredity in pea plants established the field of modern genetics.

Mendel's studies focused on the different forms or traits of seven characteristics of pea plants. Mendel observed the traits of several generations of pea plant offspring and analyzed the patterns of inheritance for each trait. He found that some traits disappeared in one generation and reappeared in the next. These observations led him to conclude that inherited traits are passed in discrete units from parent to offspring.

SEVEN CHARACTERISTICS OF PEA PLANTS STUDIED BY MENDEL

CHARACTERISTIC	*TRAITS*	
Flower color	Purple	White
Seed color	Green	Yellow
Seed shape	Round	Wrinkled
Pod color	Green	Yellow
Pod shape	Rounded	Constricted
Flower position	Terminal	Axial
Plant height	Short	Tall

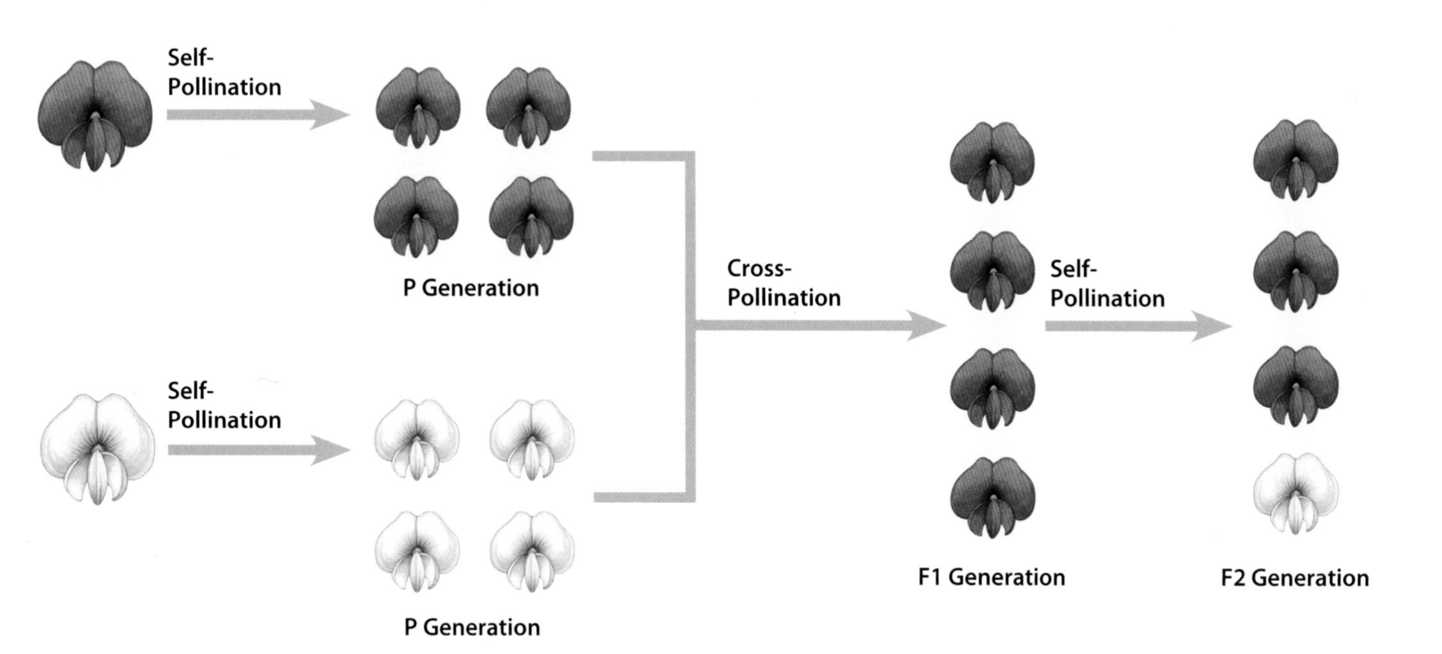

DEFINITION OF TERMS	
TERM	***DEFINITION***
Self-pollination	In flowering plants, the transfer of pollen from the anther to the stigma of the same flower or another flower on the same plant
Cross-pollination	In flowering plants, the transfer of pollen from the anther of one plant's flower to the stigma of another plant's flower
P generation	The parent generation: the first individuals crossed in a breeding study
F1 generation	The first filial generation: the offspring of the P generation
F2 generation	The second filial generation: the offspring of the F1 generation

Genetic crosses can reveal patterns of inheritance.

Scientists and plant breeders can **crossbreed** two different plants by brushing pollen from the flower of one plant onto the flower of the other plant. Mendel used this method of pollination in his pea plant experiments to control which plants were crossed.

A monohybrid cross is a cross of two parents that lets scientists examine inheritance patterns for single characteristics. Scientists can predict the traits of the offspring of a monohybrid cross by using a Punnett square. A Punnett square shows the possible gametes—or egg and sperm cells—that each parent can produce, as well as all possible combinations of alleles.

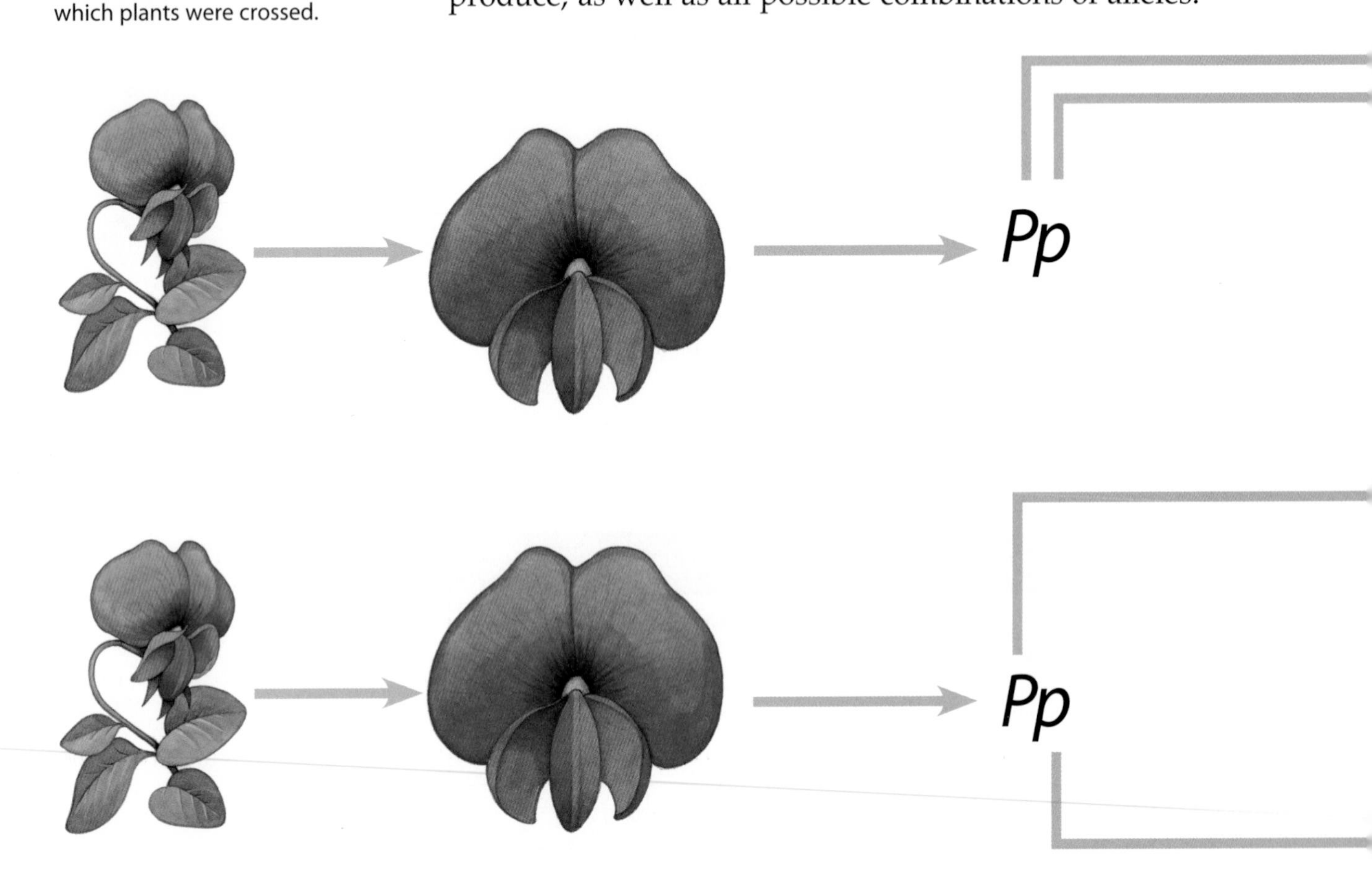

Each of these **pea plants** contains one dominant allele and one recessive allele for flower color. Both plants can produce gametes that contain either a dominant allele or a recessive allele. Because the allele for purple flowers is dominant, an offspring needs only one dominant allele to express the purple flower trait. An offspring will have white flowers only if it receives the recessive allele for white flowers from both parents.

Phenotype

An organism's **phenotype** is its physical appearance. In this example, both plants have the same purple phenotype for flower color.

Genotype

An organism's **genotype** is its actual genetic makeup. Genotype refers to the set of alleles for a particular trait, or the organism's complete set of alleles. In this example, both plants have the same genotype (*Pp*) for flower color. Since the allele for purple flowers (*P*) is dominant, both plants have purple flowers.

Using a Punnett Square

Write the alleles for one parent along the top of the **Punnett square**. Write the alleles for the other parent along the side. The separated alleles represent the possible gametes—egg and sperm cells—that each parent could produce.

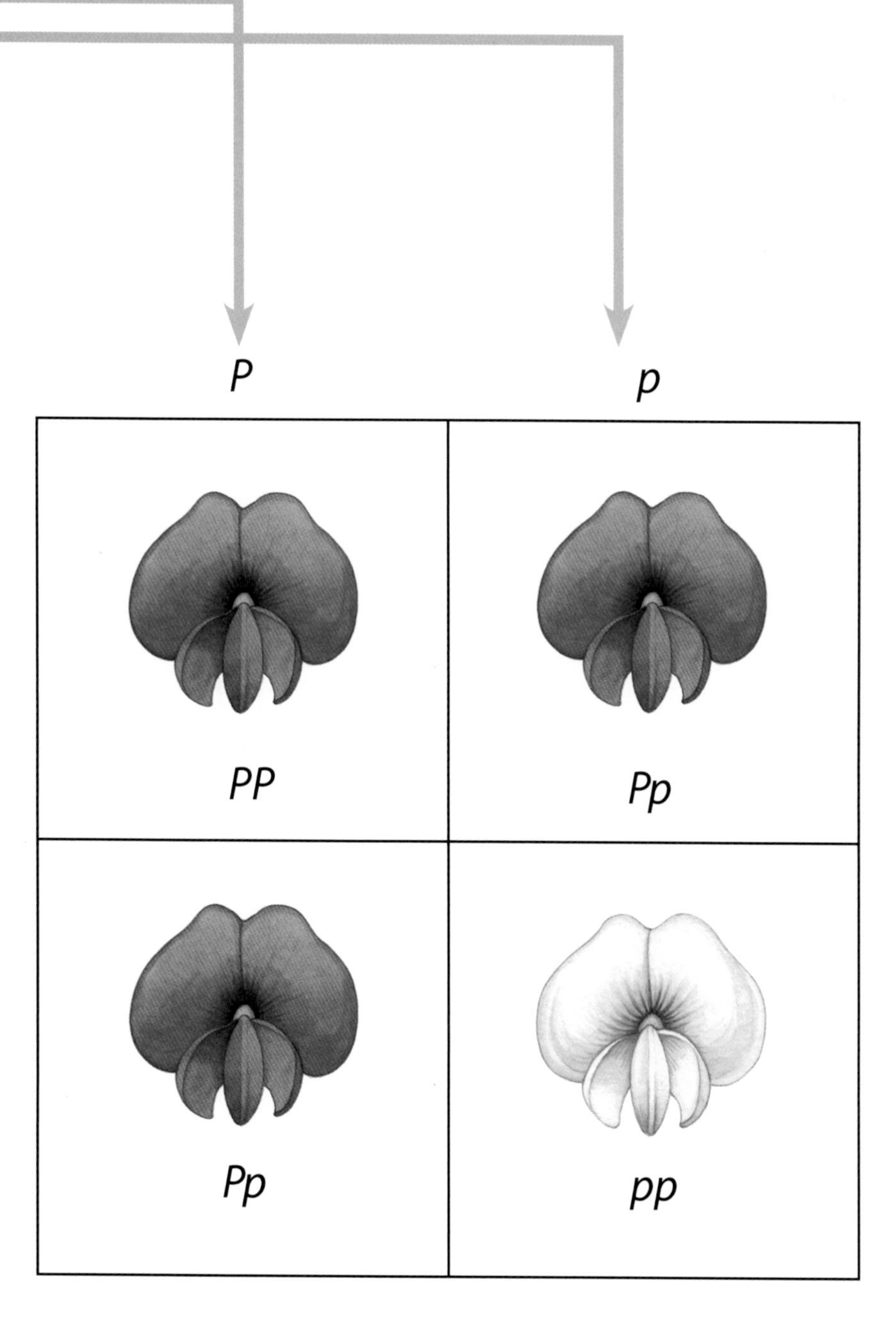

To complete the Punnett square, match each allele from one parent to each allele of the other parent. Then record these **matches** in the corresponding boxes. Each match is a possible genotype for offspring of those parents. Each genotype is a combination of two alleles.

There are three possible genotypes for the cross between the two plants in this example: *PP*, *Pp*, and *pp*. There are only two possible phenotypes: purple and white. The **outcome** of this cross-breeding can be represented by the phenotypic ratio 3:1. This ratio means that one would expect three-fourths of the offspring to have purple flowers and one-fourth of the offspring to have white flowers.

Some alleles show incomplete dominance: One allele is not dominant over another.

In the four o'clocks pictured below, neither allele for flower color shows dominance. Because of incomplete dominance, heterozygotes (*Rr*) have a different phenotype from either homozygote (*RR* or *rr*). For example, homozygotes have either dark pink flowers (*RR*) or white flowers (*rr*). Heterozygotes have light pink flowers (*Rr*).

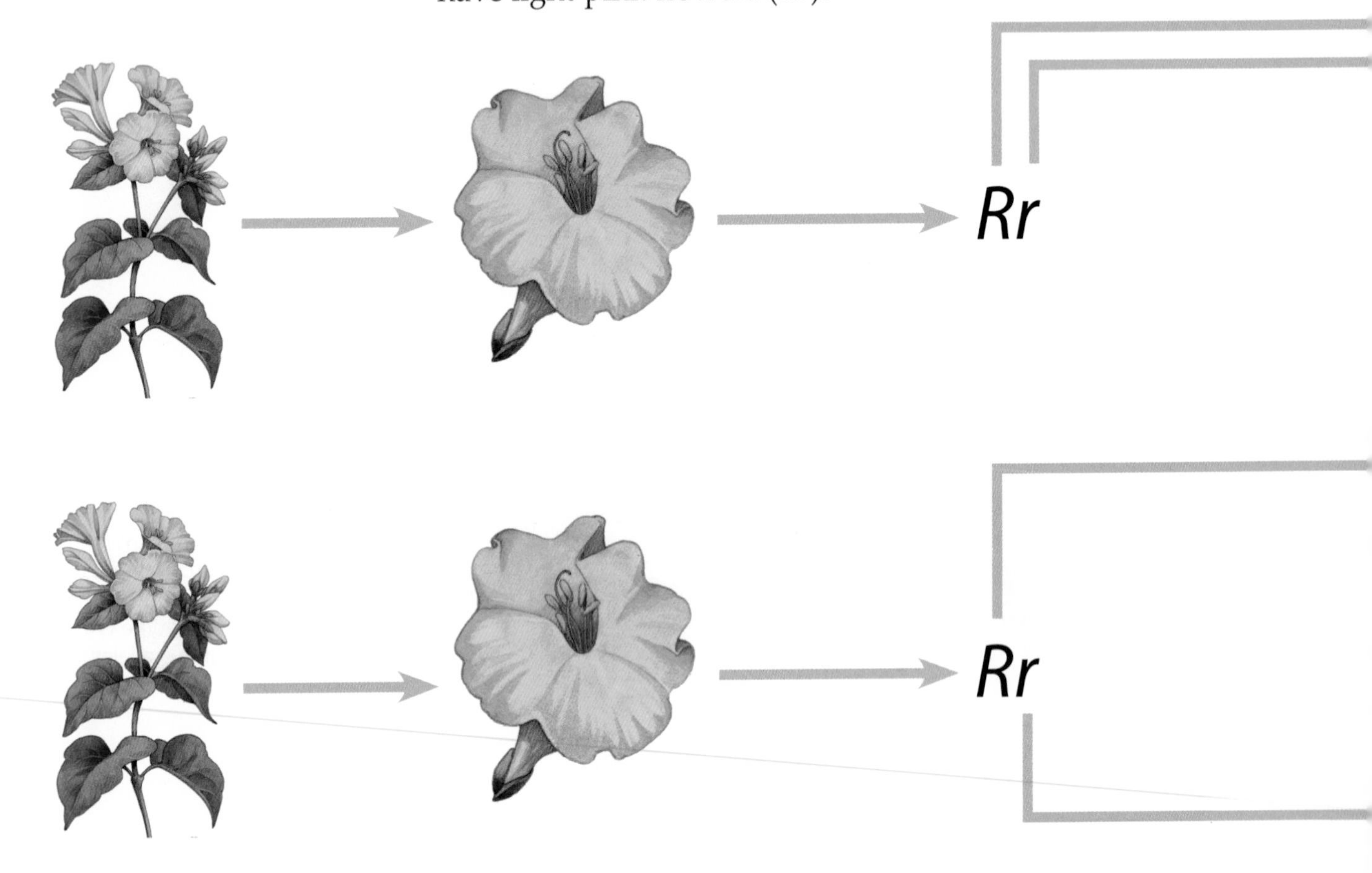

The flowers of **four o'clocks** open in the late afternoon or early evening and close in the morning. Because the flowers are open at night, they are typically pollinated by nocturnal insects such as moths.

Phenotype

An organism's **phenotype** is its physical appearance. In this example, both plants have the same light pink phenotype for flower color.

Genotype

An organism's **genotype** is its actual genetic makeup. Genotype refers to the set of alleles for a particular trait, or the organism's complete set of alleles. In this example, both plants have the same genotype (*Rr*) for flower color.

Using a Punnett Square

Write the alleles for one parent along the top of the **Punnett square**. Write the alleles for the other parent along the side. The separated alleles represent the possible gametes—egg and sperm cells—that each parent can produce.

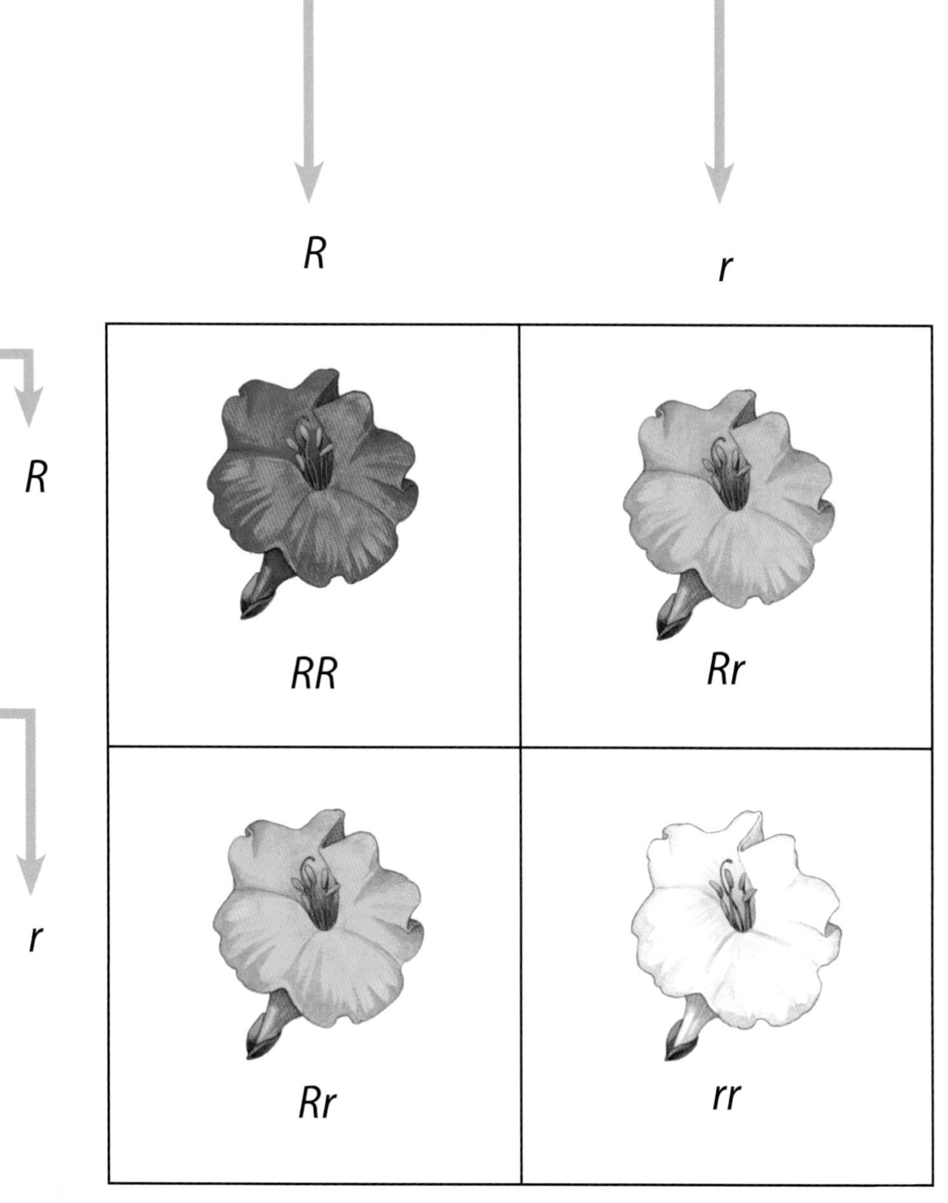

To complete the Punnett square, match each allele from one parent to each allele of the other parent. Then record these **matches** in the corresponding boxes. Each match is a possible genotype for offspring of these parents. Each genotype is a combination of two alleles.

The **outcome** of this cross-breeding can be represented by the phenotype ratio 1:2:1, which indicates the fraction of offspring of each phenotype that you would expect from this cross. Because these alleles show incomplete dominance, each genotype produces a different phenotype. You would expect one-fourth of the offspring to have dark pink flowers, one-half to have light pink flowers, and one-fourth to be white.

A pedigree is a diagram that shows how a trait is passed throughout a group of related individuals over many generations.

The key accompanying a pedigree shows which symbols represent males and females and the colors or shadings that represent individuals with the particular trait.

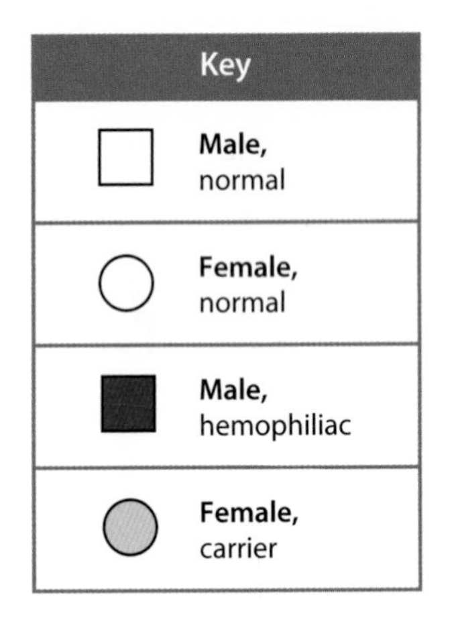

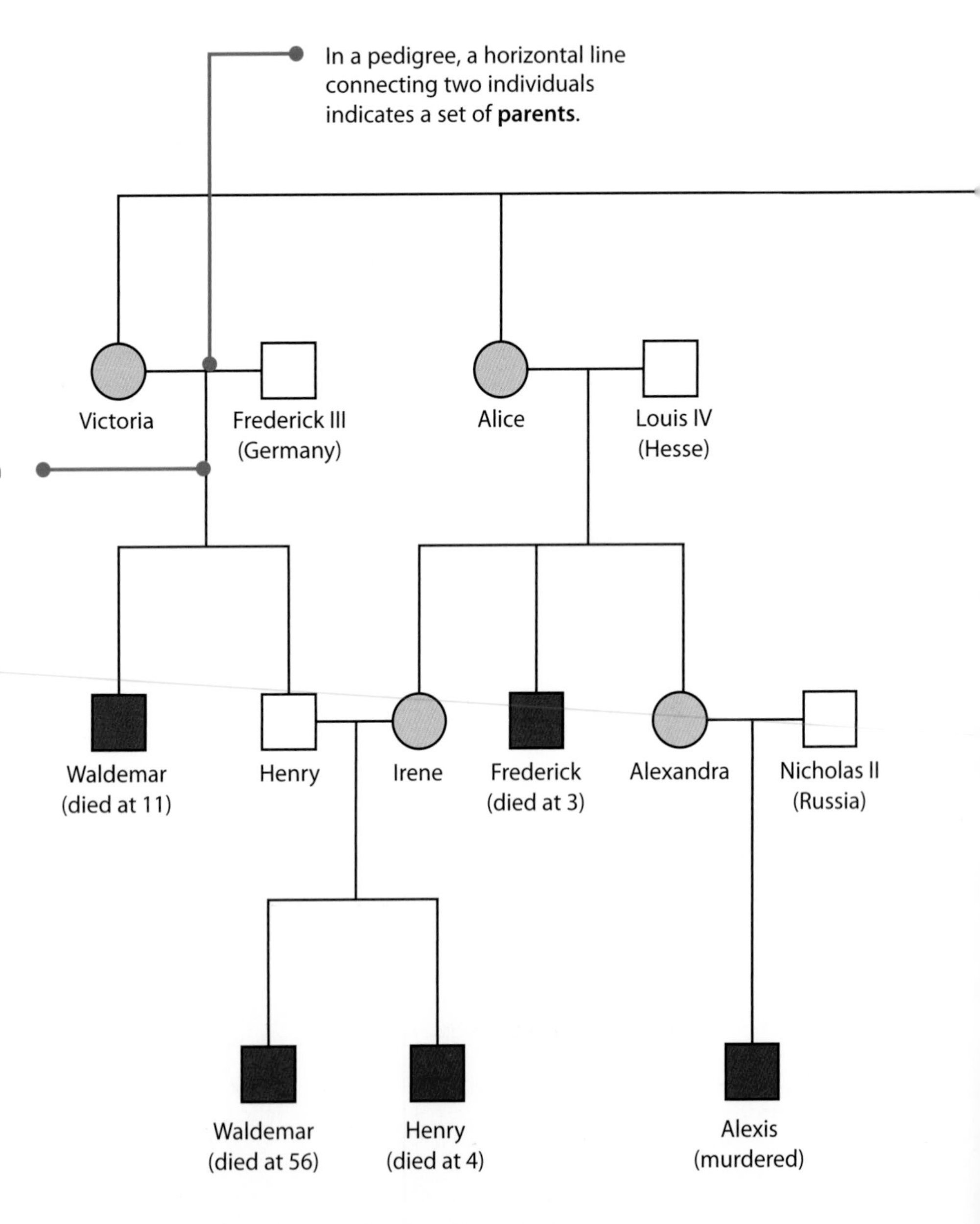

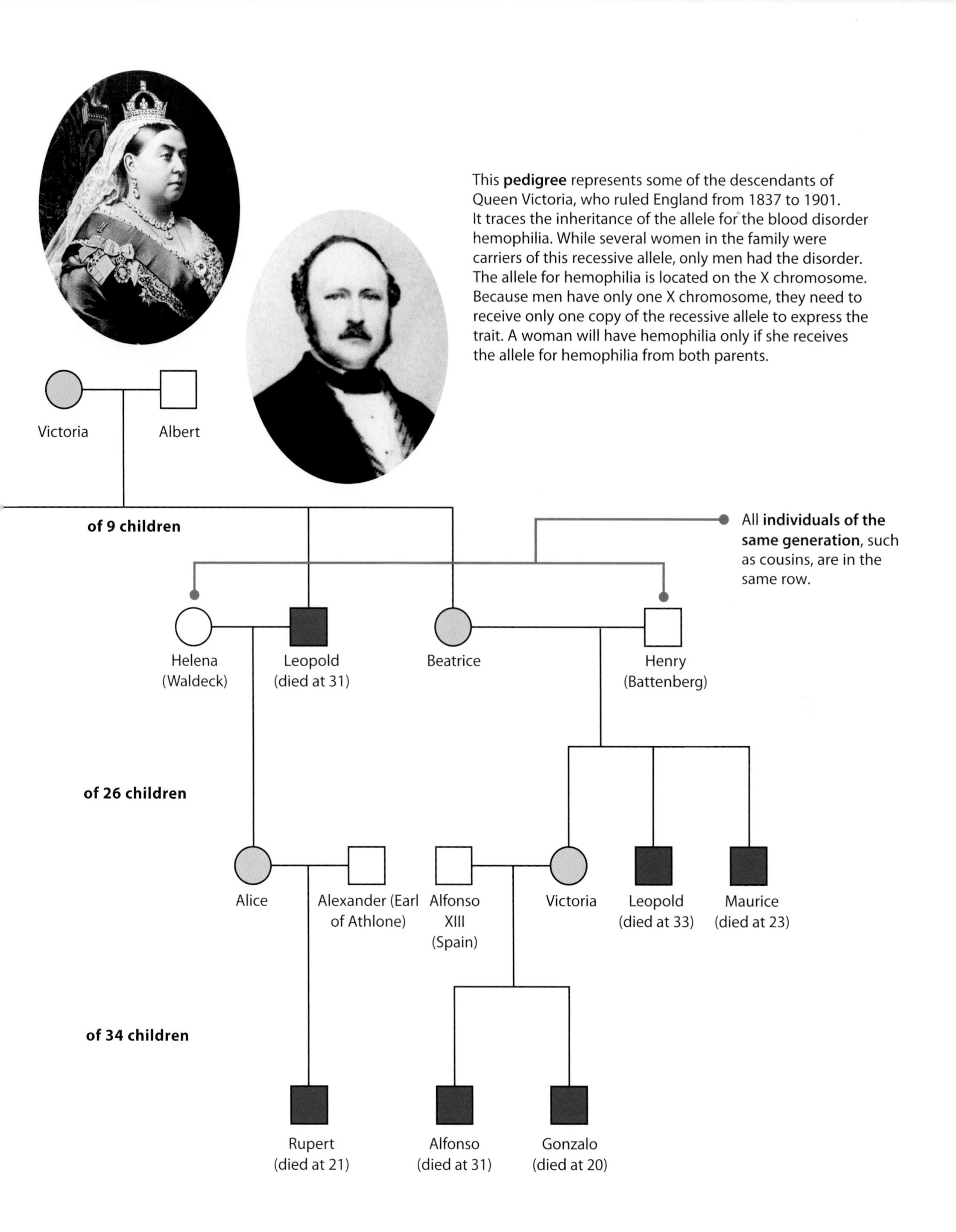

This **pedigree** represents some of the descendants of Queen Victoria, who ruled England from 1837 to 1901. It traces the inheritance of the allele for the blood disorder hemophilia. While several women in the family were carriers of this recessive allele, only men had the disorder. The allele for hemophilia is located on the X chromosome. Because men have only one X chromosome, they need to receive only one copy of the recessive allele to express the trait. A woman will have hemophilia only if she receives the allele for hemophilia from both parents.

Viruses are not living things, even though they have some characteristics of life.

Viruses are not cellular. They consist only of genetic material—either DNA or RNA—surrounded by a protein coat. Like living things, viruses reproduce, but they cannot replicate their genetic material themselves. A virus must take over a cell and use the cell's protein-making processes to produce new viruses. Viruses may infect the cells of prokaryotes (such as bacteria) or eukaryotes (such as humans).

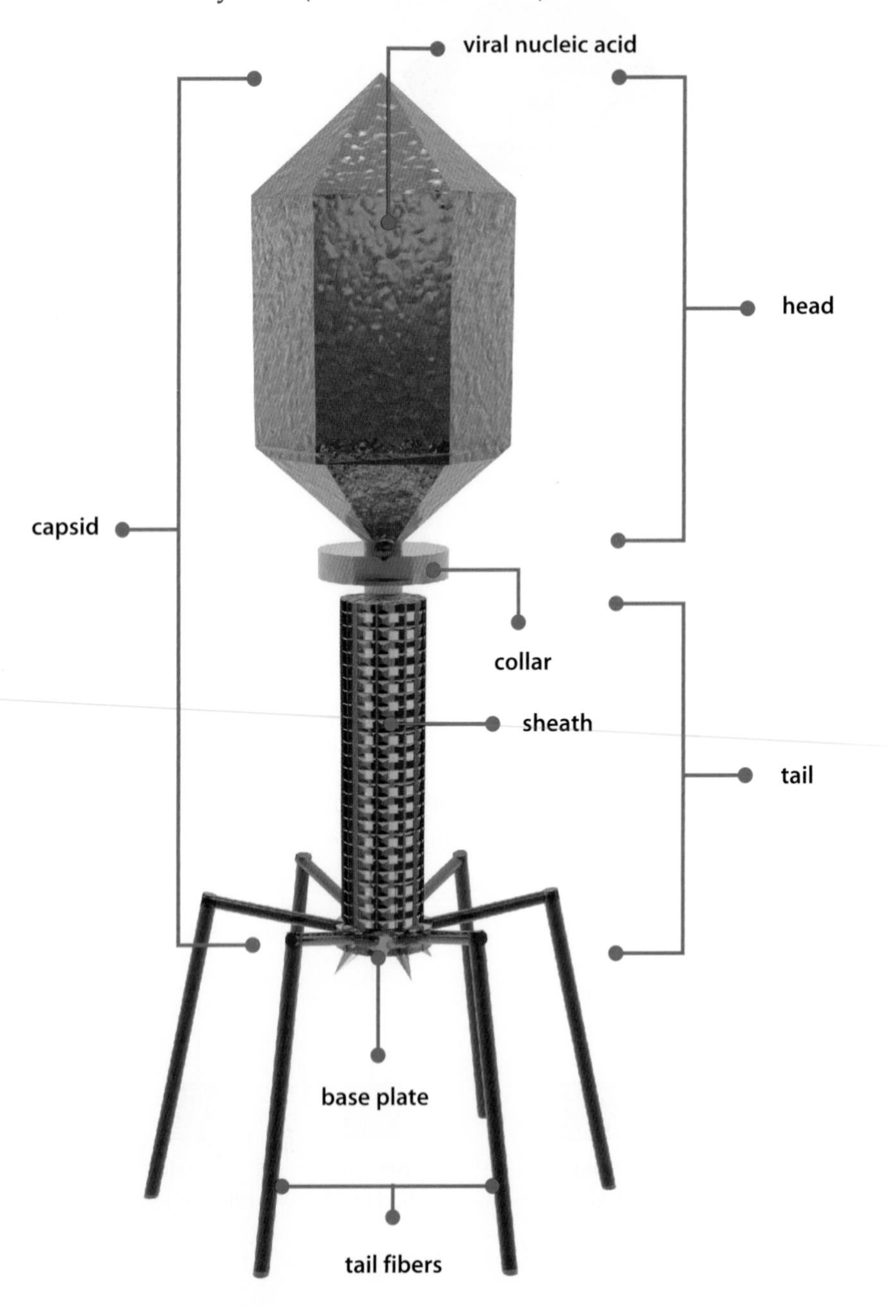

Lytic Cycle

Most viruses replicate using the lytic cycle. At the **first stage** of this cycle, a virus finds and lands on a host, and binds to its surface. Viruses that infect bacteria are called *bacteriophages*. Here a bacteriophage binds to a host bacterium.

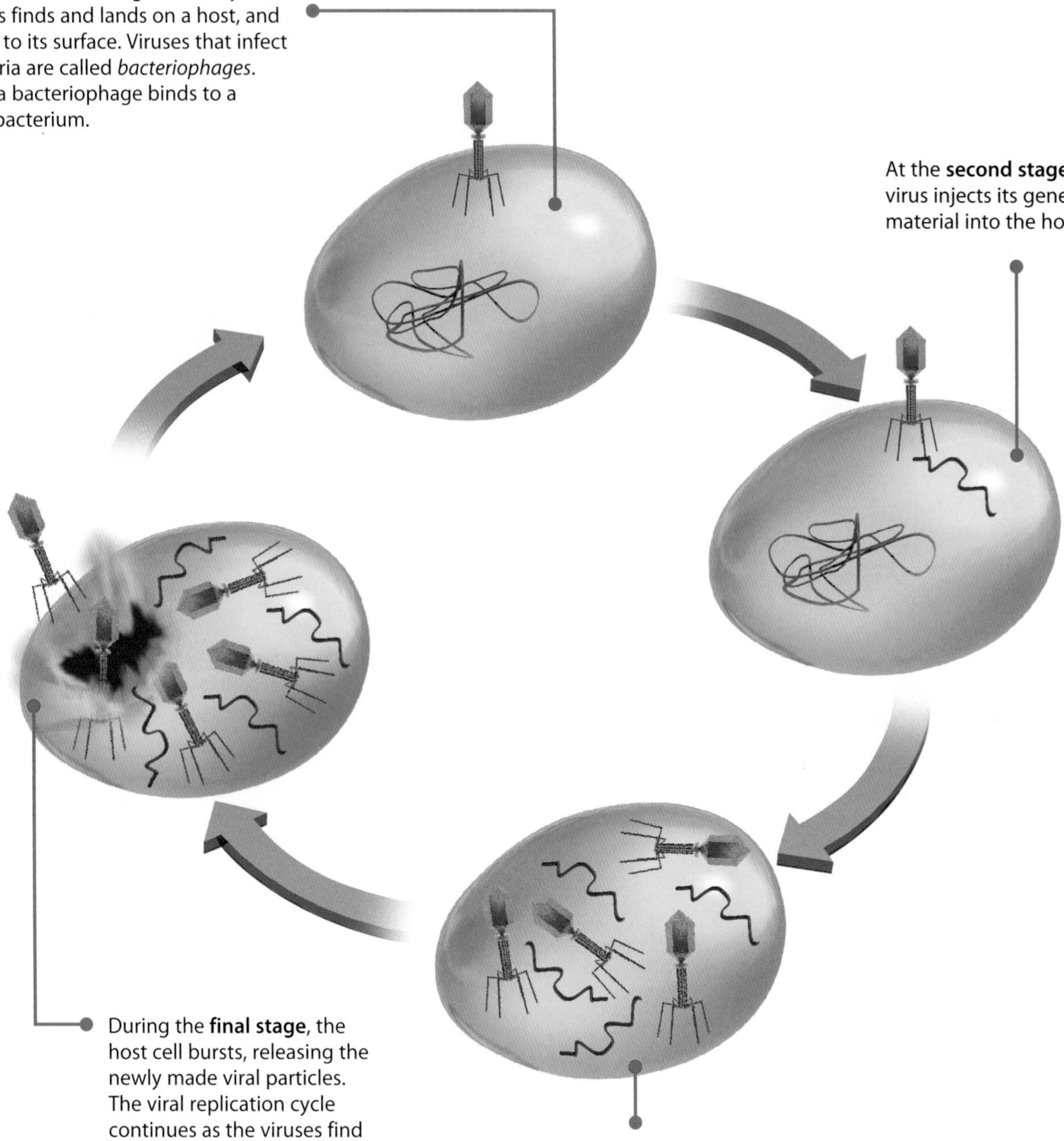

At the **second stage**, the virus injects its genetic material into the host cell.

The viral DNA takes over the host cell during the **third stage** of the lytic cycle. The bacterium begins producing viral proteins and replicating the viral DNA. New viruses form inside the host cell.

During the **final stage**, the host cell bursts, releasing the newly made viral particles. The viral replication cycle continues as the viruses find and infect new host cells.

In 1953, James Watson and Francis Crick, using work done by Rosalind Franklin, discovered that DNA is a double helix.

Solving this mystery was a vital step in understanding how DNA replicates and how it encodes the information that underlies the spectacular diversity of life.

Just like an ant, an apple tree, or any living thing, a **wombat** passes on genetic information to its offspring through DNA. All the instructions for a baby wombat's traits, such as fur color and feeding behavior, are encoded in a precise order of bases in molecules of DNA.

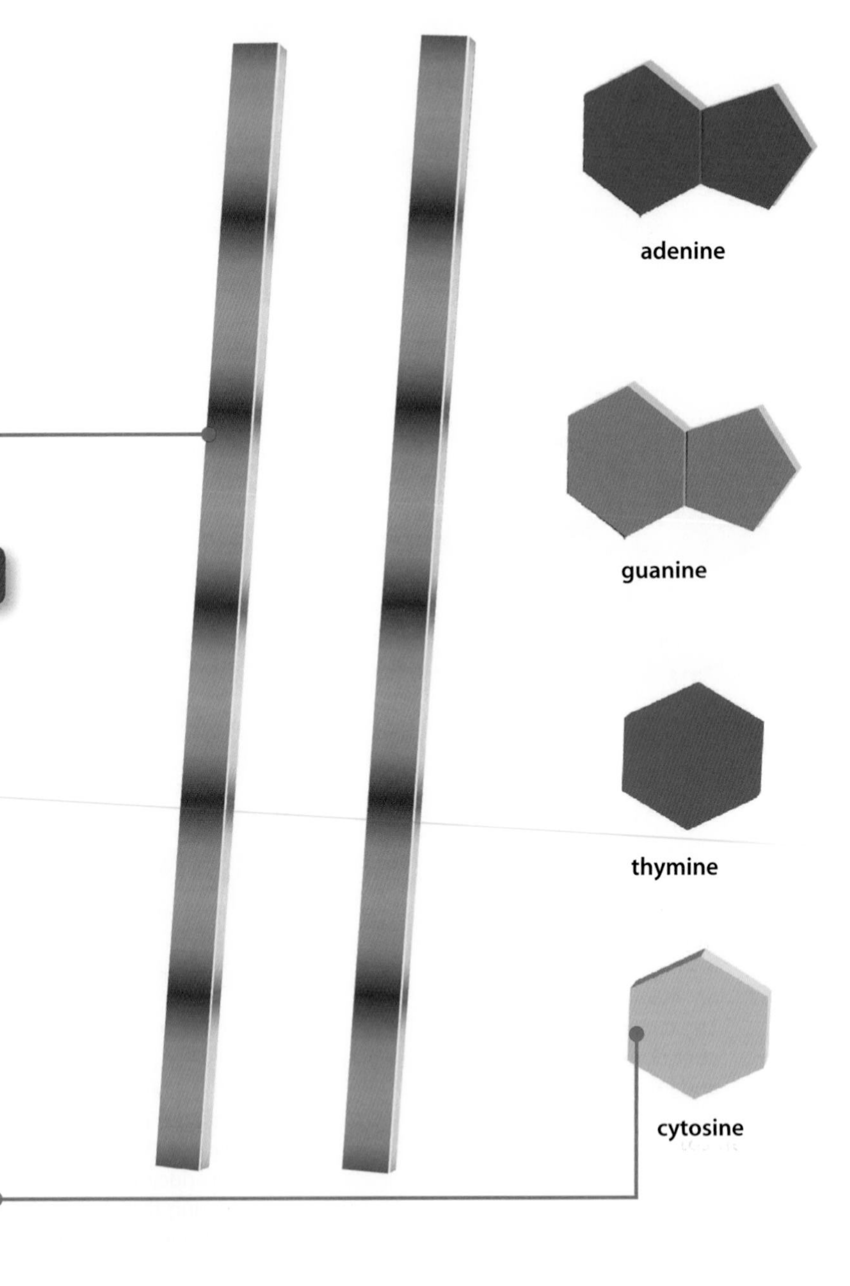

Sugar–Phosphate Backbones

A molecule of DNA looks much like a twisted ladder. The two side rails of this ladder, or **backbones**, are made of alternating deoxyribose sugars and phosphate molecules.

Nitrogenous Bases

Four different **nitrogenous bases** make up the rungs of the DNA ladder: adenine, guanine, thymine, and cytosine. Adenine and guanine are purines. Both contain two carbon–nitrogen rings. Thymine and cytosine are pyrimidines. Both contain one carbon–nitrogen ring.

Pair of Bases

Each rung of the DNA ladder is made of a **pair of bases**. Each pair has one purine and one pyrimidine. Note that adenine always pairs with thymine, and guanine always pairs with cytosine.

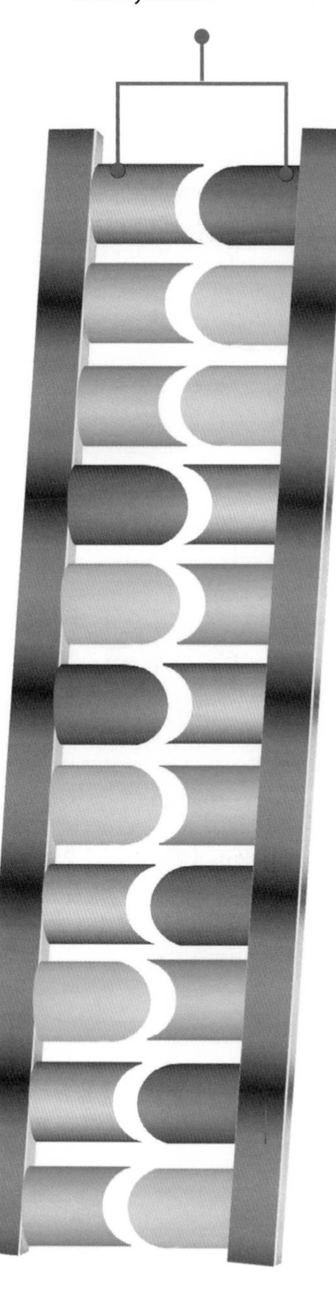

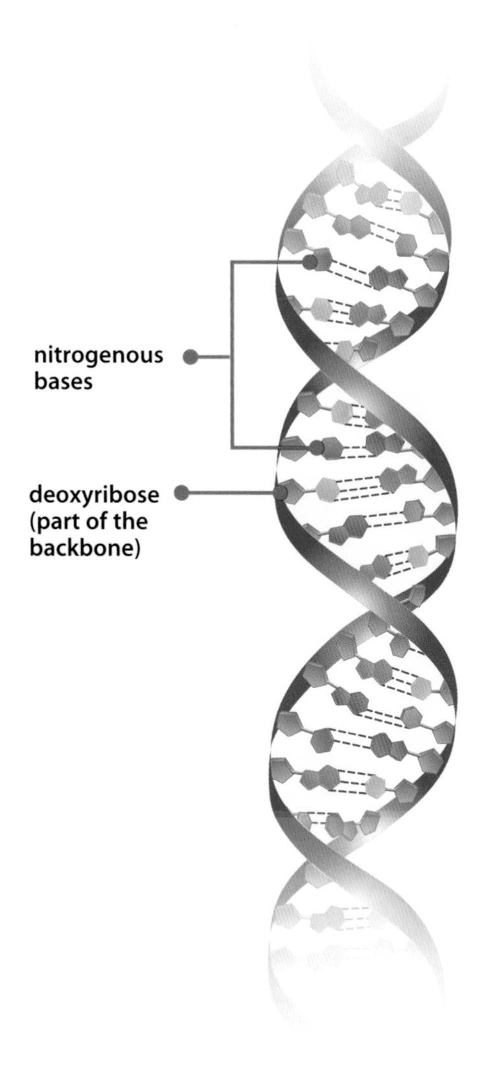

Double Helix

Imagine if you could grab the two ends of a ladder and twist them in opposite directions. You would produce a **double helix**—two helices twisted together. The double-helix shape of DNA is much like the shape of this imaginary twisted ladder.

The genetic information carried by DNA is encoded in its unique base composition and sequence.

Four chemical bases pair up—adenine with thymine and guanine with cytosine—to bind two DNA strands together, forming a double helix.

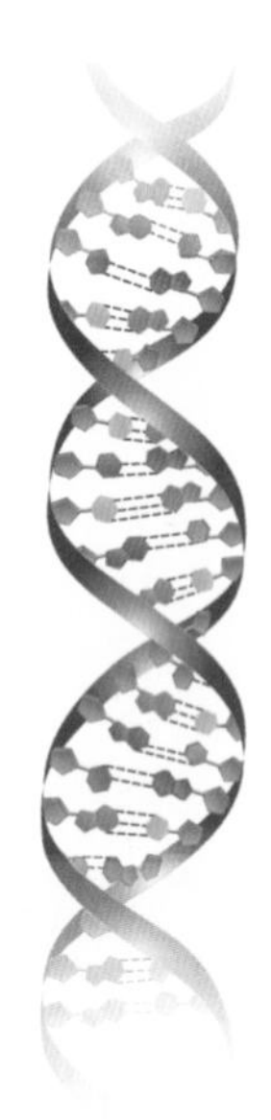

This **model** shows how the backbone faces outward and the bases stack inward. The two sugar–phosphate backbones run in opposite directions, as if one were upside down.

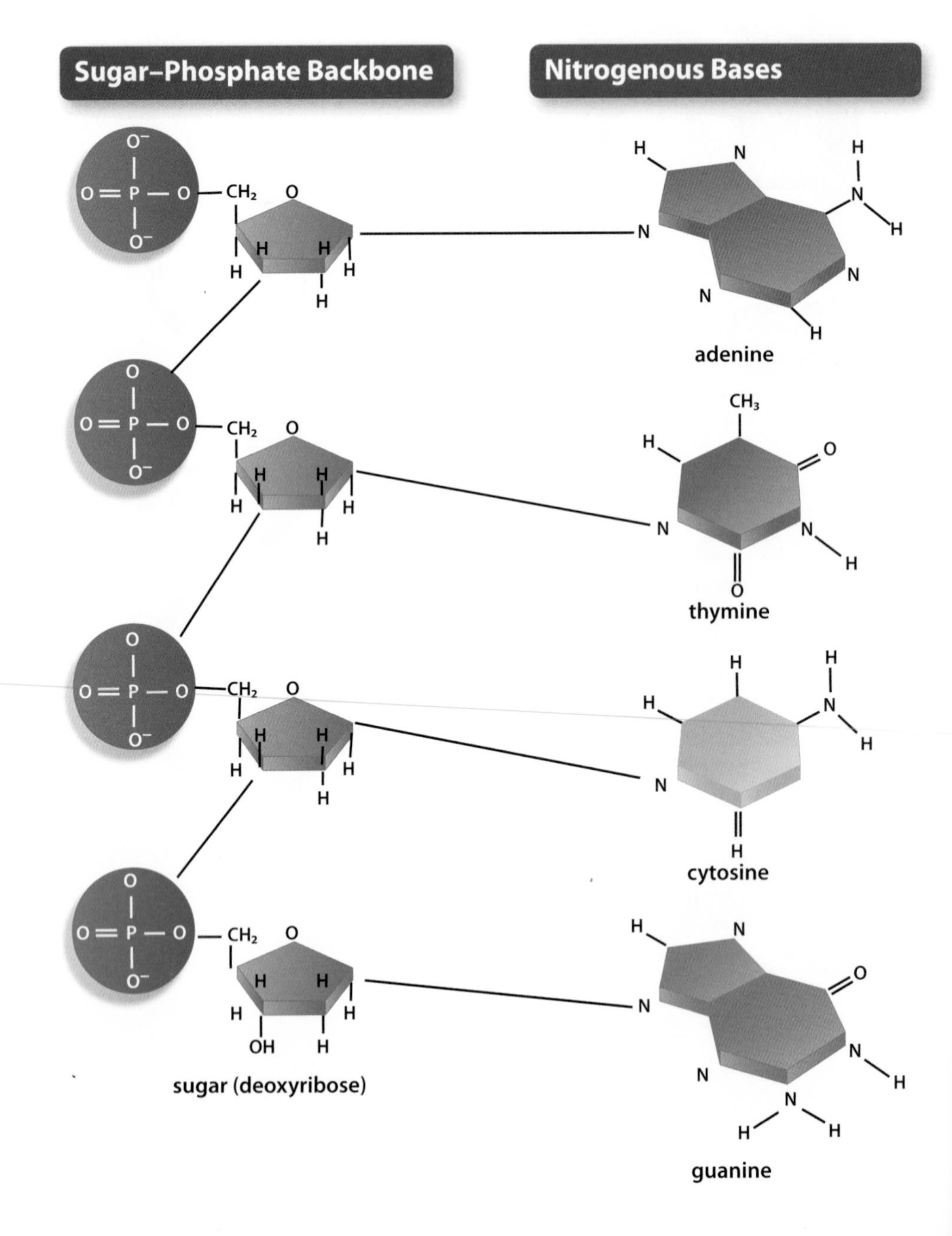

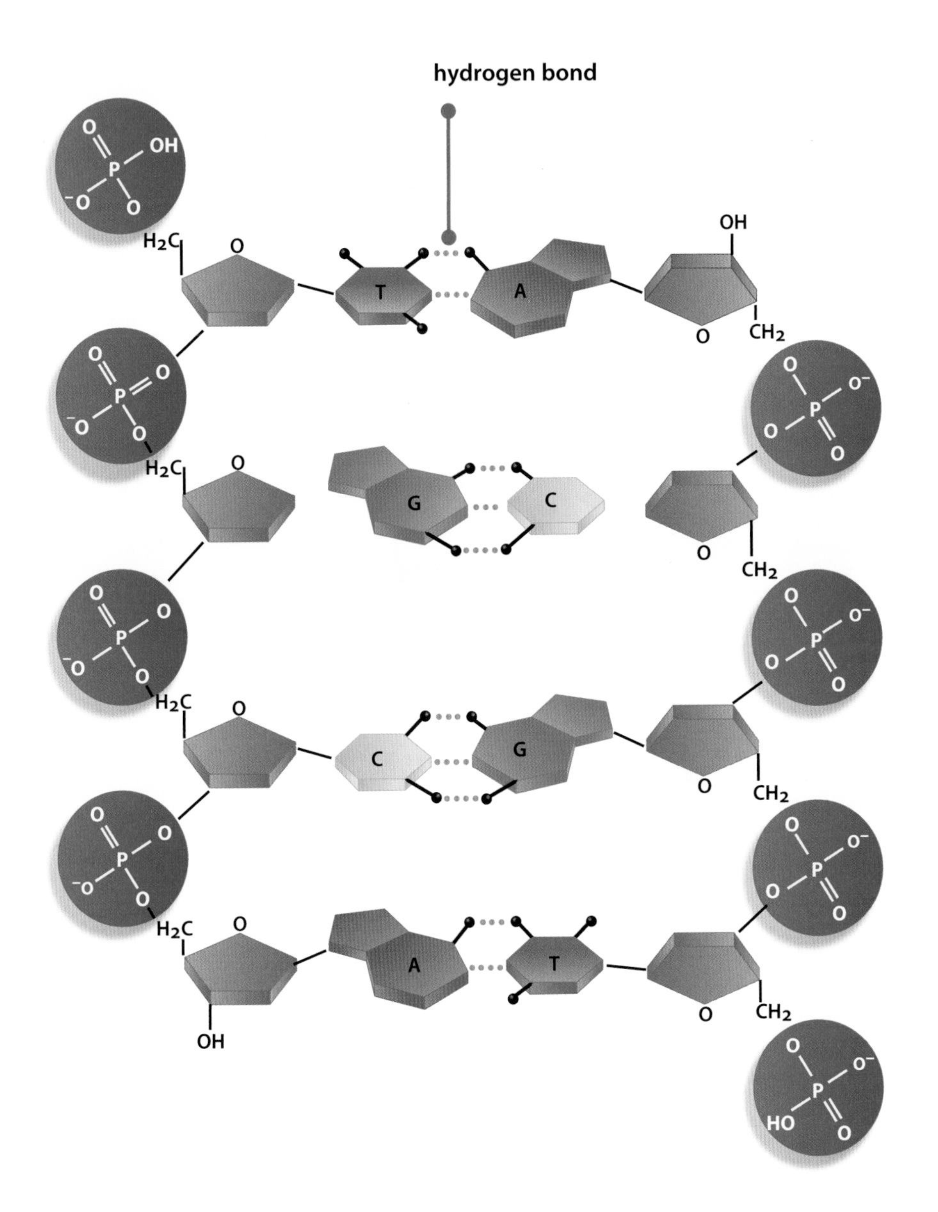

Hydrogen Bond

The two strands of the DNA double helix are held together by **hydrogen bonds** between the pairs of bases. Adenine (A) forms two hydrogen bonds with thymine (T), and guanine (G) forms three hydrogen bonds with cytosine (C). These interactions keep complementary bases together.

DNA is a molecule with the unique trait of being able to make an exact copy of itself.

The process in which DNA duplicates itself is called *replication.* Replication takes place before a cell divides. The process of DNA replication illustrates some of the vital roles that enzymes play in the body.

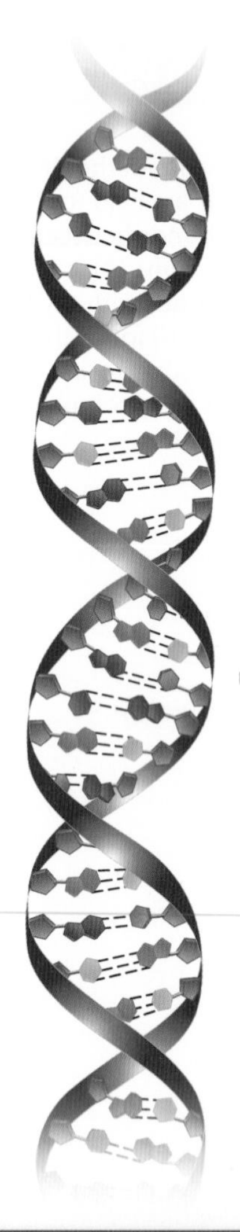

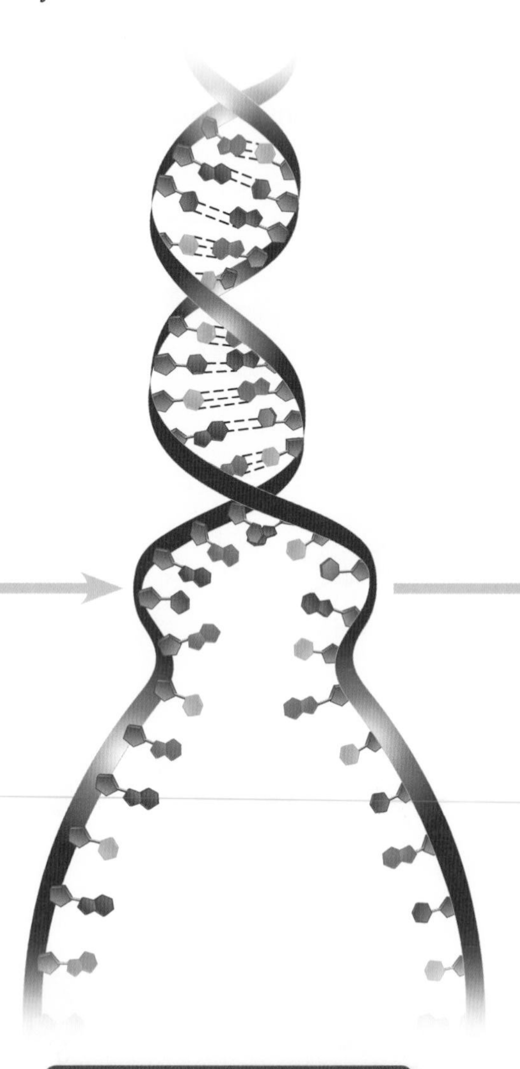

Double Helix

The shape of a DNA molecule is a double helix, which resembles a twisted ladder. Pairs of nitrogenous bases make up the rungs of the double helix. Hydrogen bonds hold the bases together.

Unwinding Helix

Before DNA replication begins, an enzyme causes the double helix to unwind on both backbones. Unwinding, which may take place all along the DNA strand, exposes the bases.

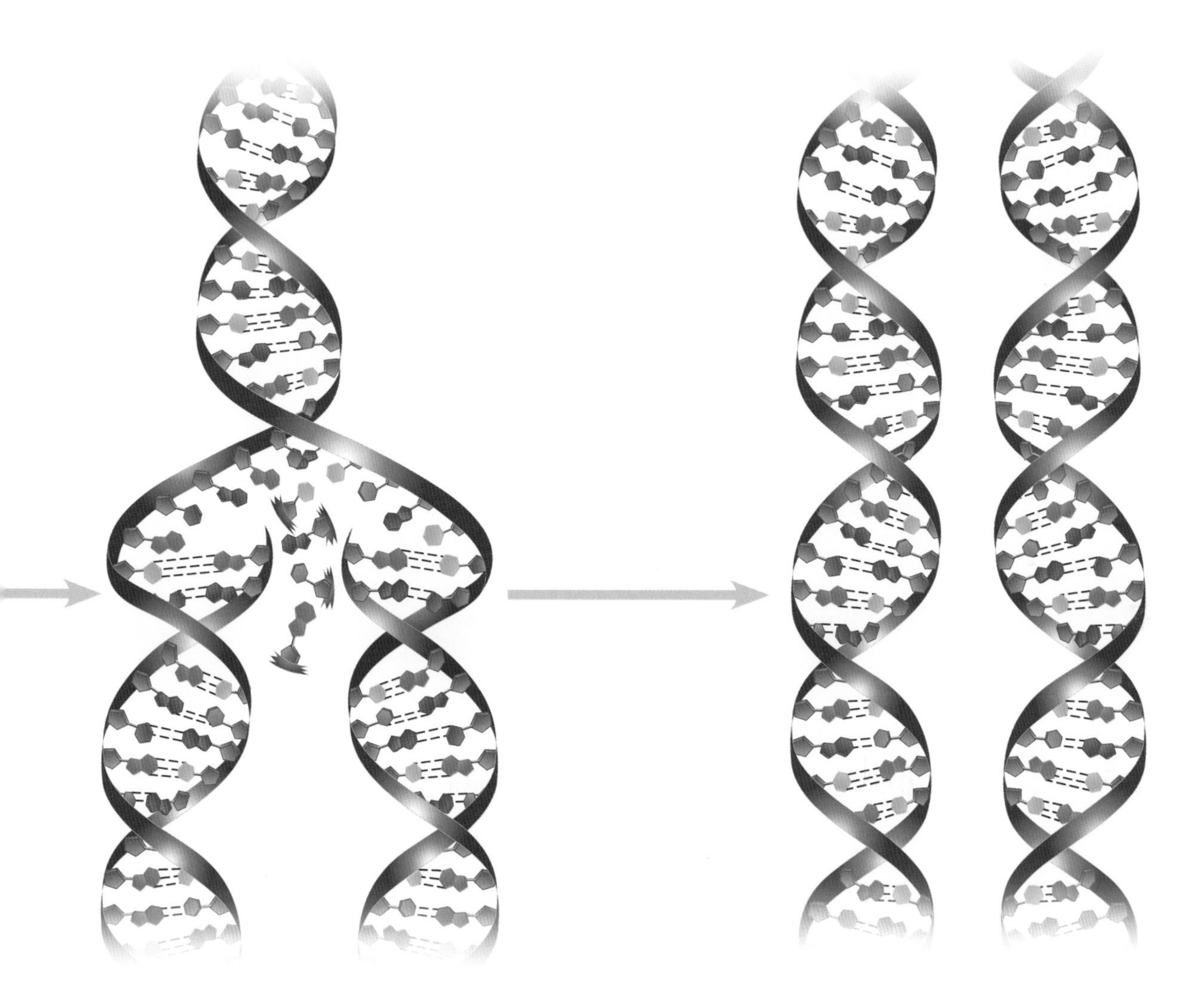

Adding Backbones and Bases

Replication starts from one end of the open portion of the DNA strand. Enzymes attach free nucleotides to the exposed bases. Each nucleotide is made of a nitrogenous base, a sugar, and a phosphate. Nucleotides continue to attach to the bases as the molecule continues to unwind. Remember that the four nitrogenous bases always attach in sets: Adenine always pairs with thymine, and guanine always pairs with cytosine. Enzymes then seal the gaps between nucleotides in the new backbones.

Two Identical DNA Molecules

The two identical DNA molecules now separate. Enzymes twist each new molecule, forming two double helices.

This **worm** belongs to a diverse class of segmented worms called *polychaetes*. Members of this group have bristles on their leglike structures. Most polychaetes live in the ocean, where some are tube dwellers. They build their tubes from their own secretions or from a combination of secretions, sand, and bits of broken shell.

The central dogma of biology states that genetic information flows from DNA to RNA to proteins.

Cells use the instructions in DNA to build the proteins that an organism needs to carry out its life processes. Most of an organism's characteristics are the result of proteins built during the processes of transcription and translation.

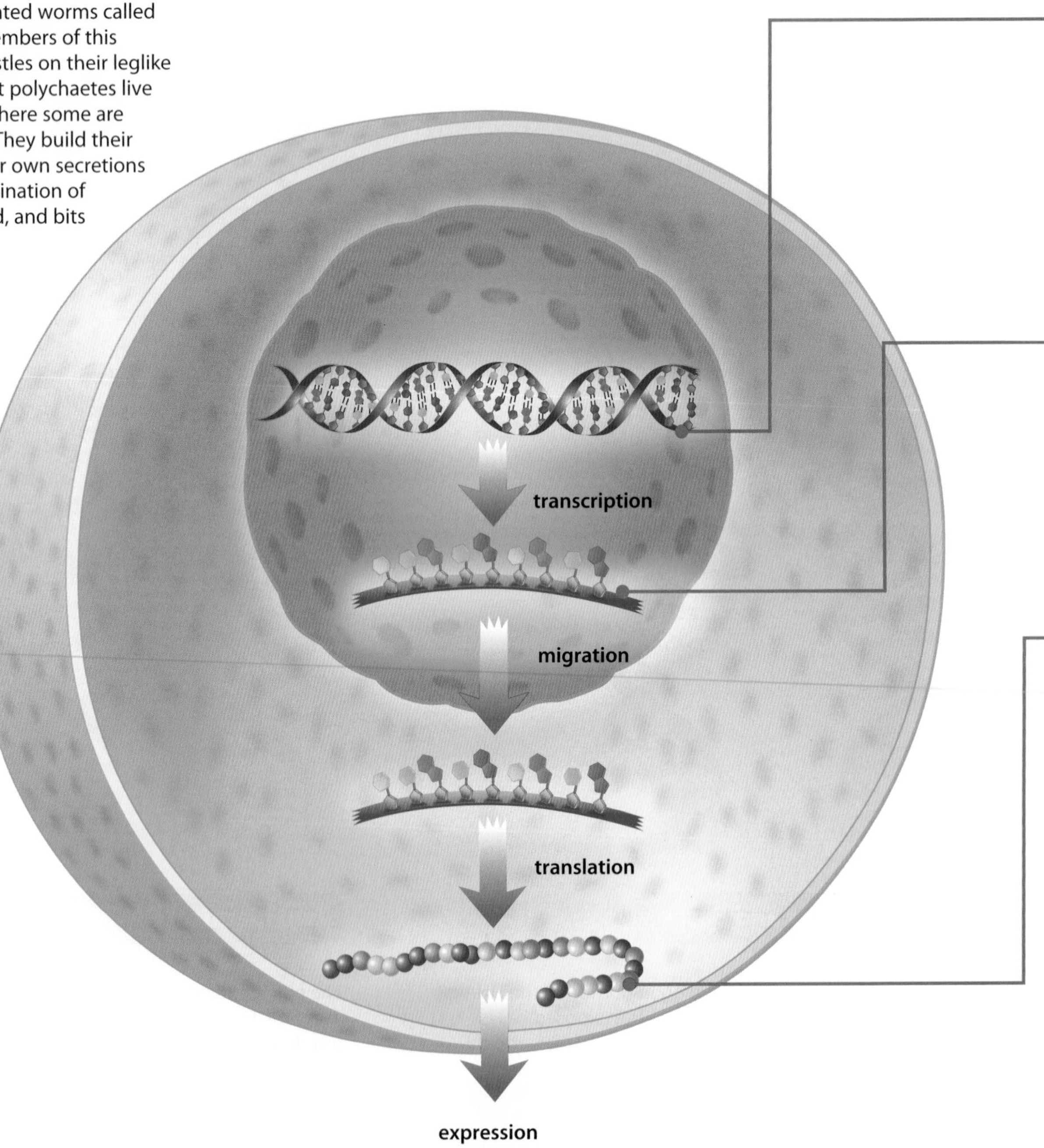

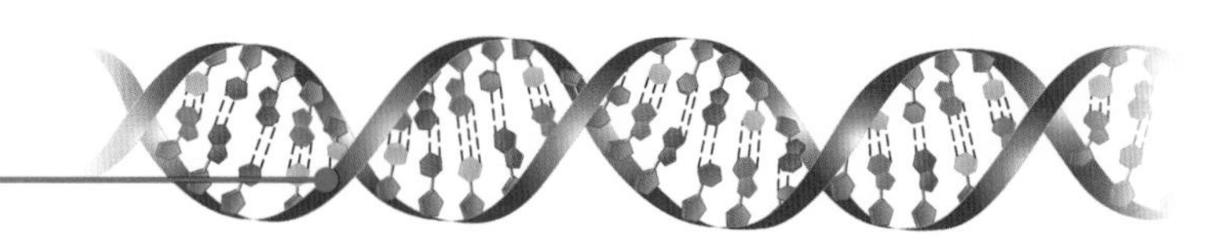

DNA carries the cell's instructions for making proteins. DNA does not leave the nucleus to deliver them. Instead, these instructions are written into a strand of messenger RNA (mRNA) during a process called *transcription.*

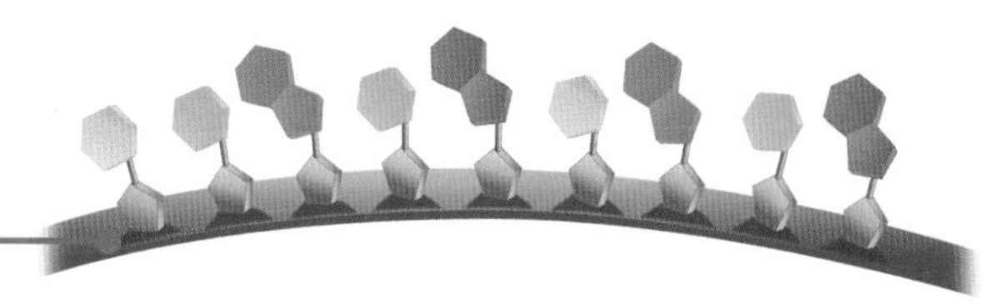

The **mRNA** is a molecule (that is smaller than DNA) that leaves the nucleus through pores in the nuclear membrane. Once outside the nucleus, the mRNA migrates to the cytoplasm where ribosomes are located.

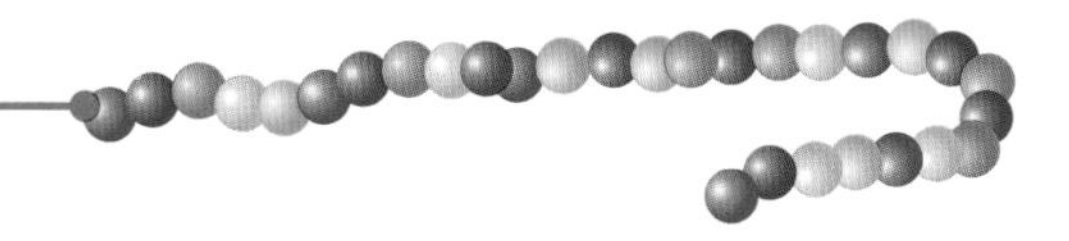

In a process called *translation*, the mRNA provides instructions for **protein production**. The protein-building instructions carried by the mRNA are translated at a ribosome. The sequence of bases in mRNA dictates the order in which free amino acids join to form proteins. Depending on its function, a newly made protein may either stay inside the cell or leave the cell.

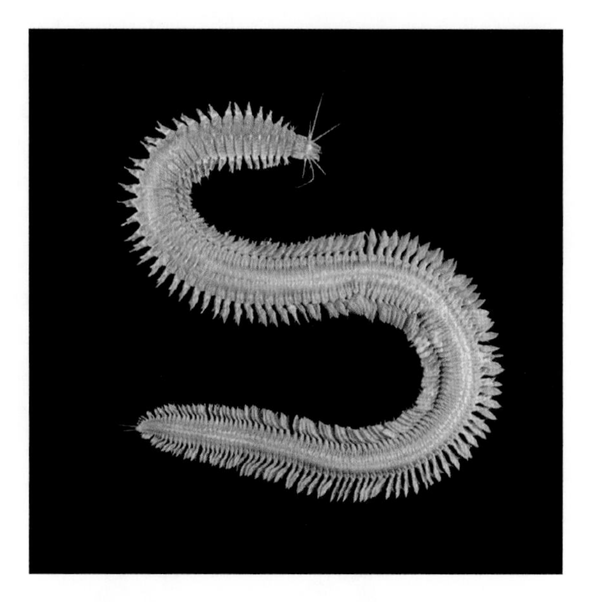

The results of transcription and translation are evident in every feature of this **worm**. Throughout the worm's life, gene expression will continue as the worm's cells produce proteins for life processes such as digestion, reproduction, growth, and repair. Proteins also make up many of the structural features of the worm.

DNA carries the instructions for building proteins. However, DNA does not build proteins directly.

Instead, DNA is the template for the production of mRNA. A molecule of mRNA is small enough to leave the nucleus through a pore in the nuclear membrane. This process of building mRNA from DNA, called *transcription,* is the first step in protein production.

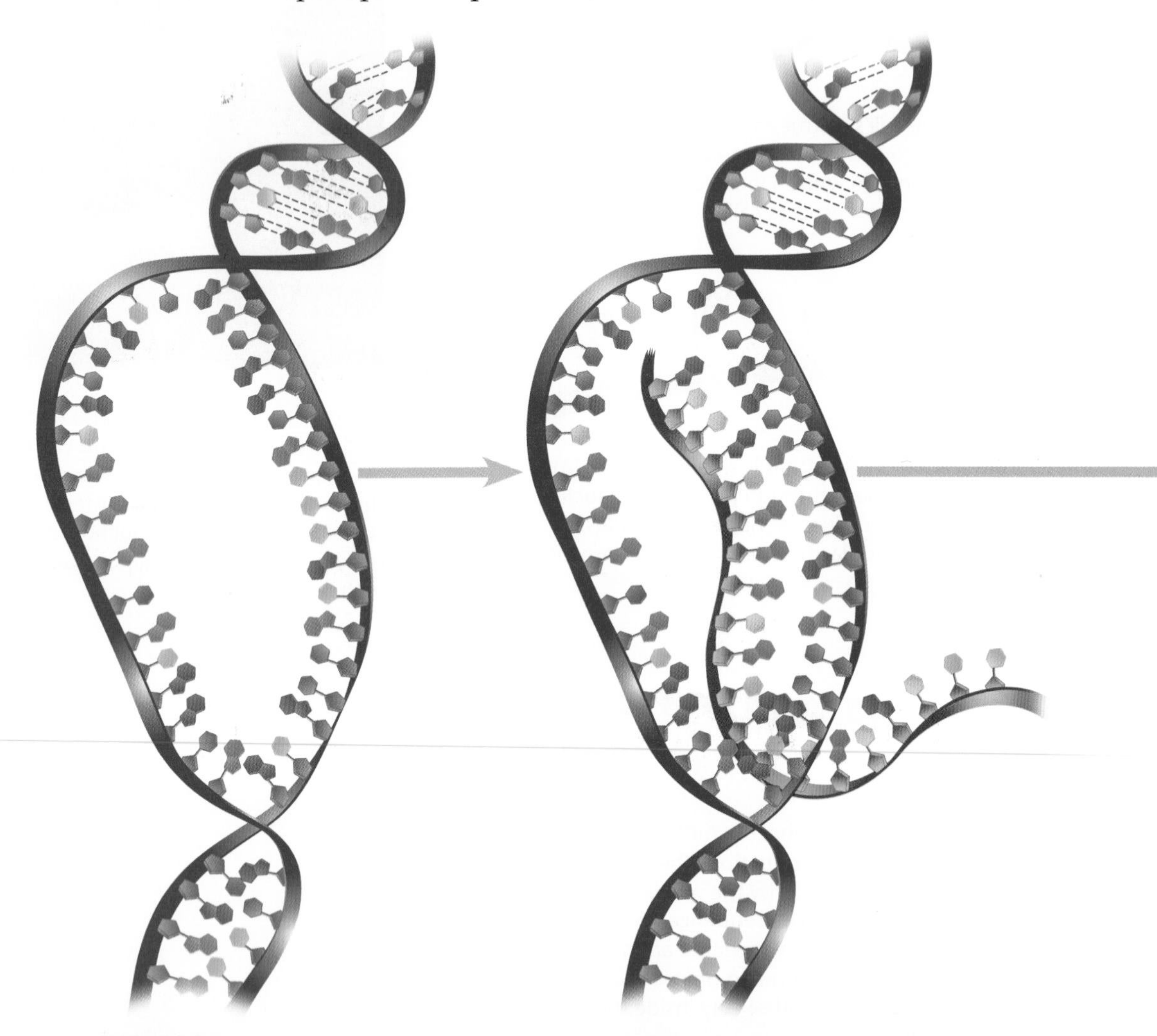

Unwinding Helix

RNA polymerase is an enzyme that binds to a DNA molecule and causes a segment of the two DNA strands to unwind and separate. Unwinding exposes the DNA's nucleotide bases. RNA polymerase then binds to the DNA segment at a particular set of bases, called a *start sequence.* This sequence indicates the beginning of a gene.

Forming the RNA Molecule

The exposed DNA bases provide a template for the production of an mRNA molecule (red). RNA polymerase adds nucleotides to form an mRNA molecule that is complementary to the DNA sequence. For example, if the DNA nucleotide sequence is TACGGT, the mRNA sequence will be AUGCCA. Recall that RNA contains the base uracil instead of thymine.

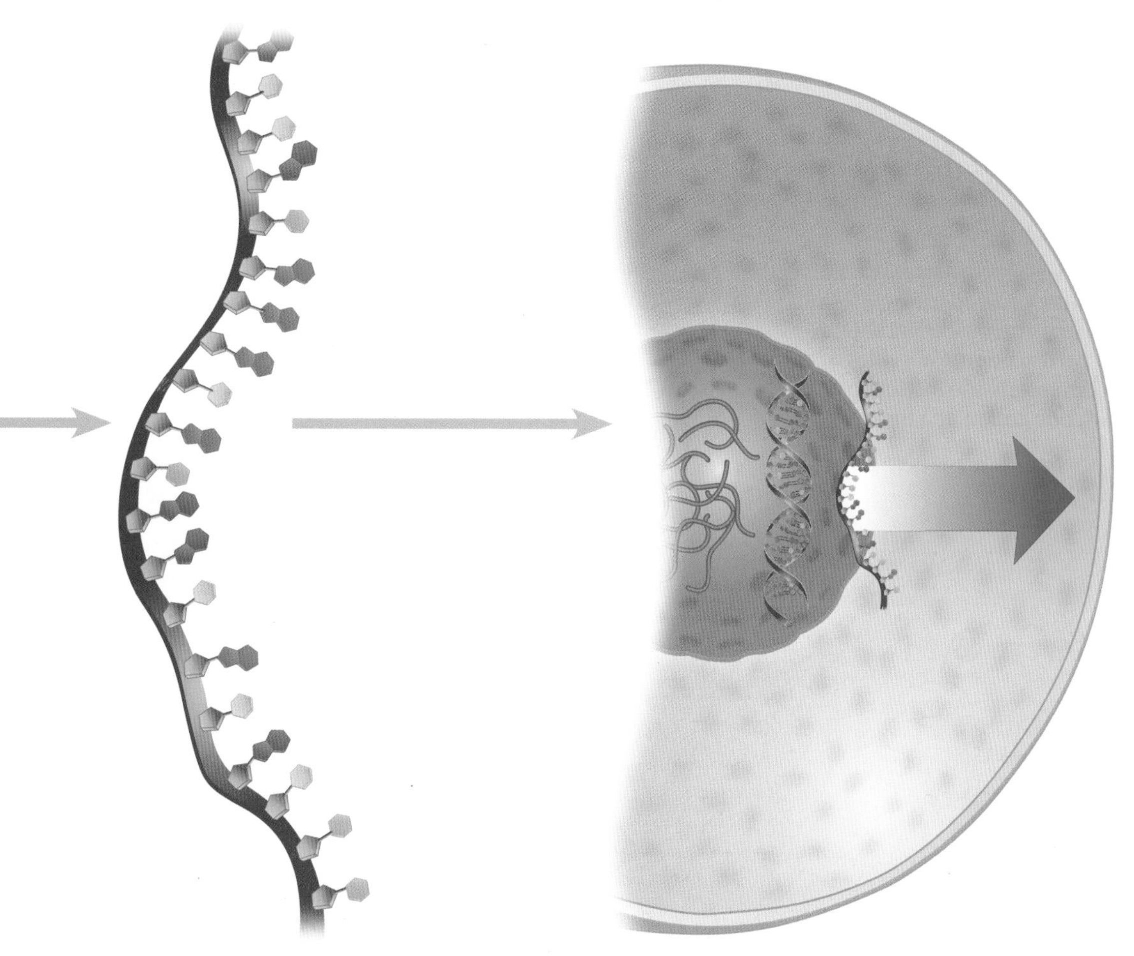

Continues with translation on next page

Releasing the RNA Molecule

When the RNA polymerase reaches a particular DNA sequence that indicates the end of a gene, it releases the DNA and the new mRNA molecule. The DNA double helix closes and rewinds.

Leaving the Nucleus

The new mRNA molecule leaves the nucleus. In the cytoplasm, the process of translation, the next stage in protein production, begins.

In the process called *translation,* three kinds of RNA help assemble amino acids into proteins.

Translation occurs at ribosomes in the cytoplasm. Transfer RNA (tRNA) molecules bring amino acids, the subunits of proteins, to the ribosomes.

Translation Begins

After the mRNA leaves the nucleus, it joins with a ribosome in the cytoplasm.

A tRNA molecule carrying the start codon—the amino acid methionine—signals the initiation of translation.

Each molecule of tRNA has an anticodon, a set of three bases complementary to a specific mRNA codon. A tRNA molecule carries a specific amino acid that corresponds to its codon. Molecules of tRNA pair up with and translate the instructions encoded in the mRNA, one codon at a time.

Elongation of the Amino Acid Chain Begins

As the mRNA molecule passes through the ribosome, a tRNA molecule pairs up with the next mRNA codon.

Each amino acid brought to the ribosome by tRNA forms a peptide bond with the amino acid from the previous tRNA.

The growing chain of amino acids is transferred to the new tRNA, and the newly empty tRNA detaches and moves back into the cytoplasm.

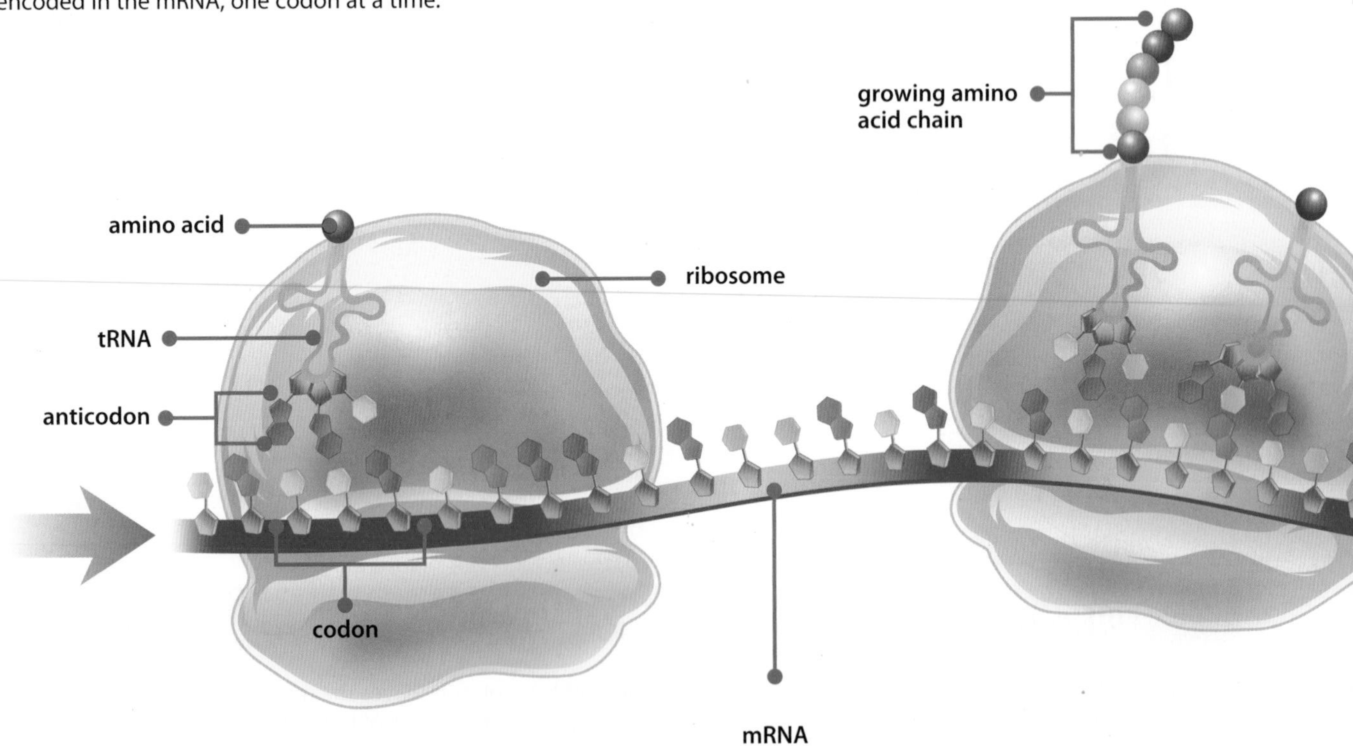

Elongation of the Amino Acid Chain Continues

The process repeats as the mRNA continues to pass through the ribosome. The amino acid chain grows as amino acids (delivered by the tRNA) bind to one another.

Translation Stops

Finally, the ribosome reaches the stop codon, a three-base sequence that specifies the end of the transcribed sequence. The new protein, or polypeptide, then falls away from the ribosome.

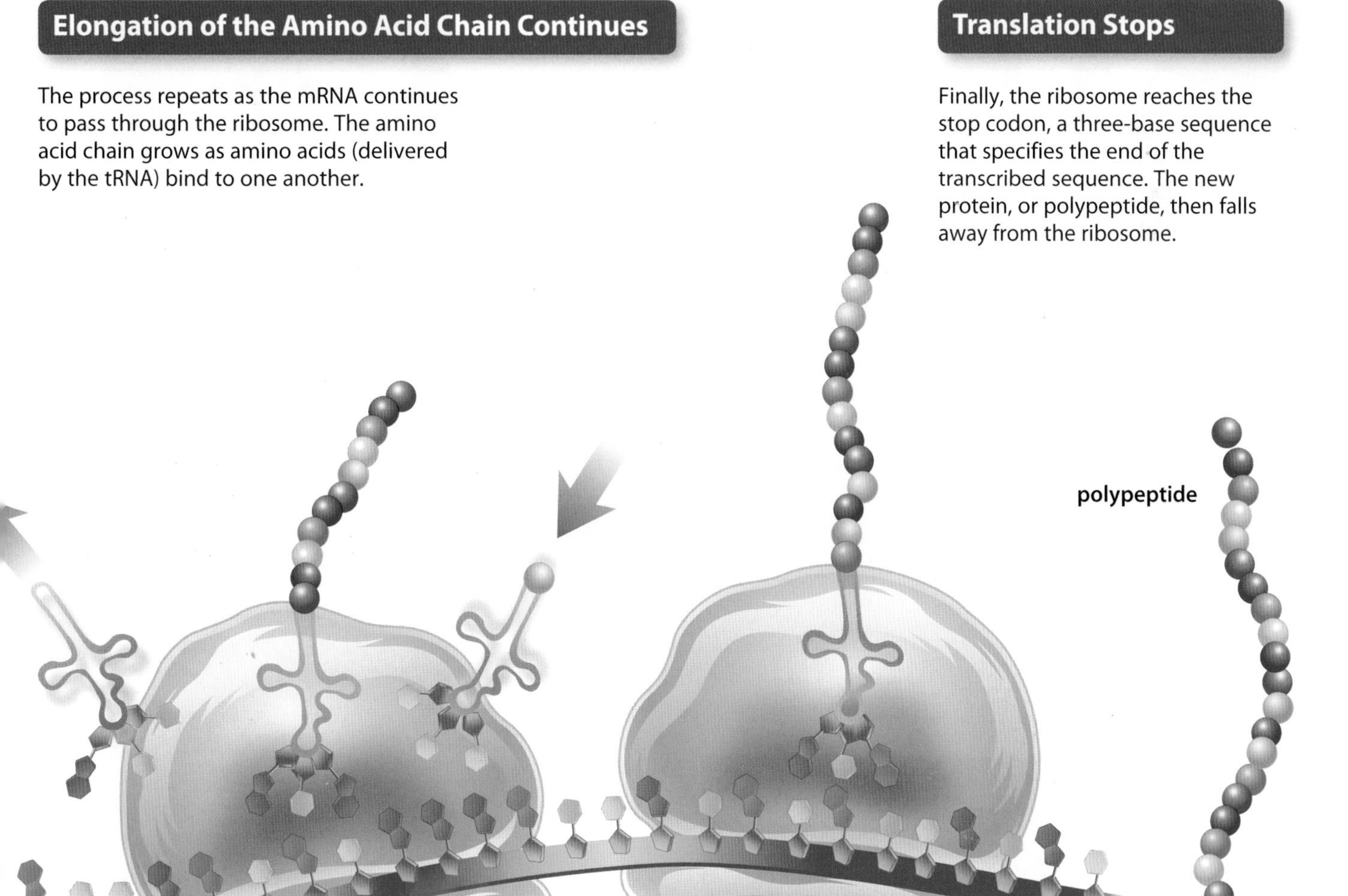

All living things share the same genetic code.

No matter what the organism—a whale or a toad or a redwood—each has the same basic genetic code. Like all codes, the genetic code conveys information using symbols. These symbols, or codons, dictate the order of amino acids in a protein.

Fungus

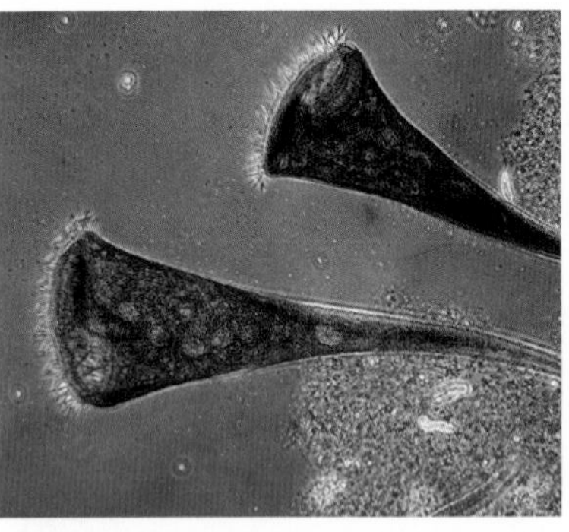

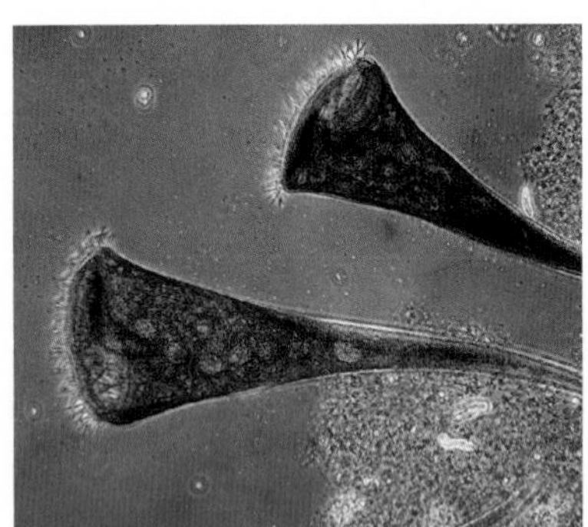

Protist

Animal

Plant

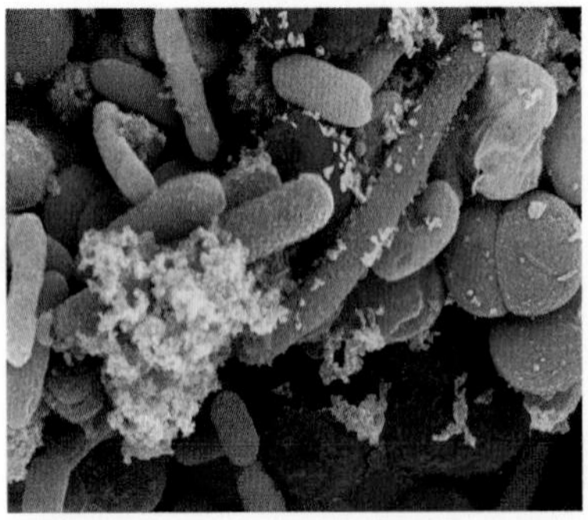

Bacterium

A **codon** is a sequence of three nucleotides in a stretch of mRNA. Within a codon, this sequence of three nucleotides provides the code for a particular amino acid. The same codon, whether in a human or a bacterium, always dictates the same amino acid.

CODONS IN mRNA					
FIRST BASE	***SECOND BASE***				***THIRD BASE***
	U	***C***	***A***	***G***	
U	UUU } Phenylalanine UUC } UUA } Leucine UUG }	UCU UCC Serine UCA UCG	UAU } Tyrosine UAC } UAA } Stop UAG }	UGU } Cysteine UGC } UGA } Stop UGG } Tryptophan	U C A G
C	CUU CUC Leucine CUA CUG	CCU CCC Proline CCA CCG	CAU } Histidine CAC } CAA } Glutamine CAG }	CGU CGC Arginine CGA CGG	U C A G
A	AUU } Isoleucine AUC } AUA } AUG } Methionine (start)	ACU ACC Threonine ACA ACG	AAU } Asparagine AAC } AAA } Lysine AAG }	AGU } Serine AGC } AGA } Arginine AGG }	U C A G
G	GUU GUC Valine GUA GUG	GCU GCC Alanine GCA GCG	GAU } Aspartic acid GAC } GAA } Glutamic acid GAG }	GGU GGC Glycine GGA GGG	U C A G

How to Read the Codon Table

1. Look down the left side of the table for the first base in the codon.
2. Match that row with the column containing the second base.
3. Once you find the box that corresponds to the first two bases, match these possible combinations with the row for the third base, found along the right side of the table. Then read which amino acid the codon specifies. In many cases, more than one codon dictates the same amino acid.

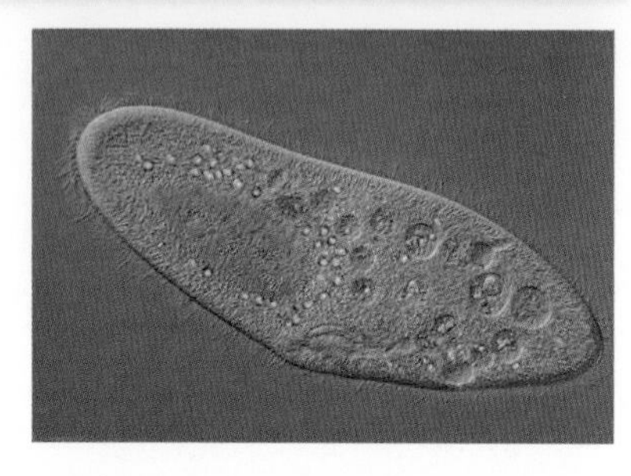

All living things, including single-cell organisms such as this **paramecium**, rely on proteins to function.

Three different kinds of RNA play a role in building proteins: messenger, transfer, and ribosomal.

DNA stores information in a cell's nucleus. That information must be moved from the nucleus to the areas of the cell where proteins are made.

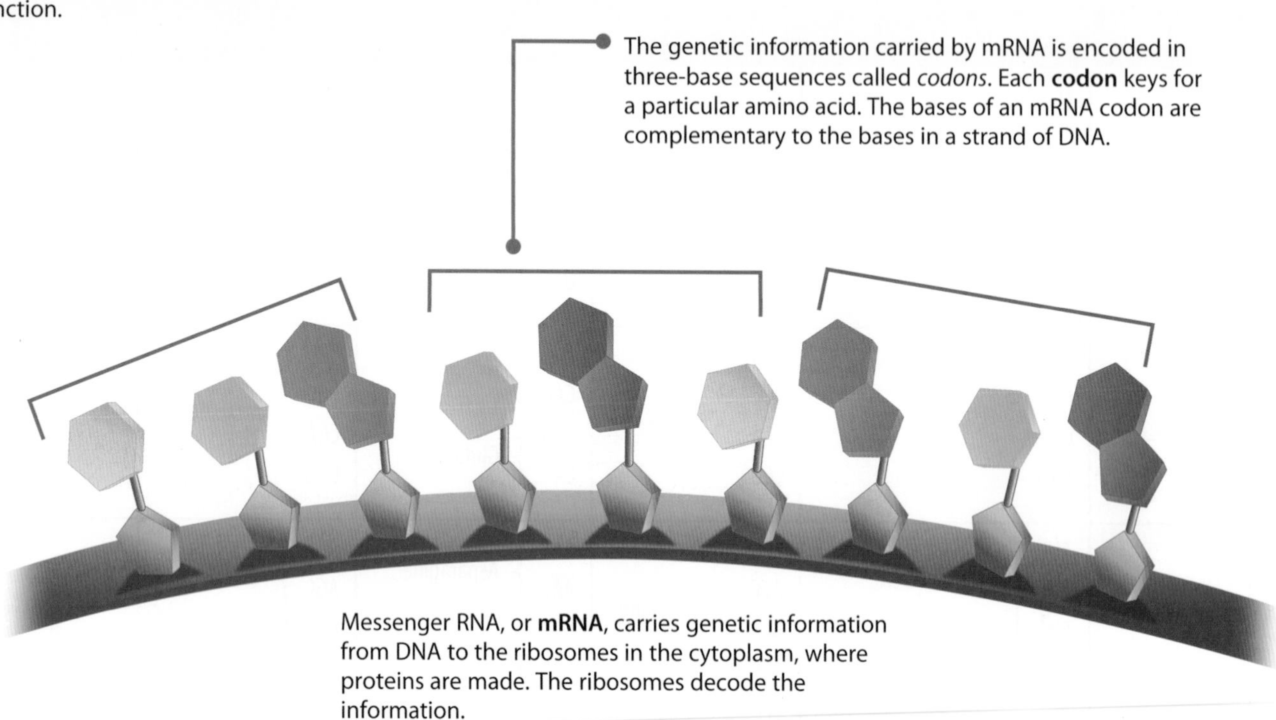

The genetic information carried by mRNA is encoded in three-base sequences called *codons*. Each **codon** keys for a particular amino acid. The bases of an mRNA codon are complementary to the bases in a strand of DNA.

Messenger RNA, or **mRNA**, carries genetic information from DNA to the ribosomes in the cytoplasm, where proteins are made. The ribosomes decode the information.

SIMILARITIES BETWEEN KINDS OF RNA
Have the same four nitrogenous bases: adenine, guanine, uracil, cytosine
Have a sugar–phosphate backbone
Have ribose as sugar
Play roles in protein production

Transfer RNA, or **tRNA**, is a small, cross-shaped RNA molecule that helps in translation. Each tRNA molecule contains an anticodon, a sequence of three bases that complements an mRNA codon. Each tRNA molecule binds to the single amino acid that corresponds to the mRNA codon.

Ribosomes are made of ribosomal RNA, or **rRNA**, and proteins. Each ribosome has two subunits that work together to make proteins.

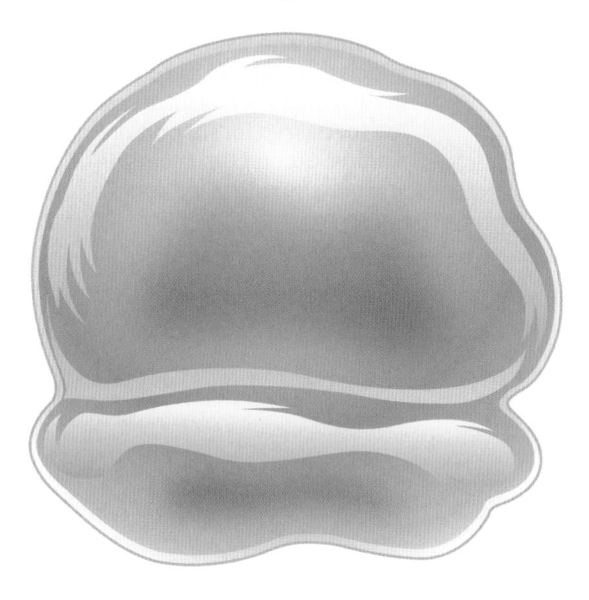

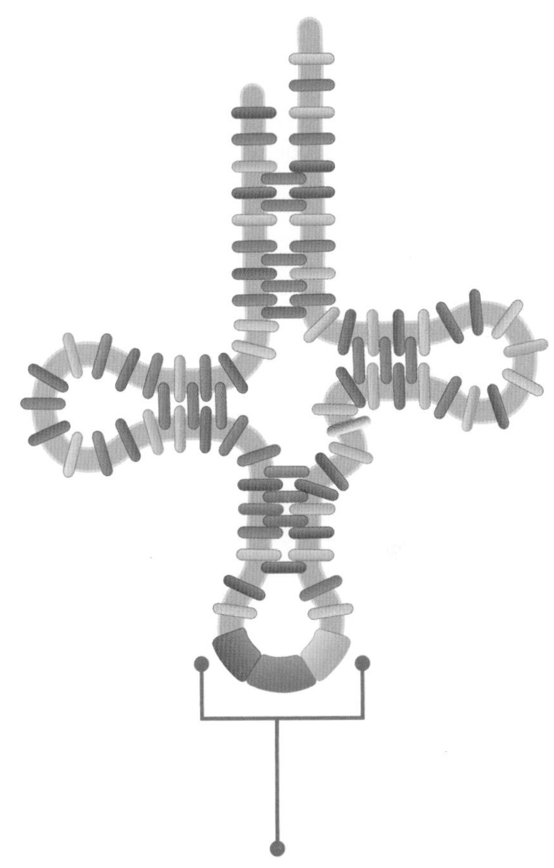

The **anticodon** in the tRNA molecule matches only one specific codon in the mRNA molecule. This very specific match ensures that the correct amino acid is incorporated into the protein.

DIFFERENCES BETWEEN KINDS OF RNA

	STRUCTURE	*LOCATION*	*FUNCTION*
mRNA	Single strand	Nucleus and cytoplasm	Transcribes DNA; carries protein-building instruction to ribosomes
tRNA	Single folded strand	Cytoplasm	Brings amino acids to ribosomes during translation
rRNA	Several molecules combined with proteins to form large and small ribosomal subunits	Cytoplasm (ribosomes)	Makes up ribosomes, which translate mRNA into proteins

As root cells mature, the cells differentiate, or become specialized, to carry out specific functions.

Some specialized cells and their similar companion cells form tissues that perform specific roles.

Onions are often used in school studies of plants because their cells are large enough to observe under a low-powered microscope.

Ground tissue, along with dermal and vascular tissues, is contained in each organ of a plant. Its cells are specialized for support or storage. Ground tissue outside of vascular tissue is called *cortex*.

The **epidermis** covers and protects the root. It is made up of a single layer of thin-walled, rectangular cells and is often covered by a waxy cuticle that helps prevent water loss. Epidermal cells may have root hairs.

The tip of the root is covered by a group of cells called the *root cap*. The **root cap** protects the tip of the root as it pushes downward through the soil. These cells produce a slimy substance that helps the root tip slide more easily through the soil.

Plants have a zone of cell division in their roots and shoots called the *apical meristem*. A **meristem** is a localized site of cell division in plants. All new cells for the onion root are formed here. This tissue of the root meristem remains undifferentiated throughout the life of the plant. The cells that originate in the meristem tissue may remain meristematic, or they may differentiate and become other tissues of the plant.

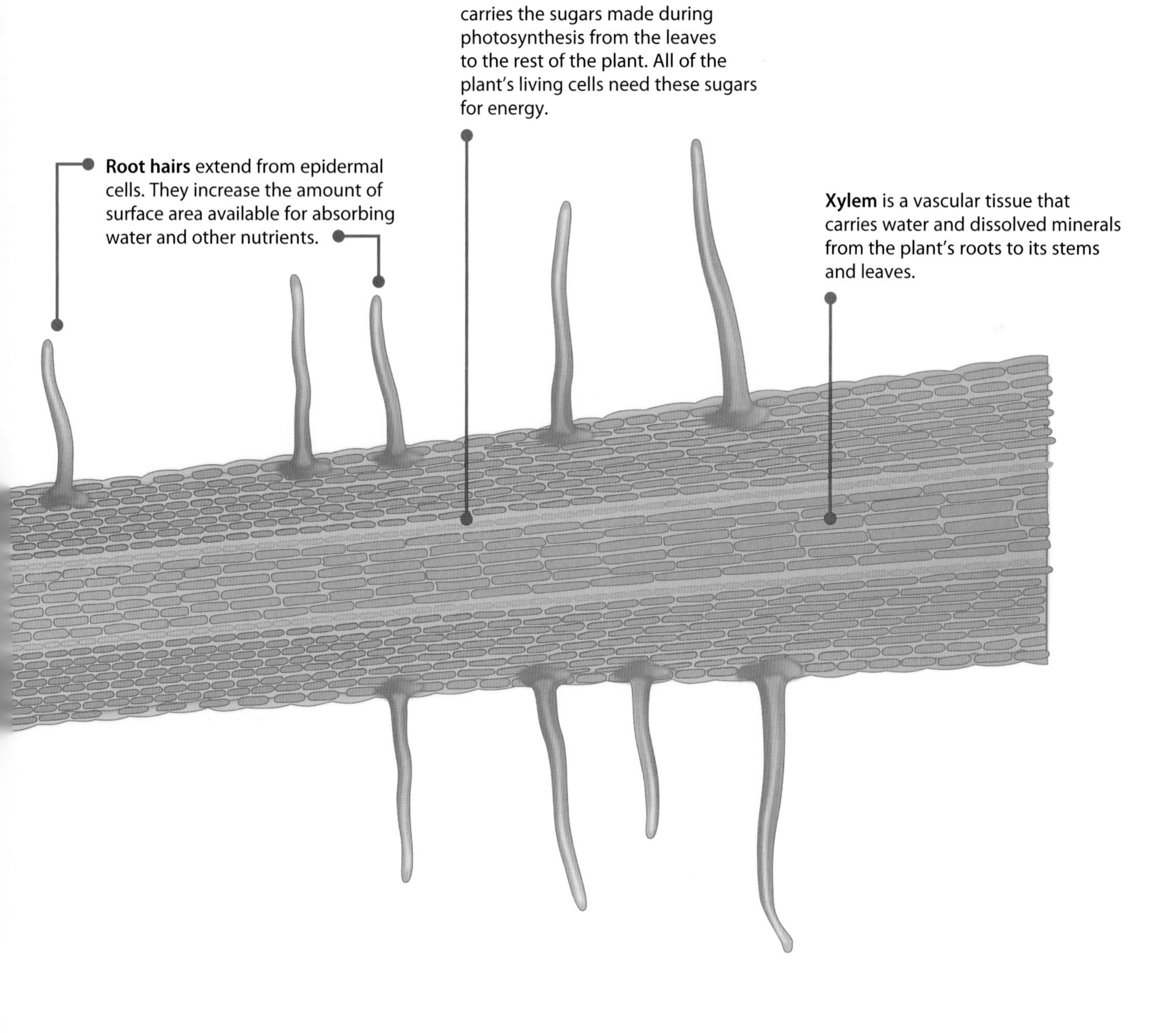
Phloem is a vascular tissue that carries the sugars made during photosynthesis from the leaves to the rest of the plant. All of the plant's living cells need these sugars for energy.
Root hairs extend from epidermal cells. They increase the amount of surface area available for absorbing water and other nutrients.
Xylem is a vascular tissue that carries water and dissolved minerals from the plant's roots to its stems and leaves.

Every cell in an animal's body originates from one cell: a fertilized egg.

As the egg cell divides and the embryo develops, the cells begin to differentiate, or change, in structure. Cell differentiation allows different cells in a multicell organism to perform different jobs.

Caenorhabditis elegans is a kind of nematode, or **roundworm**, that scientists have studied extensively. *C. elegans* is about 1 mm long and lives in the soils of temperate climates.

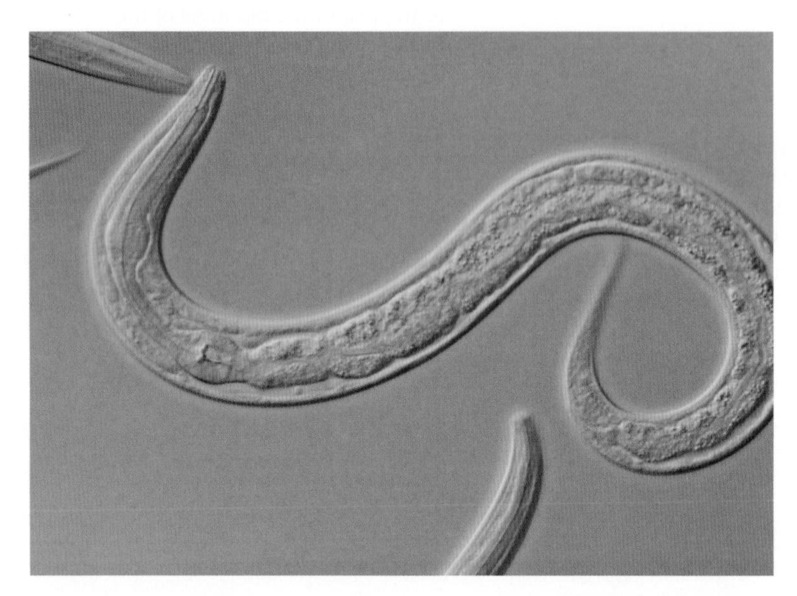

A roundworm's DNA contains instructions for how the roundworm will develop. Each cell in a developing embryo is genetically predestined to develop into a specific type of **cell**—such as an intestinal cell—in the adult organism.

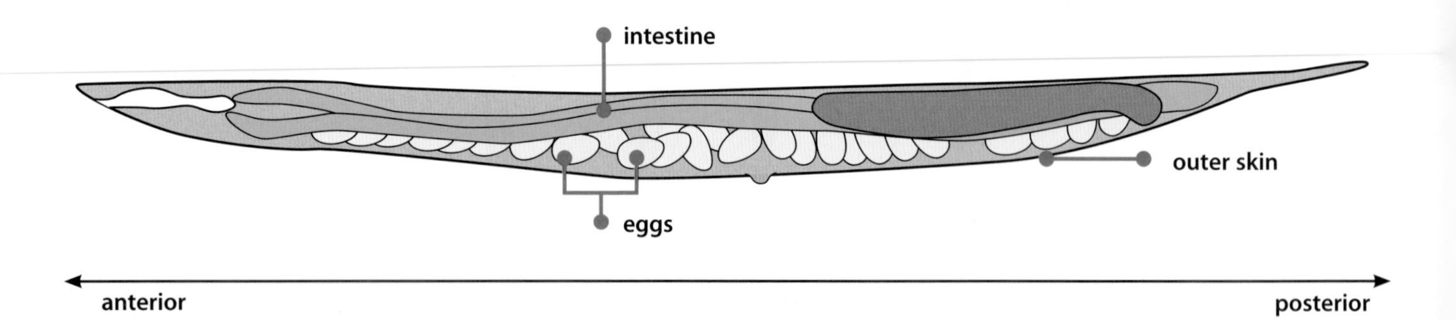

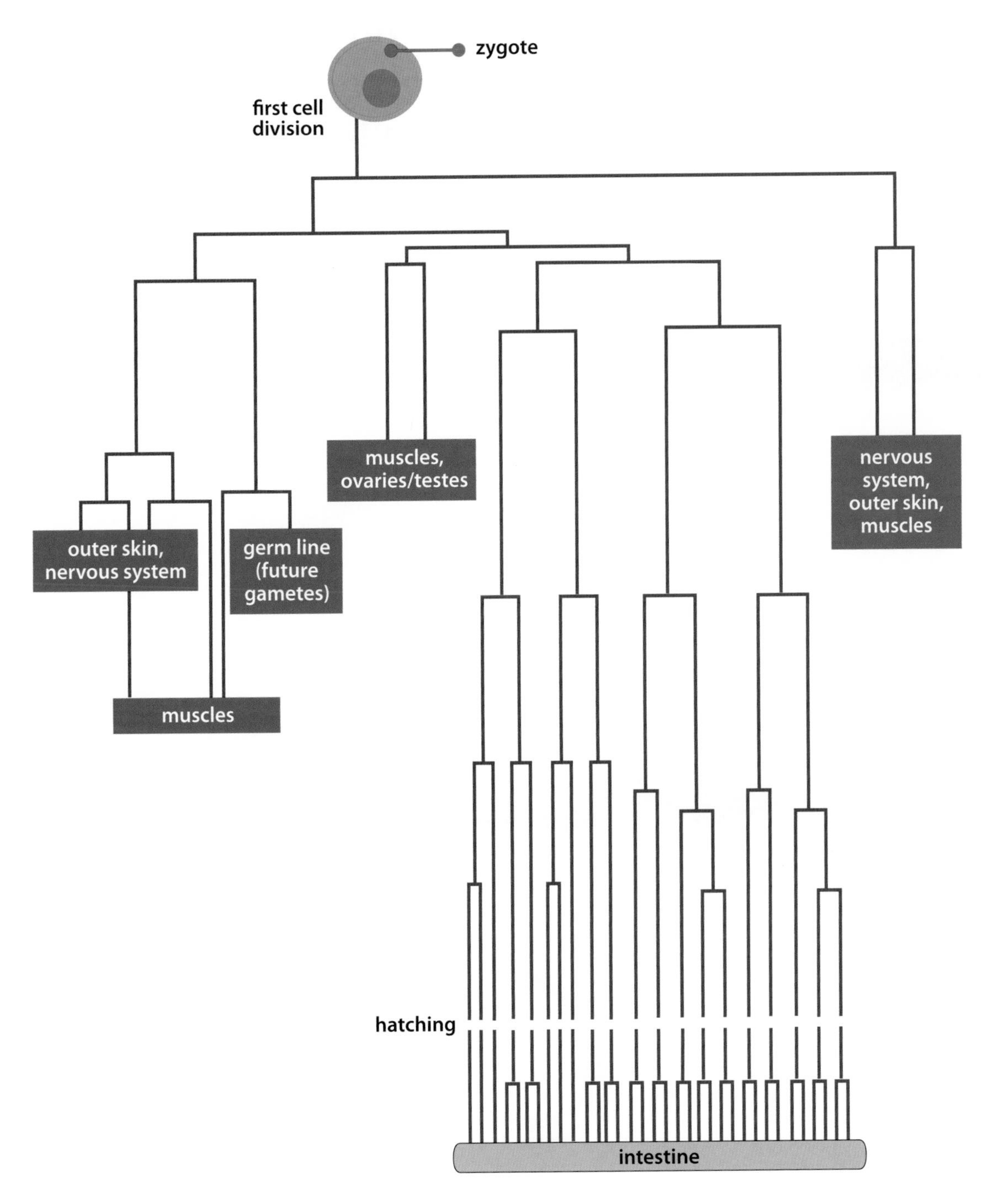

Scientists have been able to **map** how and when each cell in the body of an adult *C. elegans* develops. A roundworm starts from a single cell and develops completely within a matter of hours.

Because virtually all known living things share the same genetic code, scientists can use bacteria to produce human proteins.

Recombinant DNA technology allows scientists to use bacteria to produce human proteins such as insulin. Doctors use insulin to treat people with diabetes. Enzymes play a key role in recombinant DNA technology.

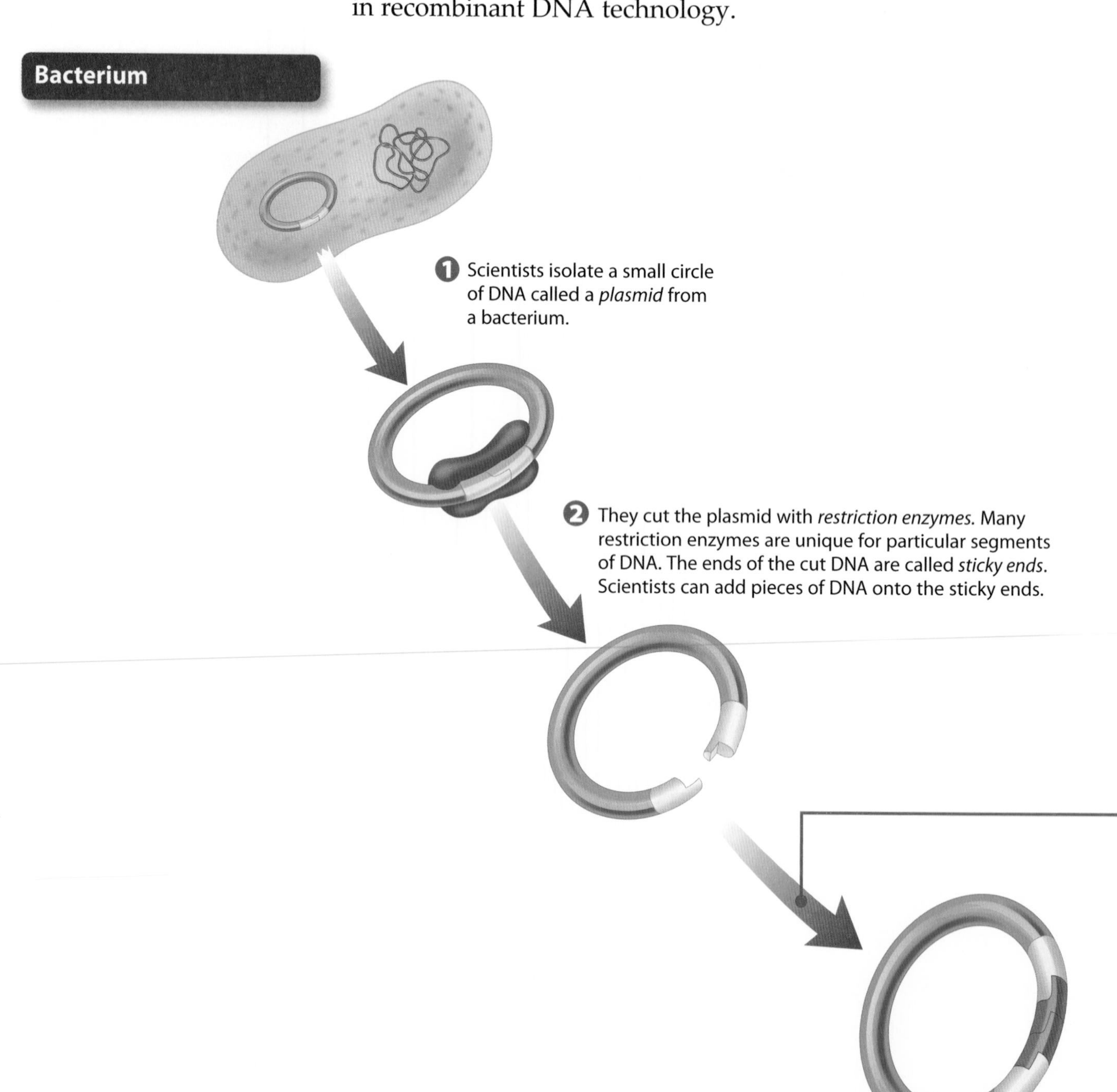

Bacterium
1 Scientists isolate a small circle of DNA called a *plasmid* from a bacterium.
2 They cut the plasmid with *restriction enzymes.* Many restriction enzymes are unique for particular segments of DNA. The ends of the cut DNA are called *sticky ends.* Scientists can add pieces of DNA onto the sticky ends.

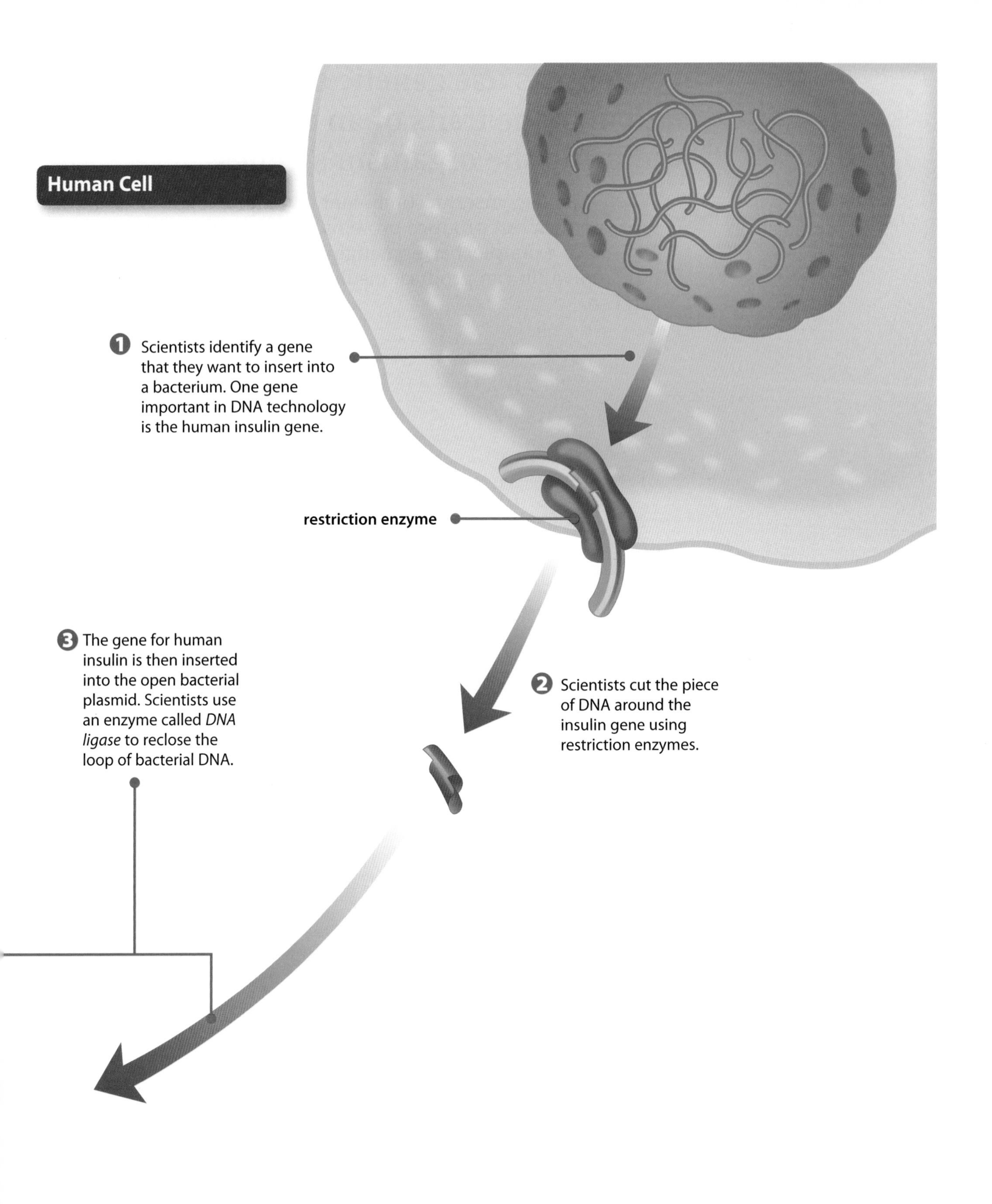
Human Cell
❶ Scientists identify a gene that they want to insert into a bacterium. One gene important in DNA technology is the human insulin gene.
restriction enzyme
❷ Scientists cut the piece of DNA around the insulin gene using restriction enzymes.
❸ The gene for human insulin is then inserted into the open bacterial plasmid. Scientists use an enzyme called *DNA ligase* to reclose the loop of bacterial DNA.

Scientists use genetic engineering to change the traits of an organism by altering the organism's genes.

When scientists insert recombinant DNA into an organism, the organism can produce proteins coded for the additional genes. For example, bacteria engineered with the gene for human insulin can produce insulin that people with diabetes can use.

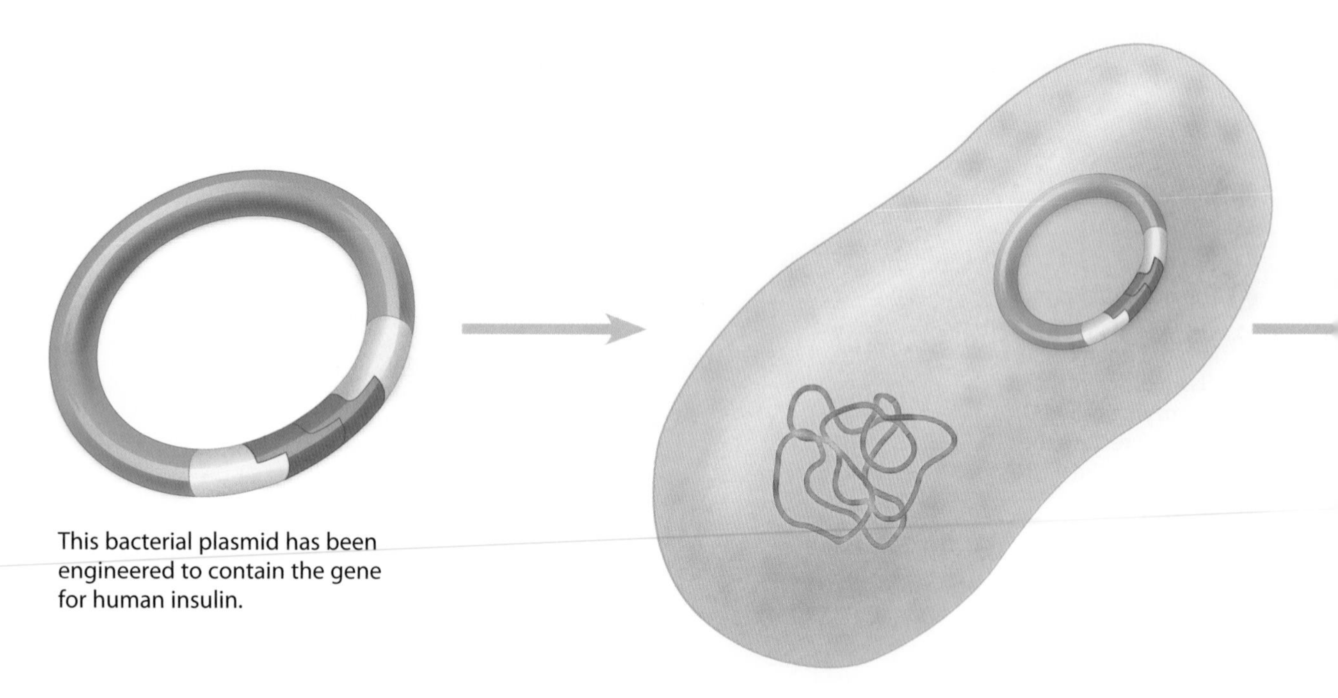

This bacterial plasmid has been engineered to contain the gene for human insulin.

Scientists insert the engineered plasmid with the human insulin gene back into the bacterium.

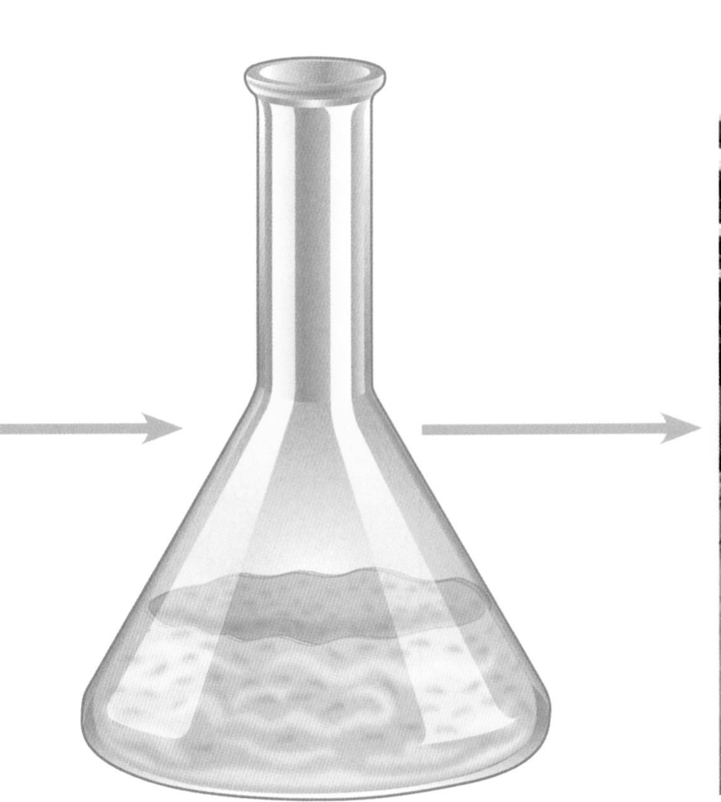

The bacterium makes copies of its DNA and divides, and its offspring grow and reproduce. All of the engineered bacterium's descendants carry the gene for insulin.

Because they carry insulin genes, the bacteria produce human insulin. Scientists extract and purify the insulin so that people with diabetes can use it.

Scientists separate earth's history into different periods of time, each of which has unique geologic and biologic characteristics.

The geologic time scale represents all of earth's history. The smallest unit of time on this scale is the epoch. Multiple epochs make up a period, multiple periods make up an era, and multiple eras make up an eon.

Eon		Era	Millions of years ago
Phanerozoic		Cenozoic	65
Phanerozoic		Mezozoic	248
Phanerozoic		Paleozoic	540
Precambrian	Proterozoic	Late	900
Precambrian	Proterozoic	Middle	1600
Precambrian	Proterozoic	Early	2500
Precambrian	Archean	Late	3000
Precambrian	Archean	Middle	3400
Precambrian	Archean	Early	3800
Precambrian	Hadean		4500

Era	Period		Epoch	Millions of years ago
Cenozoic	Quaternary		Holocene	
				0.01
			Pleistocene	
				1.8
	Tertiary		Pliocene	
				5.3
			Miocene	
				23.8
			Oligocene	
				33.7
			Eocene	
				54.8
			Paleocene	
				65.0
Mesozoic	Cretaceous			
				144
	Jurassic			
				206
	Triassic			
				248
Paleozoic	Permian			
				290
	Carboniferous	Pennsylvanian		
				323
		Mississippian		
				354
	Devonian			
				417
	Silurian			
				443
	Ordovician			
				490
	Cambrian			
				540
Precambrian				

There is strong evidence that life on earth has changed over time.

The first organisms appeared on earth about 3.5 billion years ago. They were tiny bacteria-like cells that did not need oxygen to survive. All life on earth evolved from those early organisms.

Era	Period	Epoch	Millions of years ago
Cenozoic	Quaternary	Holocene	0.01
		Pleistocene	1.8
	Tertiary	Pliocene	5.3
		Miocene	23.8
		Oligocene	33.7
		Eocene	54.8
		Paleocene	65.0
Mesozoic	Cretaceous		144
	Jurassic		206
	Triassic		248
Paleozoic	Permian		290
	Carboniferous	Pennsylvanian	323
		Mississippian	354
	Devonian		417
	Silurian		443
	Ordovician		490
	Cambrian		540
Precambrian			

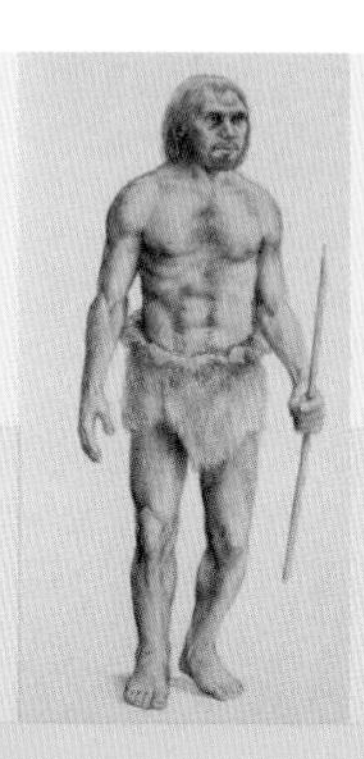

The oldest known fossils of **hominids**, or humanlike primates, are between 5 million and 8 million years old. The earliest modern humans, *Homo sapiens*, evolved more than 130,000 years ago.

Hyracotherium (Eohippus), an early ancestor of the modern horse, lived 60 million years ago. The Cenozoic era, in which most modern mammals (including horses) evolved, is sometimes called the Age of Mammals.

The end of the Cretaceous period (about 65 million years ago) is defined by the **extinction** of nearly half of all animal and plant species on earth.

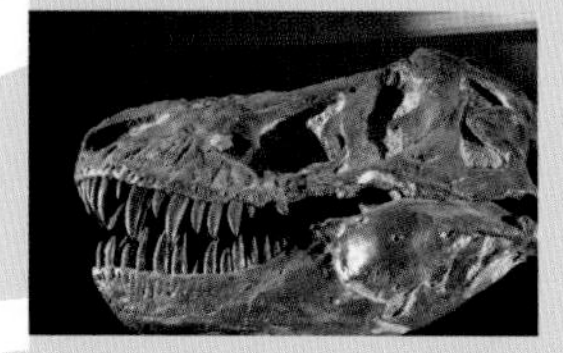

Tyrannosaurus rex lived during the Cretaceous period (between about 144 million and 65 million years ago). All dinosaurs, including *Tyrannosaurus rex*, lived during the Mesozoic era. For this reason, the Mesozoic era is sometimes called the Age of Reptiles.

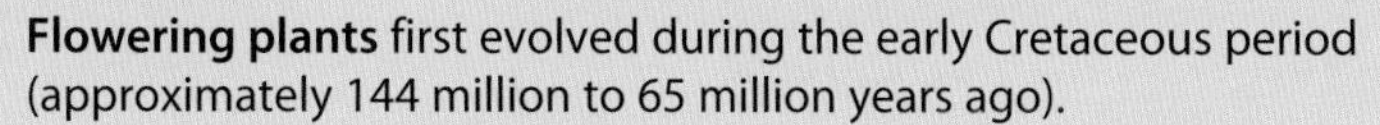

Flowering plants first evolved during the early Cretaceous period (approximately 144 million to 65 million years ago).

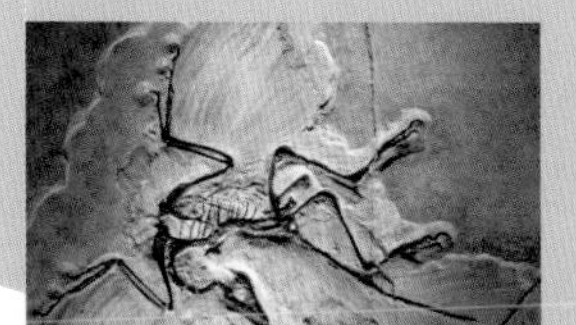

Archaeopteryx lived during the late Jurassic and early Cretaceous periods (about 206 million to 144 million years ago). It had characteristics of both modern birds and of dinosaurs, suggesting that modern birds evolved from dinosaurs.

The largest **mass extinction** event in earth's history occurred at the end of the Permian period (about 250 million years ago). About 90 percent of the marine organisms at the time went extinct.

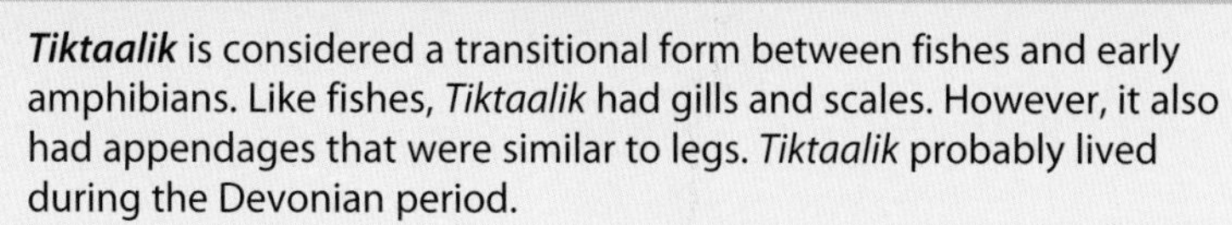

During the Carboniferous period (354 million to 290 million years ago), **huge swamps** filled with many kinds of plant life covered earth. When those plants died, they were buried in sediment and eventually became massive coal deposits.

Tiktaalik is considered a transitional form between fishes and early amphibians. Like fishes, *Tiktaalik* had gills and scales. However, it also had appendages that were similar to legs. *Tiktaalik* probably lived during the Devonian period.

The first **fishes** evolved during the Ordovician and Silurian periods (between 490 million and 417 million years ago). Fishes dominated the oceans during the Devonian period (between 417 million and 354 million years ago), so this period is sometimes called the Age of Fishes.

Trilobites, an extinct class of arthropods, flourished during the Cambrian period (between 540 million and 490 million years ago) and died out at the end of the Permian period (between 290 million and 248 million years ago).

Many different lines of scientific evidence support the theory of evolution.

One line of evidence is the observation that many species have similar characteristics. The best scientific explanation for these similarities is that all species evolved from a common ancestral species.

Comparative Embryology

Many **vertebrate embryos** look very similar, even though the adult organisms may look very different. For example, fish, turtle, and human embryos have similar features, including gills and tails. The developmental stages of these embryos are controlled by their genes. The fact that these embryos develop in similar ways suggests that the species share genes derived from a common ancestor.

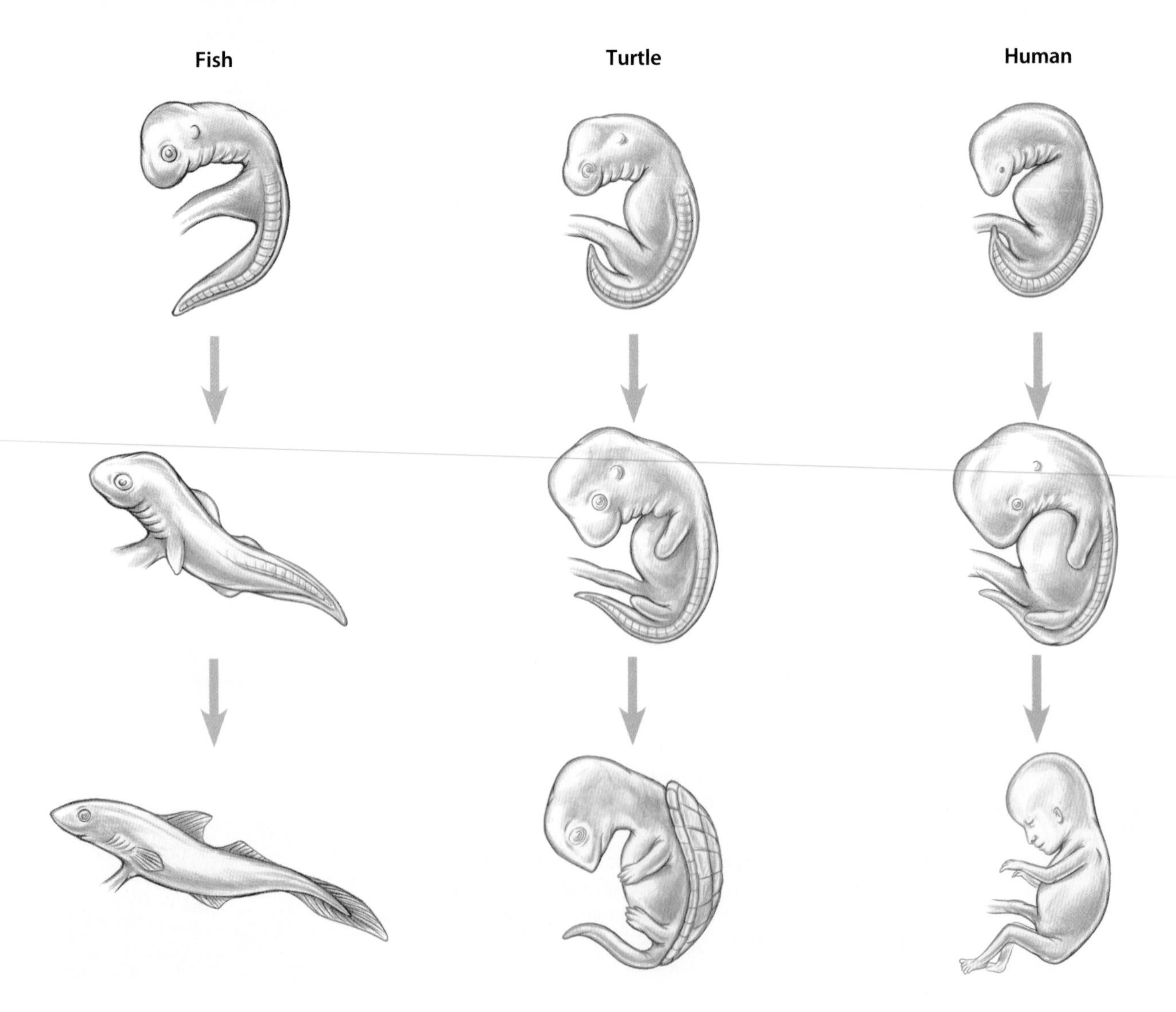

Limb Homology

At first glance, the limbs of these four animals appear to have nothing in common. However, a closer look reveals that the limbs have a similar bone structure. The similarities imply that the underlying structure arose in a common ancestor and became modified as different populations adapted to different environments. Similar structures in different species that are modified from those of a common ancestor are known as **homologous structures**. In this diagram, similar colors represent similar bones.

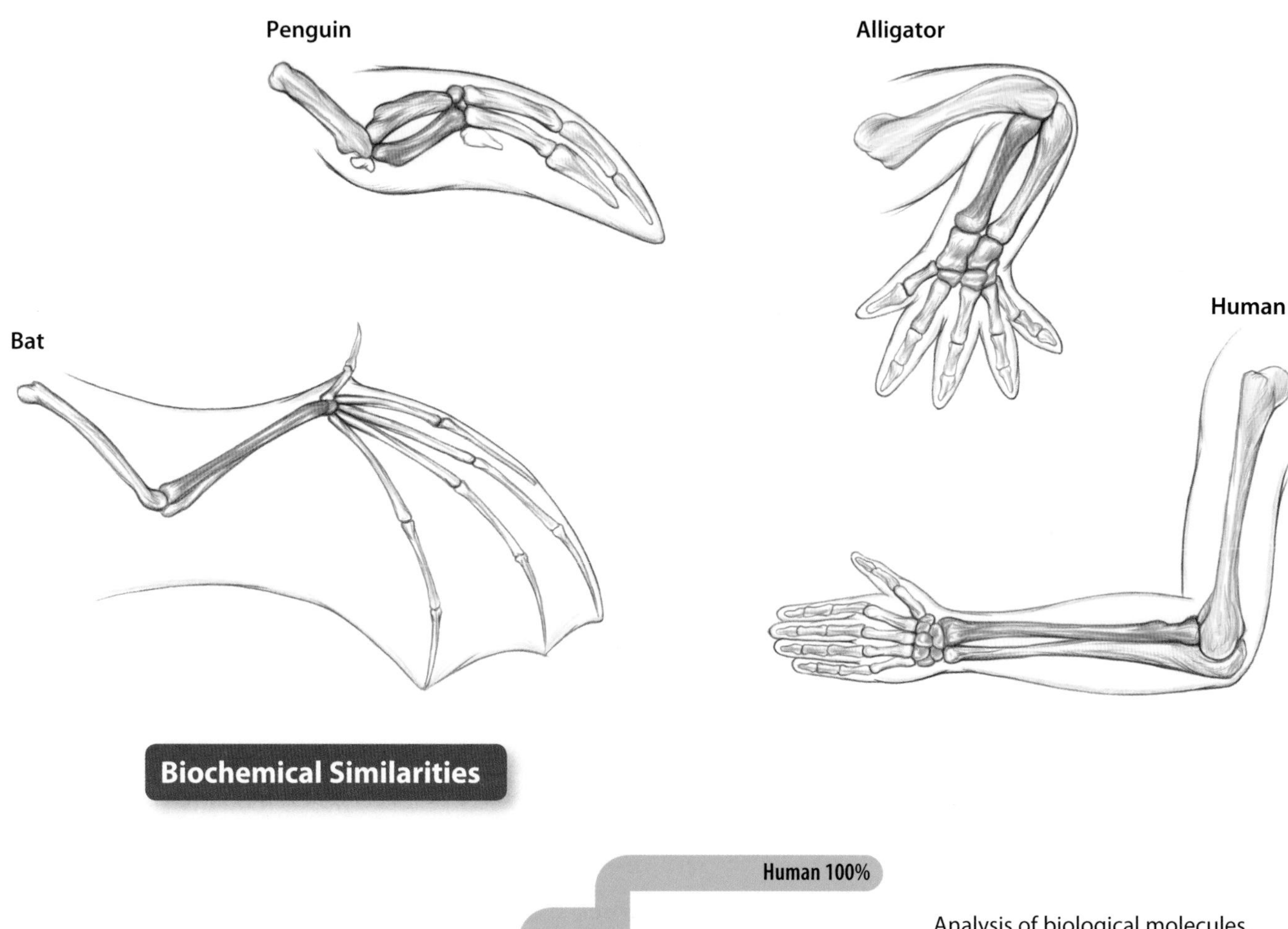

Biochemical Similarities

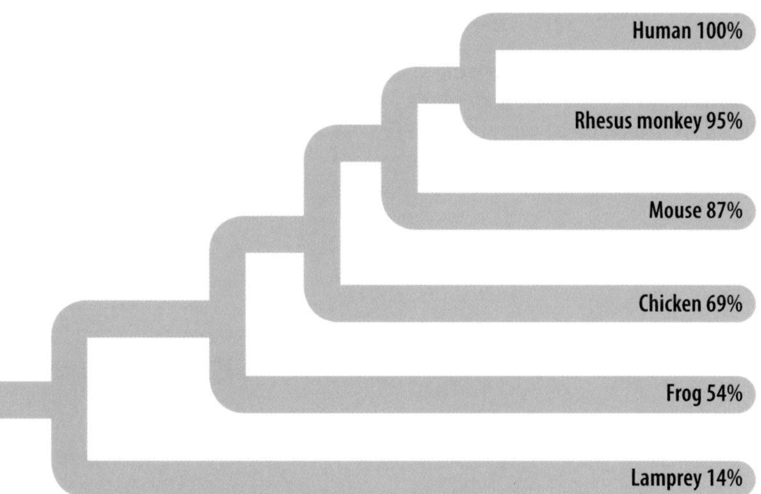

Analysis of biological molecules, such as proteins, also gives evidence for evolution. This **phylogenetic tree** shows how similar the amino acids in hemoglobin are in several chordate species compared to a human. The more similar the amino acids in hemoglobin, the more closely related the organisms are likely to be. For example, based on analysis of a hemoglobin polypeptide, rhesus monkeys are more closely related to humans than to chickens.

This little girl has **Williams syndrome**, a condition caused by the deletion of a tiny piece of chromosome 7. The deletion results in the loss of the gene that controls production of the protein elastin. The absence of elastin in the body generally leads to cardiovascular problems and premature skin aging. Individuals with Williams syndrome tend to have small, upturned noses; wide mouths; and large ears.

Chromosome mutations involve a change in the structure of a chromosome.

Part of a chromosome may break off or part of one chromosome may join another. In some cases, chromosome mutations are lethal. In many cases, however, individuals with chromosome mutations survive, and some may be minimally affected.

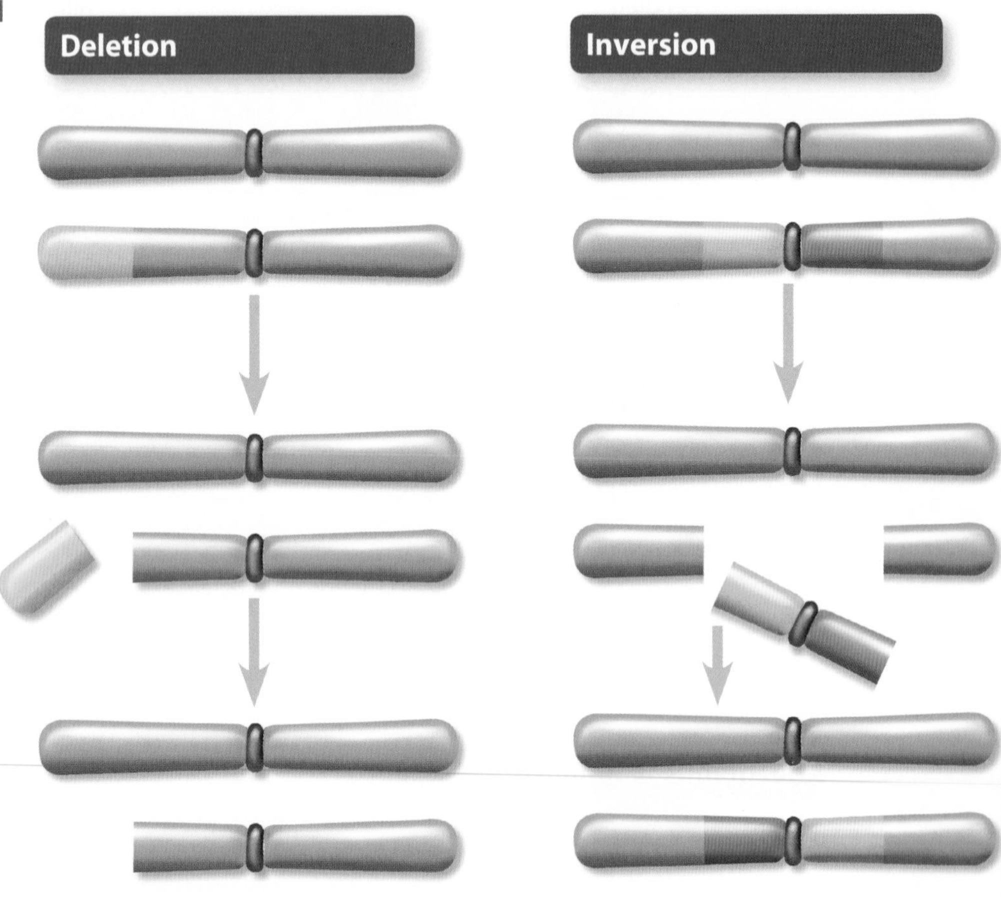

Sometimes part of a chromosome breaks off and is lost. This is known as a **deletion**. This type of mutation may cause entire genes to be lost; therefore, many deletions are fatal.

A piece of a chromosome may break off and reattach itself backward, which is known as an **inversion**. This type of mutation may cause serious problems if it disrupts genes at the site of the break.

Translocation

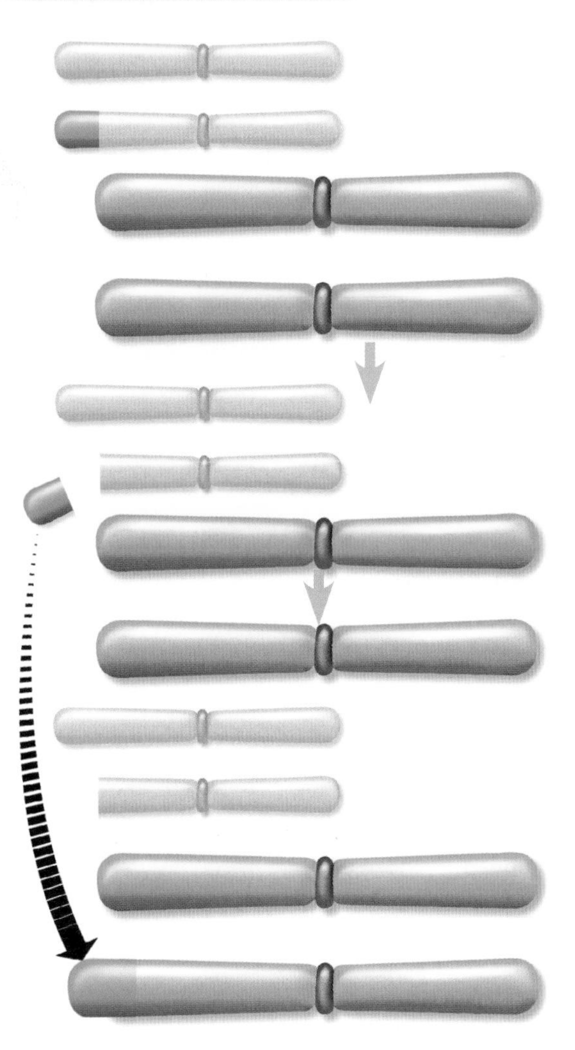

One piece of a chromosome may break off and attach to a nonhomologous chromosome, which is known as a **translocation**.

Nondisjunction

In a mutation called *nondisjunction*, a chromosome or part of a chromosome does not separate from its homologous chromosome during meiosis. When that happens, a gamete ends up with two copies of the same chromosome. If that gamete fuses with another at fertilization, the resulting offspring will have three copies of a chromosome instead of two. **Down syndrome** is a common nondisjunction that involves chromosome 21. Individuals with Down syndrome have three copies of chromosome 21 in every one of their cells.

During the metaphase stage of mitosis, the chromosomes inside a cell nucleus can be seen with a microscope. Photographs of these chromosomes are arranged to produce a **karyotype**. A karyotype shows the pairs of homologous chromosomes lined up in order of their assigned numbers. Scientists can examine the sex chromosomes in a karyotype to determine whether the individual from whom the cell was taken is male or female. A karyotype can also reveal if an individual has extra chromosomes. This karyotype is from an individual with Down syndrome (see number 21).

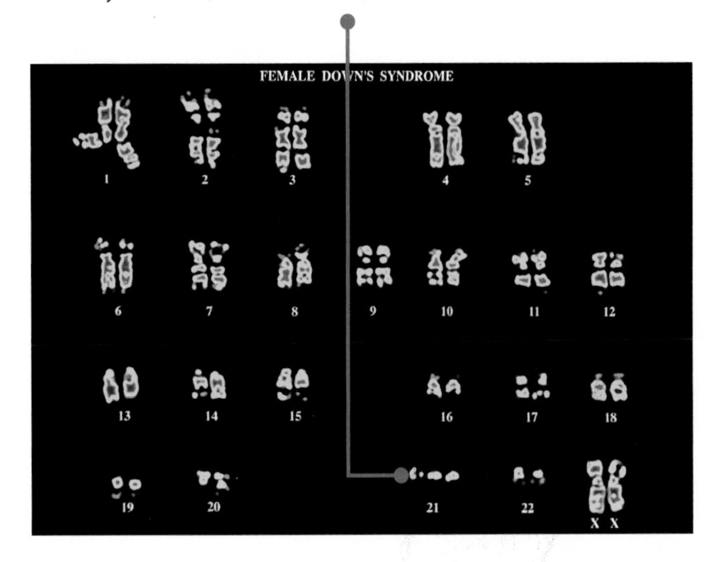

DNA mutations are changes in the sequence of nucleotide bases in a DNA molecule.

A change in an individual base is a point mutation. The three main types of point mutations are substitution, deletion, and insertion. Such mutations can cause a cell to produce incorrect or nonfunctional proteins.

Substitution Mutation

A **substitution mutation** occurs when one base replaces another in DNA. This replacement leads to a change in the DNA, the mRNA transcript, and ultimately the amino acid itself. In this case, guanine is substituted for cytosine, and mRNA has transcribed the error. At translation, the amino acid serine is acquired instead of tryptophan.

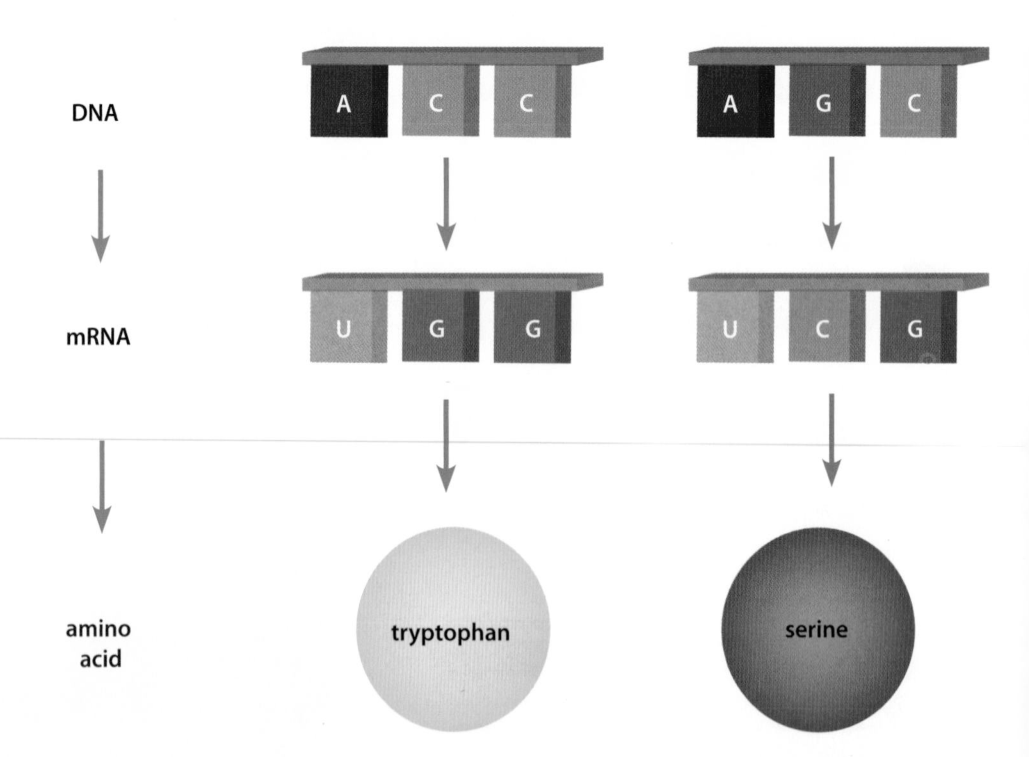

No Mutations

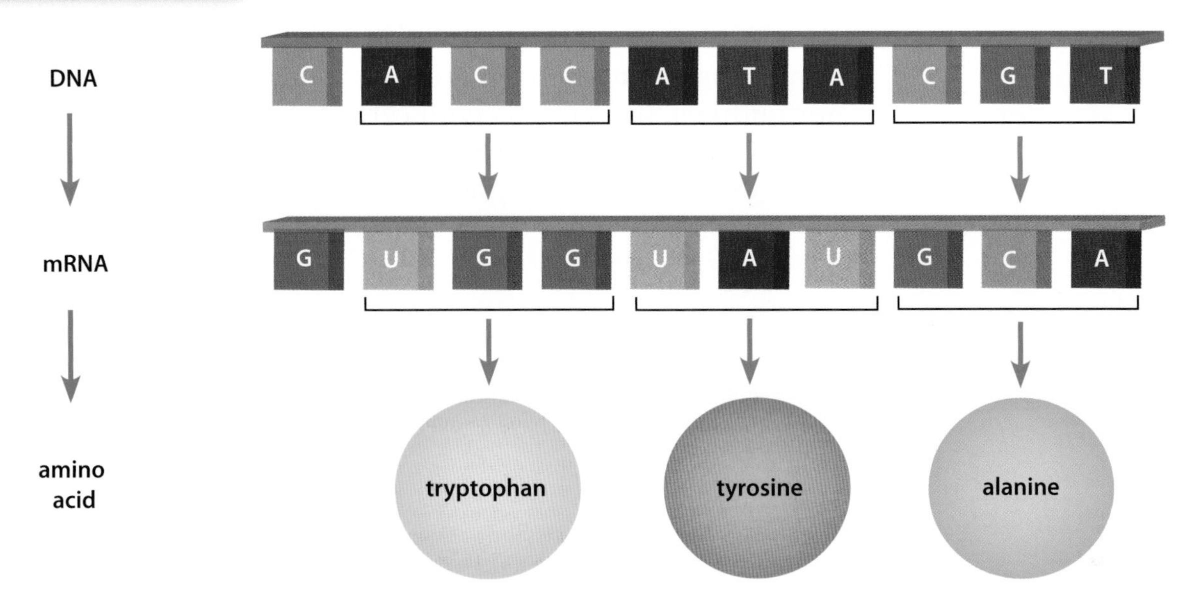

Nucleotide bases occur in groups of three along a DNA molecule. In a nonmutated segment of DNA, a ribosome transcribes and translates the sequence into a precise amino acid sequence. These amino acids will form a particular protein. When **no mutations** occur, the correct sequence of amino acids allows the protein to carry out its function.

Mutations: Frameshift

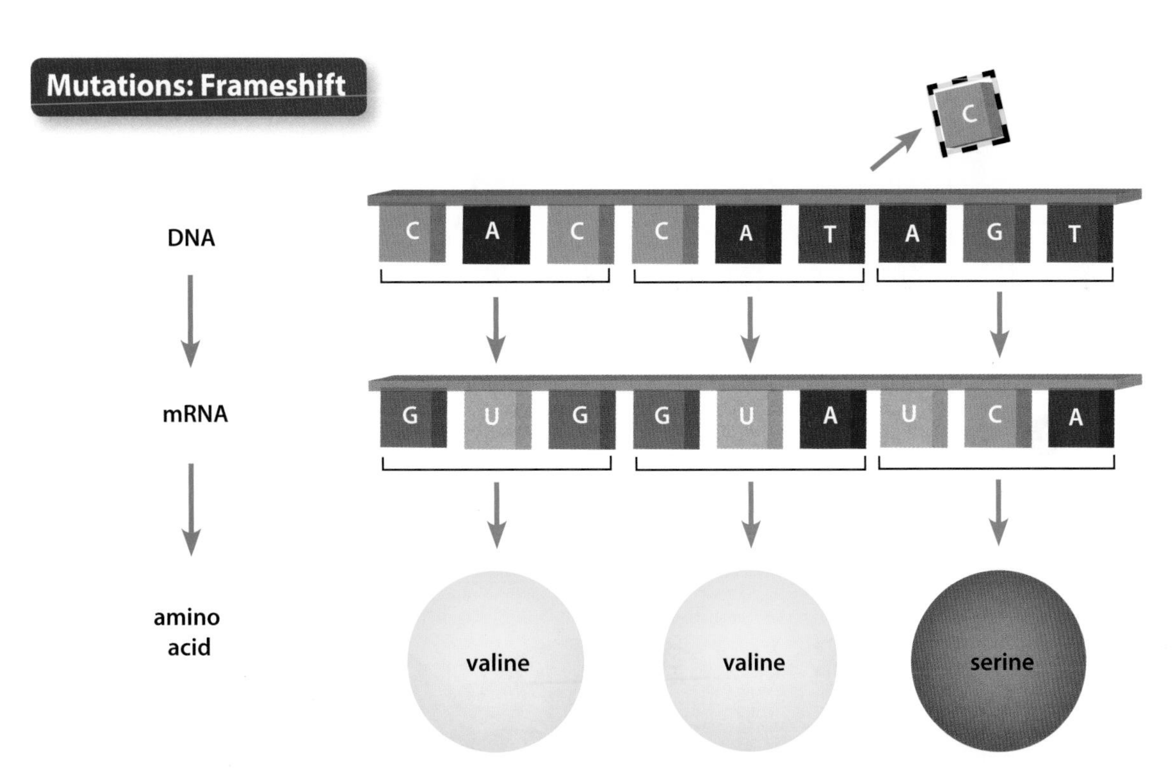

A point mutation can affect more than one codon. If a base is deleted, all codons in line after the deletion are disrupted, which is a **frameshift**. This same kind of shift results when an extra base is inserted. At translation, the wrong amino acids will likely be used. In most cases, the final protein does not have its correct structure and is not able to carry out its function.

Natural selection works on the variation in traits within a population.

In natural populations, there is genetic variation among individuals. Individuals with certain phenotypes may be better able to survive and reproduce in a particular environment than individuals with other phenotypes.

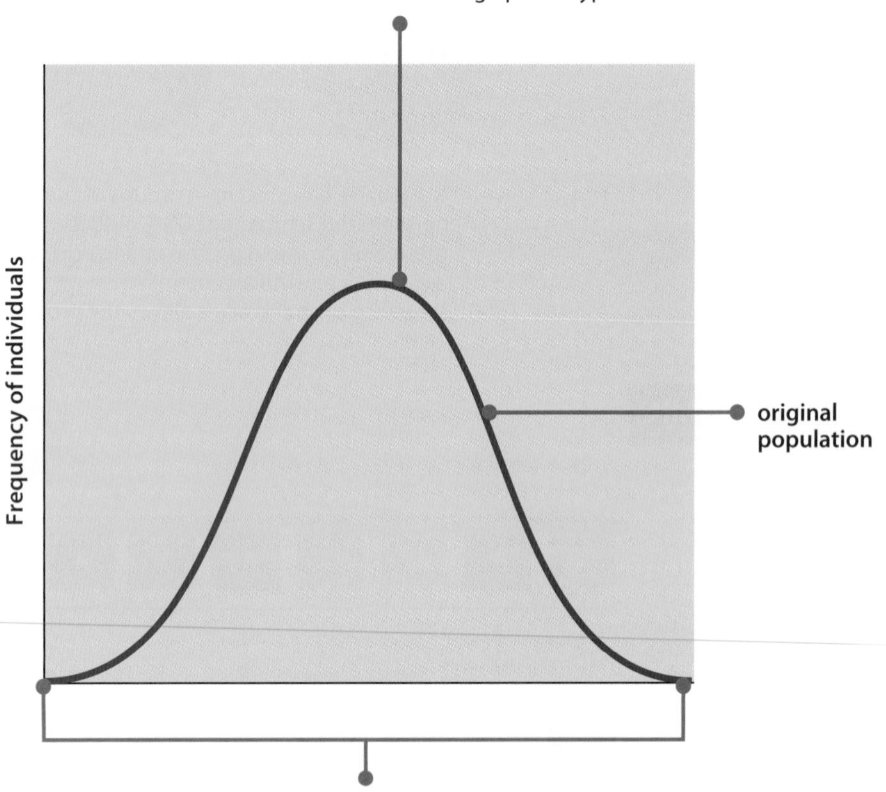
A general distribution of traits in a population can be represented by a bell curve. A **standard bell curve** shows that most individuals have an average phenotype.
Frequency of individuals
original population
In a population whose distribution of phenotypes follows a **standard bell curve**, few individuals have the extreme forms of a trait.

In this butterfly population, individuals **range in color** from light green to dark green. The distribution of phenotypes follows the standard bell curve. If the shape of a population's phenotype distribution curve differs from a standard bell curve, some type of natural selection is likely at work.

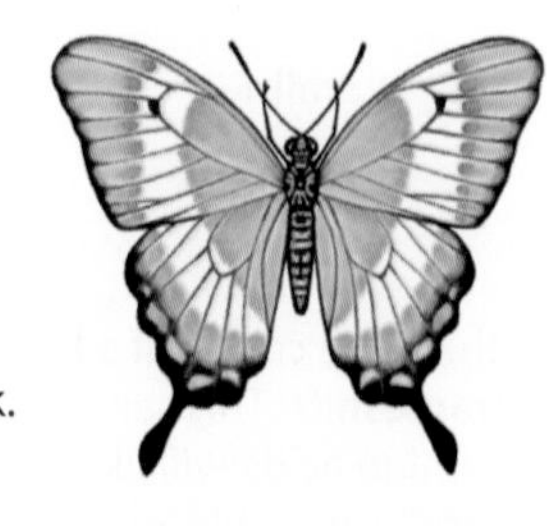

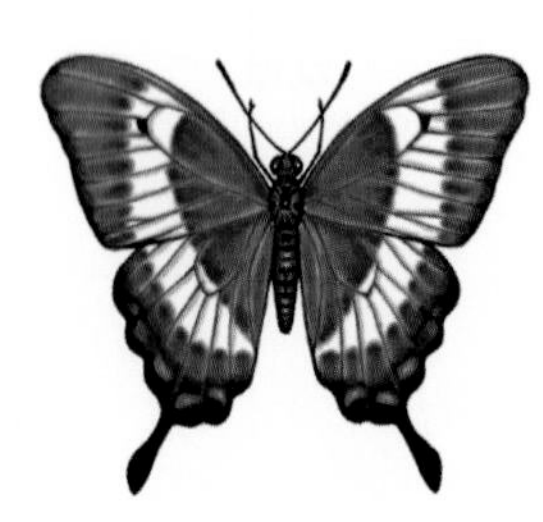

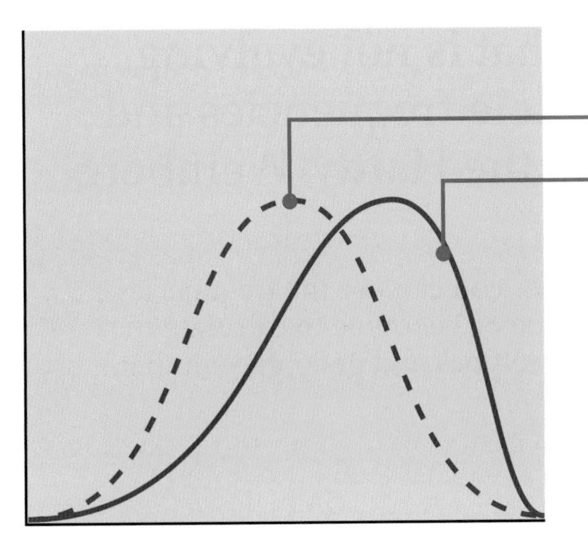

In some environments, individuals with one extreme form of a trait are more successful at surviving and reproducing than individuals with a more average form or the other extreme of the trait. For example, if dark green butterflies blend in with their surroundings better than light green butterflies, fewer dark green butterflies will be eaten by predators. More dark green butterflies will survive to reproduce. Over time, more individuals in the population will be dark green. This type of natural selection is known as **directional selection**. In this butterfly population, the dark green butterflies survive and reproduce at higher rates than butterflies with lighter phenotypes.

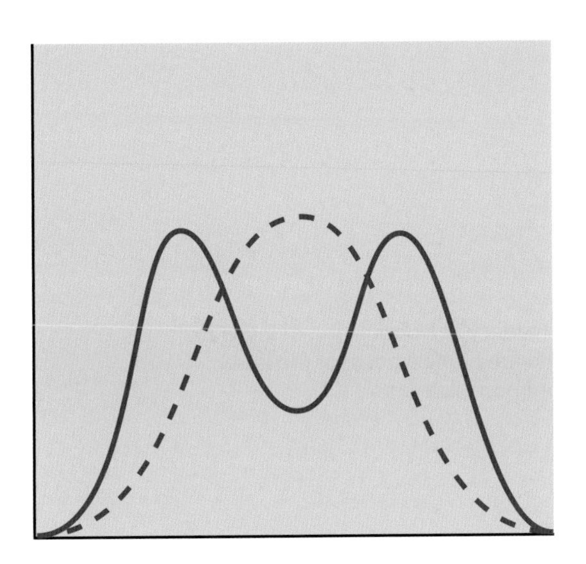

In some environments, individuals with forms of a trait at opposite extremes from the average are most successful at surviving and reproducing. Over time, fewer individuals will have the average trait and more individuals will have phenotypes at the extremes. This type of natural selection is known as **disruptive selection**. In this butterfly population, the lightest individuals and the darkest individuals survive and reproduce at higher rates than average-colored individuals.

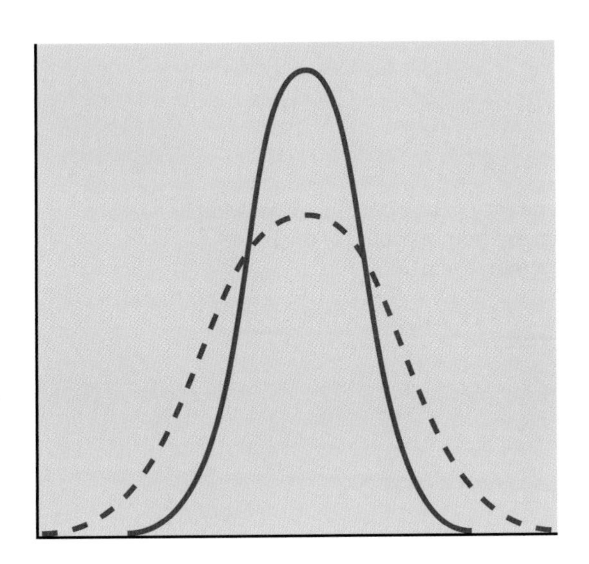

In some environments, individuals with the average form of a trait are more successful at surviving and reproducing than individuals with extreme forms of a trait. Over time, more individuals will have the average trait and fewer individuals will show extreme phenotypes. This type of natural selection is known as **stabilizing selection**. In this butterfly population, average-colored individuals with a moderately dark green color survive and reproduce at higher rates than either light green or dark green butterflies.

For a population that is not evolving, you can predict allele frequencies and phenotypes using the Hardy-Weinberg equation.

For a trait that has two alleles, you can use the frequencies of one homozygote phenotype or genotype to calculate the frequencies of the other phenotypes and genotypes in that population.

Hardy-Weinberg Equation

$$p^2 + 2pq + q^2 = 1$$

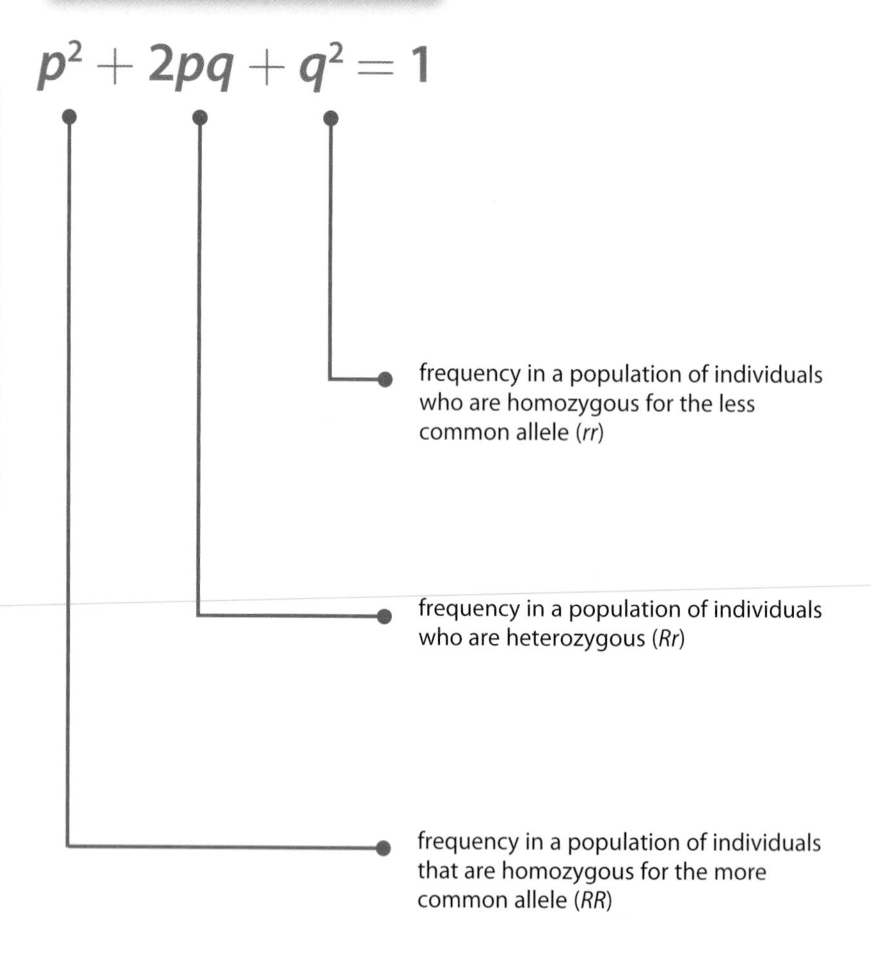

$p =$ frequency (decimal) of more common allele

$q =$ frequency (decimal) of less common allele

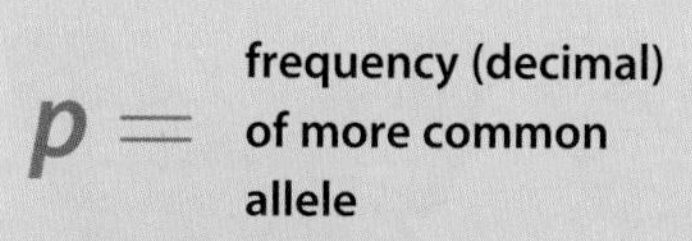

$$p + q = 1$$

Using the Hardy-Weinberg Equation

How can you use the Hardy-Weinberg equation to solve problems involving allele frequencies in the population?

$$p^2 + 2pq + q^2 = 1$$
$$p + q = 1$$

Solving a Problem

Individuals with cystic fibrosis suffer from production of mucus that is very sticky and thick. This thick mucus can build up in the lungs and breathing passages, causing respiratory problems. Mucus buildup can also affect the pancreas, an organ that secretes digestive enzymes, preventing the normal breakdown and absorption of food. Individuals with more severe forms of the disease may die at a young age.

The allele for cystic fibrosis is recessive. The more common allele (*R*) is a dominant allele. Because of this, an individual must have two copies of the recessive allele (*r*) to have the disorder. Individuals with only one copy of the recessive allele are known as carriers. These individuals can pass the allele to offspring, but they do not have the disorder.

In the general population, 0.048 percent of individuals have cystic fibrosis. Use this information and the Hardy-Weinberg equation to calculate the frequency of individuals who are heterozygous carriers of the cystic fibrosis allele, but who do not have the disorder.

1. Given: $q^2 = 0.048\% = 0.00048$

   $q = \sqrt{.00048} = 0.022$

2. If $q = 0.022$, and $p + q = 1$, then $p = 1 - q = 1 - 0.022 = 0.978$

3. $2pq = 2(0.978)(0.022) = 0.043 = 4.3\%$

   This means that 43 out of every 1,000 people in this particular population carry the allele for cystic fibrosis but do not have the disorder. These individuals are heterozygous carriers.

4. $p^2 + 2pq + q^2 = 1$

   - q^2: In this population, 0.048 percent of individuals have cystic fibrosis.
   - $2pq$: In this population, 4.3 percent of individuals are carriers of the cystic fibrosis allele.
   - p^2: In this population, 95.6 percent of individuals do not have cystic fibrosis and do not carry the cystic fibrosis allele.

Many scientists organize all living things into three main groups, or domains, based on shared traits.

Domains are further divided into kingdoms. As scientists learn more about earth's living things, they may adjust this classification structure. For now, scientists think a system of three domains best represents our understanding of how organisms are related.

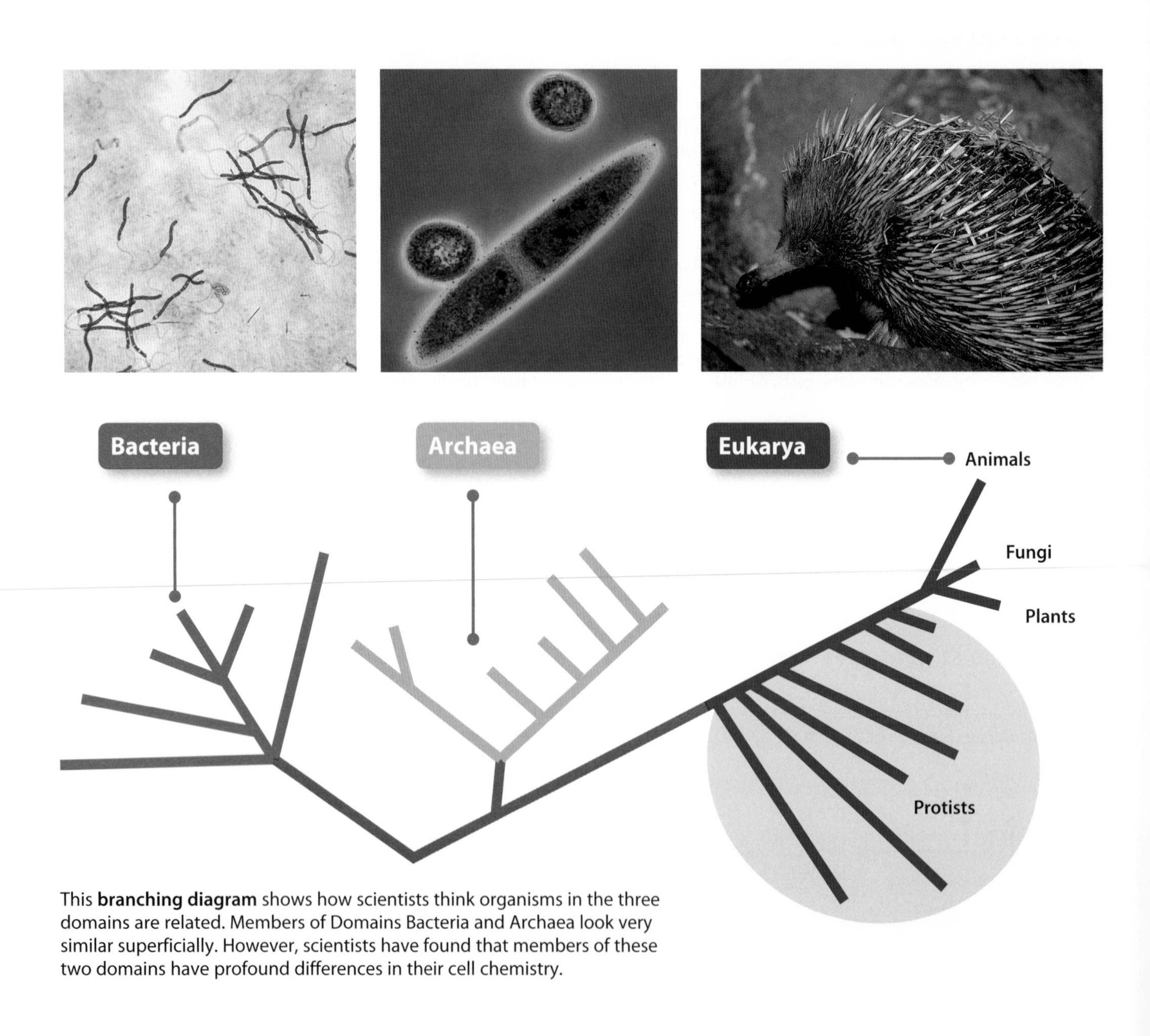

This **branching diagram** shows how scientists think organisms in the three domains are related. Members of Domains Bacteria and Archaea look very similar superficially. However, scientists have found that members of these two domains have profound differences in their cell chemistry.

DOMAIN AND KINGDOM CHARACTERISTICS

DOMAIN	*KINGDOM*	*CHARACTERISTICS*				*EXAMPLES*
		BODY TYPE	*CELL TYPE*	*CELL STRUCTURE*	*MEANS OF NUTRITION*	
Bacteria	Eubacteria	Single cell	Prokaryotic	Cell wall containing peptidoglycan	Autotrophic and heterotrophic	*Escherichia coli*
Archaea	Archaebacteria	Single cell	Prokaryotic	Cell wall containing no peptidoglycan	Autotrophic and heterotrophic	Halophiles Thermophiles
Eukarya	Protista	Single cell and multicell	Eukaryotic	Various	Autotrophic and heterotrophic	*Amoeba* *Paramecia*
Eukarya	Fungi	Single cell and multicell	Eukaryotic	Cell wall containing chitin	Heterotrophic	Yeast Mushrooms
Eukarya	Plantae	Multicell	Eukaryotic	Cell wall containing cellulose	Autotrophic	Mosses Conifers Orchids Oak trees
Eukarya	Animalia	Multicell	Eukaryotic	No cell wall	Heterotrophic	Jellyfish Spiders Earthworms Birds

This individual belongs to the species ***Phoeniconaias minor***.

Within each kingdom, species are further classified into groups based on similarities. For example, the **full classification** for a lesser flamingo is shown here:

Domain: Eukarya
Kingdom: Animalia
Phylum: Chordata
Subphylum: Vertebrata
Class: Aves
Order: Ciconiiformes
Family: Phoenicopteridae
Genus: *Phoeniconaias*
Specific epithet: *minor*

A phylogenetic tree shows how groups of organisms are related through common ancestry.

Scientists create phylogenetic trees to show evolutionary relationships at different levels of classification, from domains to species. This phylogenetic tree outlines evolutionary relationships among organisms in the three domains of life.

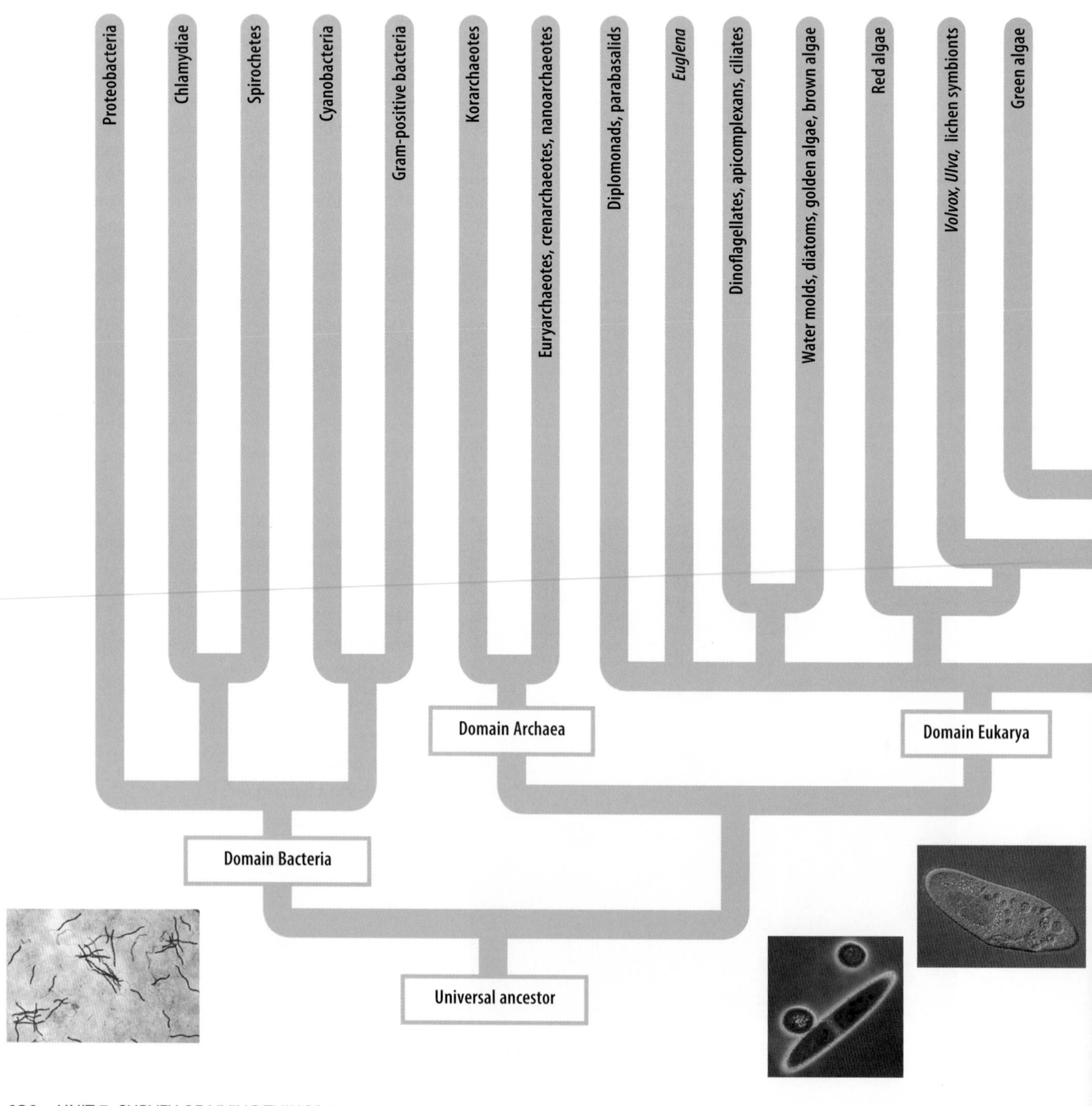

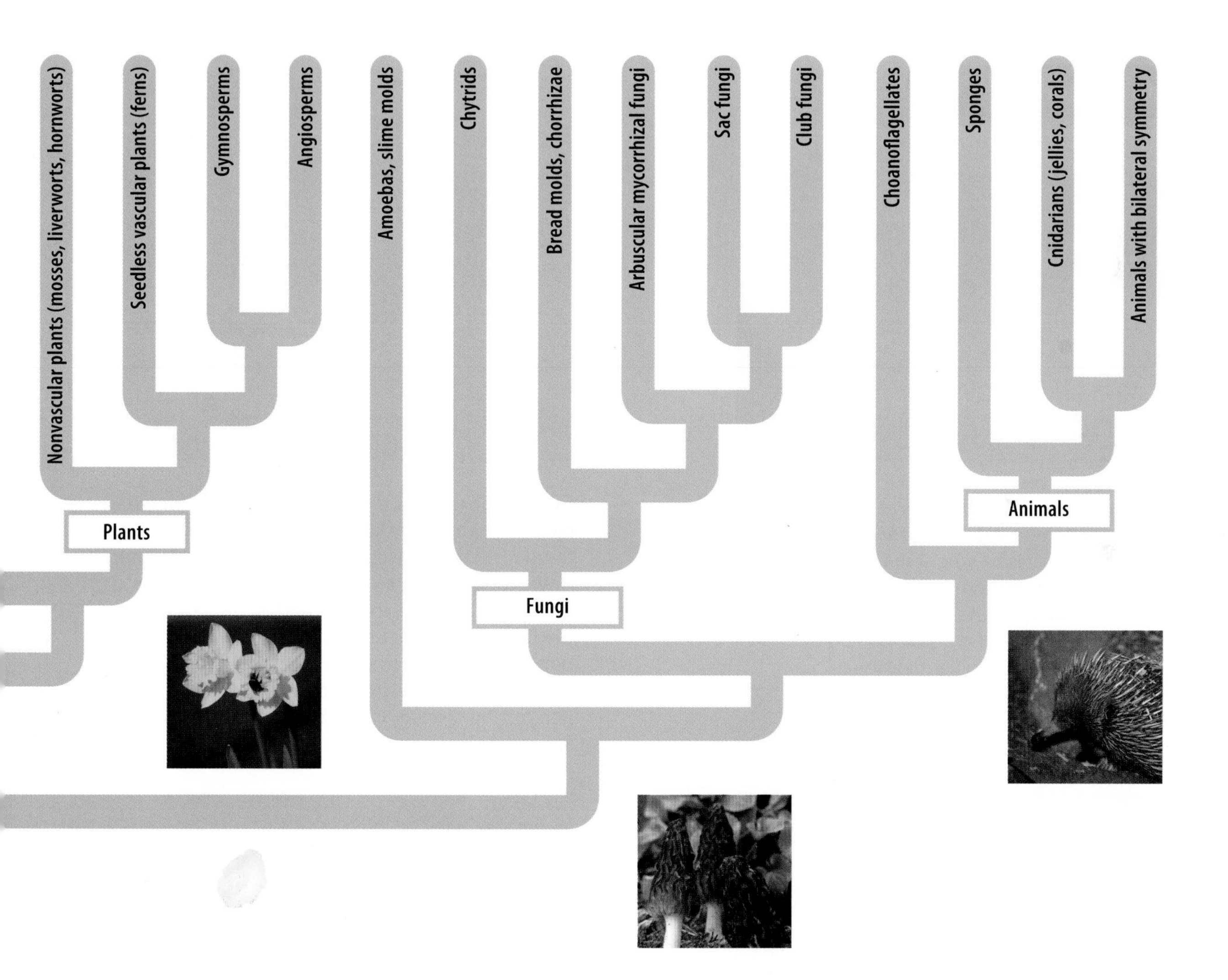
Nonvascular plants (mosses, liverworts, hornworts)
Seedless vascular plants (ferns)
Gymnosperms
Angiosperms
Amoebas, slime molds
Chytrids
Bread molds, chorrhizae
Arbuscular mycorrhizal fungi
Sac fungi
Club fungi
Choanoflagellates
Sponges
Cnidarians (jellies, corals)
Animals with bilateral symmetry
Plants
Fungi
Animals

Two of the three domains contain only prokaryotes as members.

Organisms in these two domains were once classified into a single kingdom, Monera. Scientists discovered, however, that bacteria and archaeans are as different from each other as they are from us. This led to the reclassification that most scientists accept today.

Domain Bacteria

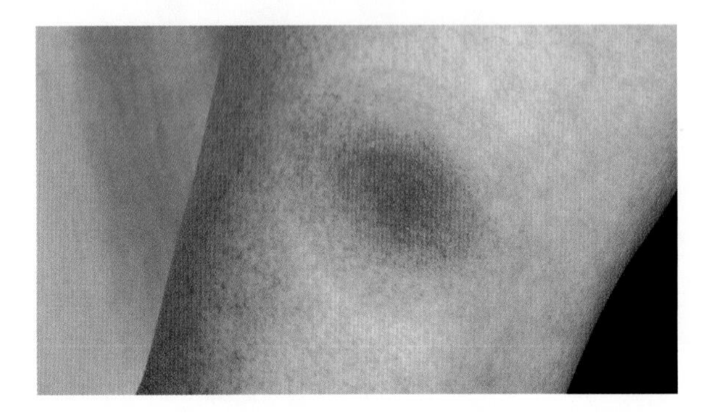

Spirochetes are a group of corkscrew-shaped bacteria. One spirochete species, *Borrelia burgdorferi*, is the cause of Lyme disease. Lyme disease is carried by ticks. One of the first symptoms of the disease is a rash that resembles a bull's-eye. As the disease progresses, symptoms may be flu-like and accompanied by stiffness in joints and an irregular heartbeat.

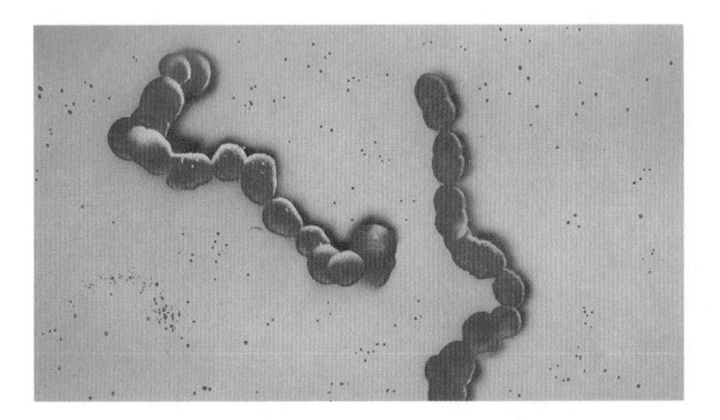

Group A ***Streptococcus***, which are gram-positive bacteria, commonly live in the human throat and on the skin. In most cases, their presence is harmless. However, *Streptococcus* can cause life-threatening diseases when they invade parts of the body where the bacteria are not usually found, or when their populations get too large. One of the most severe diseases caused by *Streptococcus* bacteria is necrotizing fasciitis. In this disease, flesh-eating *Streptococcus* destroy muscle, fat, and skin tissue.

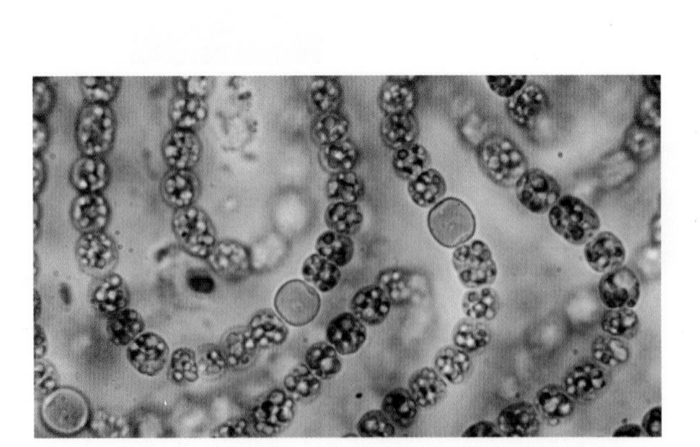

Cyanobacteria, once known as blue-green algae, carry out photosynthesis. Scientists think that much of the oxygen in our atmosphere today is due to the large amounts of oxygen produced by cyanobacteria around 2 billion years ago.

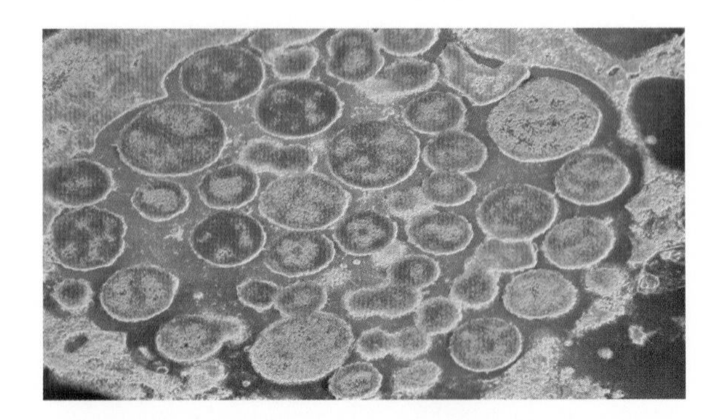

Chlamydiae are coccoid or spherical bacteria. There are three species of *Chlamydiae*, all of which cause disease in humans. One species of *Chlamydiae* causes a sexually transmitted disease that is very common. Scientists have found that another species of *Chlamydiae* causes a mild pneumonia.

Domain Archaea

In the 1970s, scientists discovered archaeans living in the hot springs of Yellowstone National Park. Previously, scientists had thought these springs were too hot to allow any life to survive. Archaeans that thrive in extremely hot conditions are known as **thermophiles**.

The very salty north arm of the Great Salt Lake is home to salt-loving archaeans known as **halophiles**. These archaeans thrive in extremely salty conditions that other organisms could not tolerate.

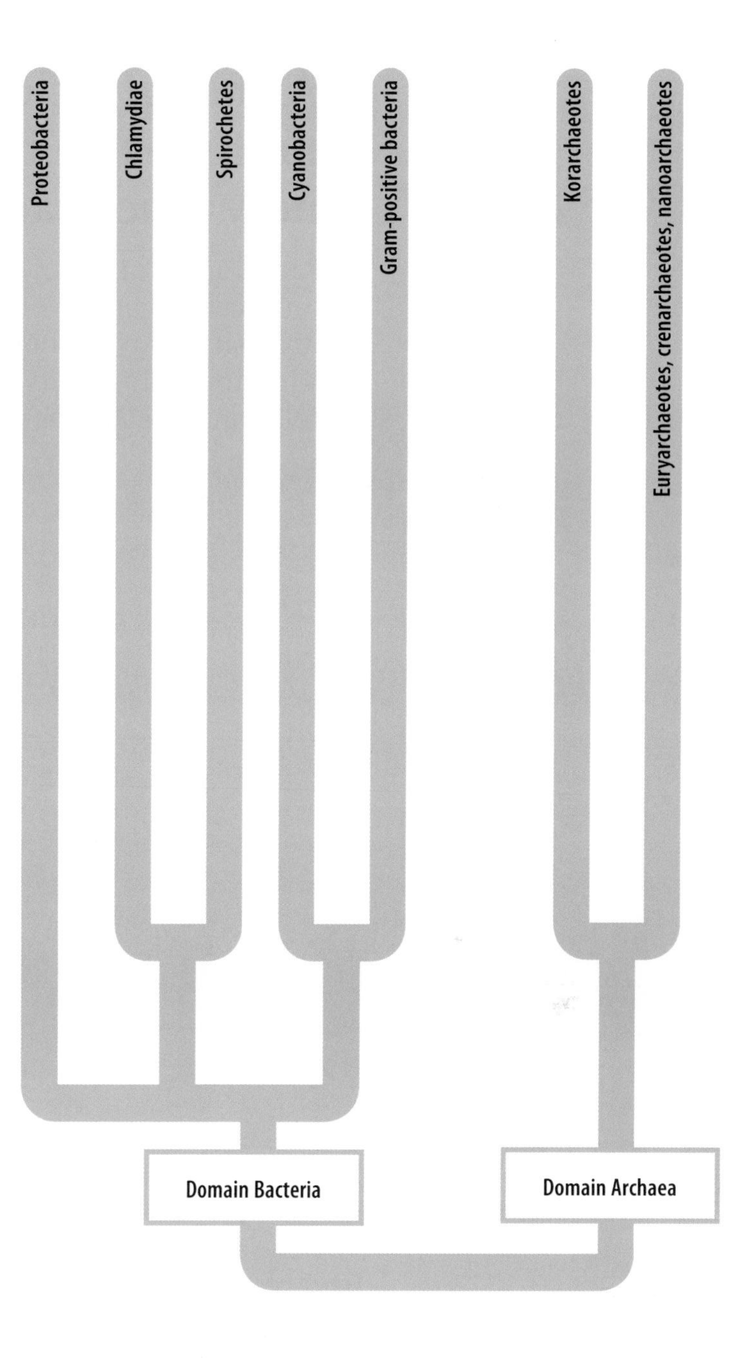

Although scientists once classified protists and fungi with plants, scientists now place each in its own kingdom.

Kingdom Protista contains a wide variety of single-cell and multicell organisms that are characterized more by their diversity than by their shared characteristics. Members of Kingdom Fungi play important ecological roles in symbiotic relationships and as decomposers.

Diplomonads, parabasalids
Euglena
Dinoflagellates, apicomplexans, ciliates
Water molds, diatoms, golden algae, brown algae
Red algae
Volvox, *Ulva*, lichen symbionts
Green algae
Amoebas, slime molds
Chytrids
Bread molds, mychorrhizae
Arbuscular mycorrhizal fungi
Sac fungi
Club fungi
Domain Bacteria
Domain Eukarya

Kingdom Protista

Red algae are abundant in the tropics, but are also found in cooler waters. Most red algae live in the oceans, but some live in freshwater. Although red algae have chloroplasts that allow them to photosynthesize, the organisms often appear red due to pigments called *phycobilins*.

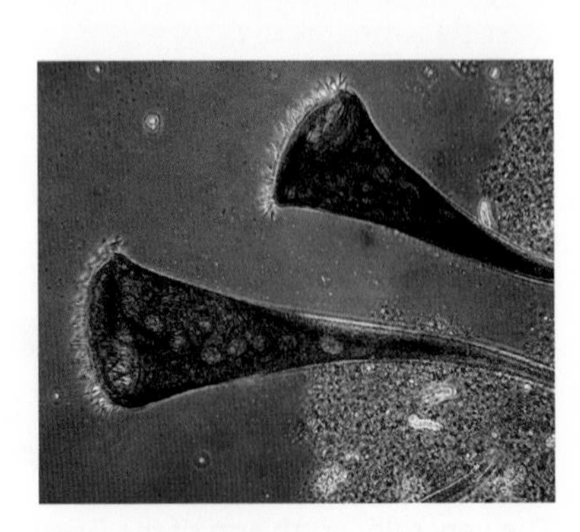

Stentor is a trumpet-shaped, single-cell protist that uses its cilia to sweep food down its gullet. This protist is commonly found in pond water.

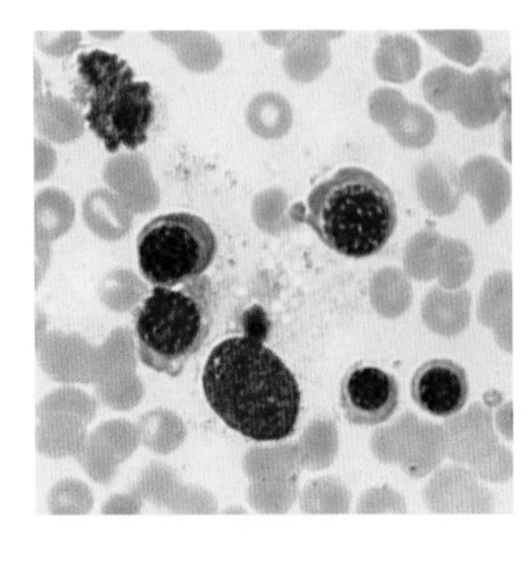

Protists in the genus ***Plasmodium*** are heterotrophic parasites—they consume other organisms. The various species of *Plasmodium* generally infect vertebrates such as humans and are carried by invertebrates such as mosquitoes. Some species of *Plasmodium* are the cause of malaria in humans.

Kingdom Fungi

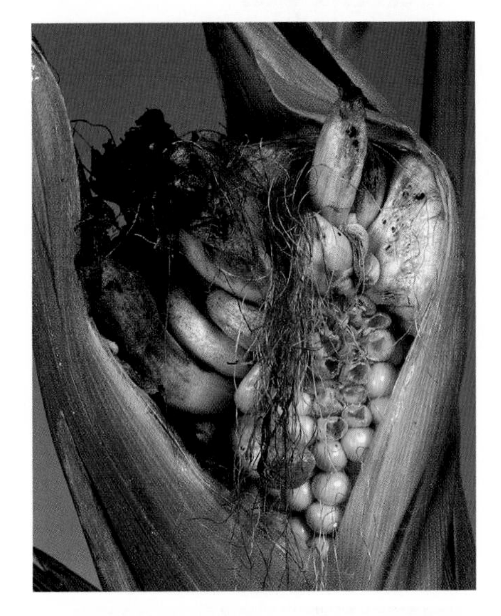

Corn smut is a fungus closely related to mushrooms, puffballs, and stinkhorns. Known as *huitlacoche* in Mexico, this fungus is considered by some people to be a delicacy.

The phylum **Basidiomycota** includes some of the most familiar fungi, such as those commonly referred to as mushrooms. Although many members of this phylum are edible, some are highly poisonous. You should never eat a wild mushroom before having it identified as nonpoisonous by a fungus expert.

Yeast are single-cell fungi that can reproduce both sexually and asexually. These organisms produce carbon dioxide and alcohol as they ferment sugars. For thousands of years, humans have used yeast in the production of foods such as bread and beer.

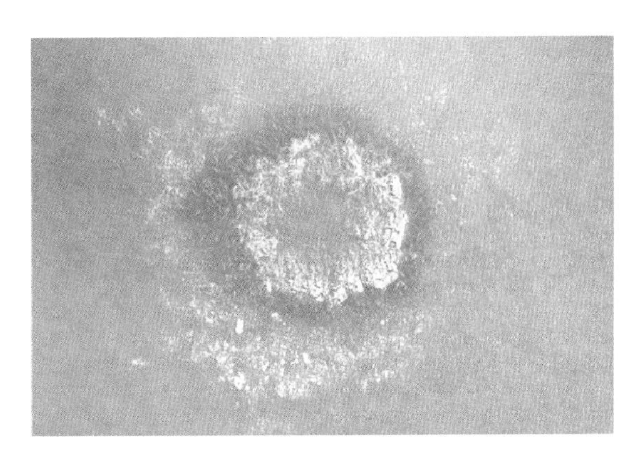

In spite of its name, **ringworm** is actually a fungus. Ringworm is a very common, and very contagious, skin infection. The fungus prefers warm, moist patches of skin. Infections are generally mild, and most can be treated easily.

Scientists classify all plants in Kingdom Plantae within Domain Eukarya.

The huge variety of modern plant species is a result of evolution over millions of years. The first land plants were small and restricted to moist environments. Later plant species developed adaptations—such as thick cuticles and seeds—that made survival in new environments possible.

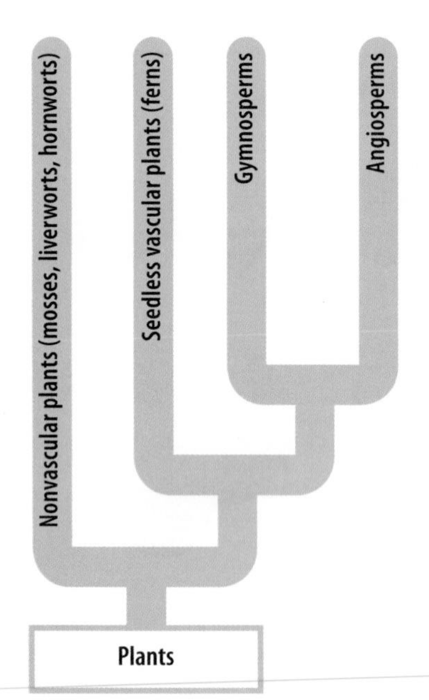

Plants Without Seeds

Mosses are nonvascular plants. They lack specialized tissues for transporting water and other nutrients. Nutrients move through and between the cells of nonvascular plants by diffusion. Because of this, most nonvascular plants grow low to the ground and live in or near sources of water.

Ferns are seedless vascular plants. Like other vascular plants, they have specialized tissues—xylem and phloem—that transport water and other nutrients throughout their bodies. These tissues allow vascular plants to grow much larger than nonvascular plants. Seedless vascular plants first evolved during the Devonian period (more than 390 million years ago), or even earlier in the late Silurian period.

Plants With Seeds

Bristlecone pines, also known as Methuselah trees, are the oldest known living things. Individuals can live more than 5,000 years. The bristlecone pine is a gymnosperm, one of two groups of seed plants. Gymnosperms carry their gametes and seeds in cones and are generally pollinated by wind.

Many people mistake **cycads** for palms, but these plants are actually gymnosperms. Though they make up only a tiny percentage of living species today, cycads were a dominant part of earth's vegetation during the Mesozoic era (between 248 million and 65 million years ago). Cycads generally thrive in warm climates; only one genus occurs naturally in the United States (in southern Florida).

Day lilies are angiosperms, or flowering plants. Angiosperms are divided into two main groups: monocots and dicots. Monocots like this day lily have seeds that contain only one seed leaf or cotyledon. In general, monocots' leaves have parallel veins, and their flowers have three parts (or multiples of three). Angiosperms first appeared in the fossil record during the Cretaceous period (between 144 million and 65 million years ago). Some scientists think the first angiosperms may have evolved as early as 200 million years ago.

Oaks are also angiosperms, although their flowers are small and inconspicuous. Oaks are dicots. Their seeds contain two seed cotyledons. In general, the leaves of dicots have netlike veins, and the flowers have four or five parts.

Scientists classify all animals in Kingdom Animalia within Domain Eukarya.

Scientists classify animals together because they all share some common features. All animals are multicellular, and their cells do not have cell walls. In addition, animals can reproduce sexually, are heterotrophic, and digest their food inside their bodies.

Animals

Choanoflagellates

Sponges

Cnidarians (jellies, coral)

Animals with bilateral symmetry

Animals

Sponges (phylum Porifera) are some of the simplest animals and were among the earliest animals to evolve on earth. To feed, sponges filter tiny microorganisms and other organic matter from the water in which they live. Like all animals, sponges can reproduce sexually. However, many sponges can also reproduce asexually by producing tiny buds of tissue that can grow into mature sponges.

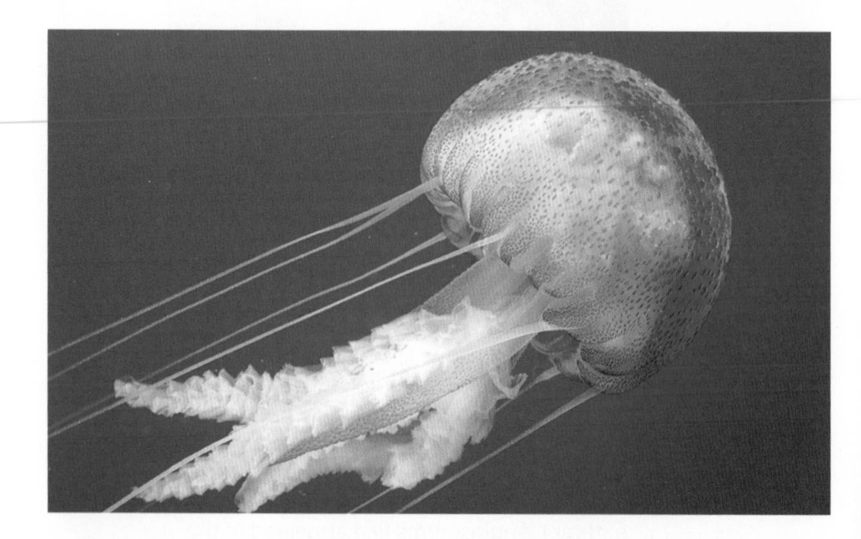

Jellyfish are members of phylum Cnidaria, which also includes corals and sea anemones. Cnidarians have very simple tissues arranged in two main layers. In jellyfish, these layers form a hollow sac. The tissues inside the sac act as a simple digestive system. Most cnidarians, including jellyfish, have tentacles that contain stinging cells called *nematocysts*. The organisms use their nematocysts to stun and disable prey.

Flatworms (phylum Platyhelminthes) are simple invertebrates with bodies made of three tissue layers. Most flatworms are small and, as their name suggests, flat. Flatworms do not have circulatory systems. However, their small size and flattened body shape allow oxygen and other gases to diffuse into and out of every cell. Although some flatworms are free-living, most are parasites that live on other animals.

Humans are members of phylum Chordata. Chordates have a central nerve cord, or notochord, that carries information between the brain and other parts of the body. Most chordates have internal skeletons made of bone or cartilage, or both. They also have complete digestive systems, and most have complex, closed circulatory systems.

Phylum Mollusca includes more than 125,000 species of **mollusks**. All mollusks have a muscular foot and a tough mantle, which help protect the animal. Most mollusks, including clams and snails, have hard shells that protect their soft bodies. The shells of some mollusks, such as octopuses and squid, are greatly reduced. Mollusks have complex digestive systems.

Sea stars are members of phylum Echinodermata. This phylum also includes sand dollars and sea urchins. Echinoderms have hard endoskeletons made mainly of calcium carbonate. They also have water-vascular systems, which are networks of tubes filled with water. These animals can control the pressure of this water within their tubes. Extensions of the tubes protrude from the skeleton. When these extensions fill with water, they can act as feet and allow the animals to move or grasp objects such as prey.

Grasshoppers, like other members of phylum Arthropoda, have hard, jointed shells called *exoskeletons* that provide support to their bodies. An exoskeleton is generally made up of the protein chitin, although some also contain minerals such as calcium carbonate. Arthropods have complete, closed digestive tracts and complex nervous systems. Scientists estimate that nearly 75 percent of all species on earth belong to this phylum.

Flatworms are invertebrate, free-living or parasitic animals that have distinct head ends with primitive brains.

Some flatworms are free-living, and some are parasitic. Flatworms have organs, but their digestive, respiratory, and circulatory systems are simple. There are three major groups of flatworms: free-living flatworms, flukes, and tapeworms.

Phylum Platyhelminthes

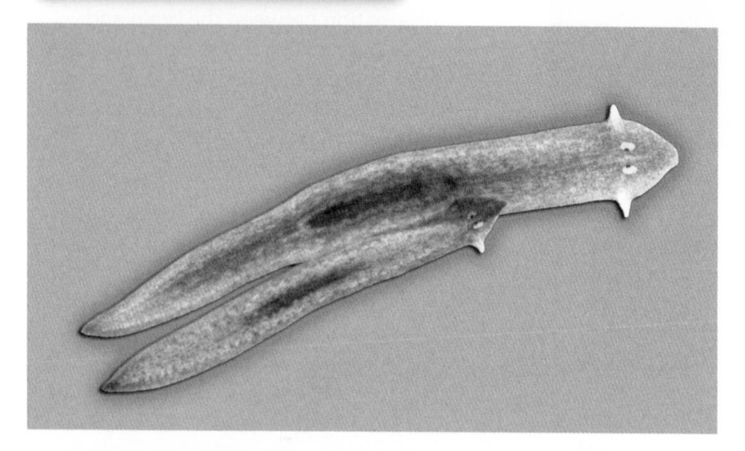

Free-living flatworms, many of which are planarians, do not require hosts for survival. However, they may still feed on other animals or parts of animals. Many planarians live in freshwater environments. Some live on land in moist soils.

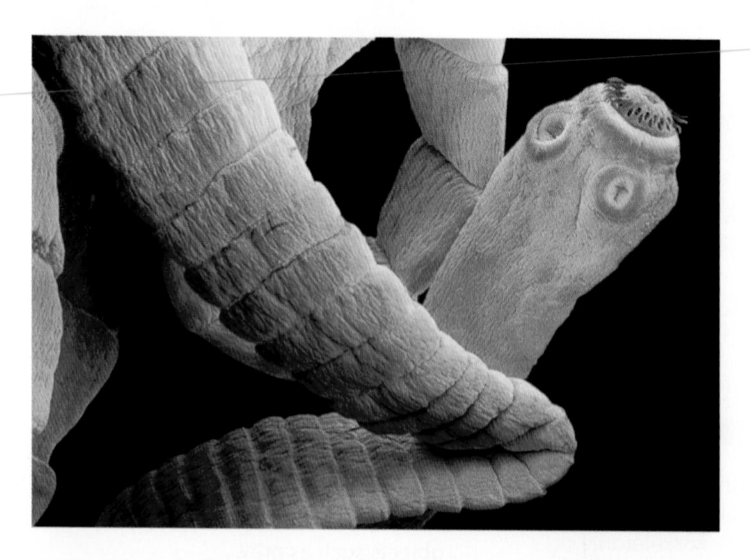

Tapeworms are parasitic flatworms. They have no digestive tract; they absorb nutrients from the guts of their hosts. A tapeworm's body is made up almost entirely of reproductive segments called *proglottids*.

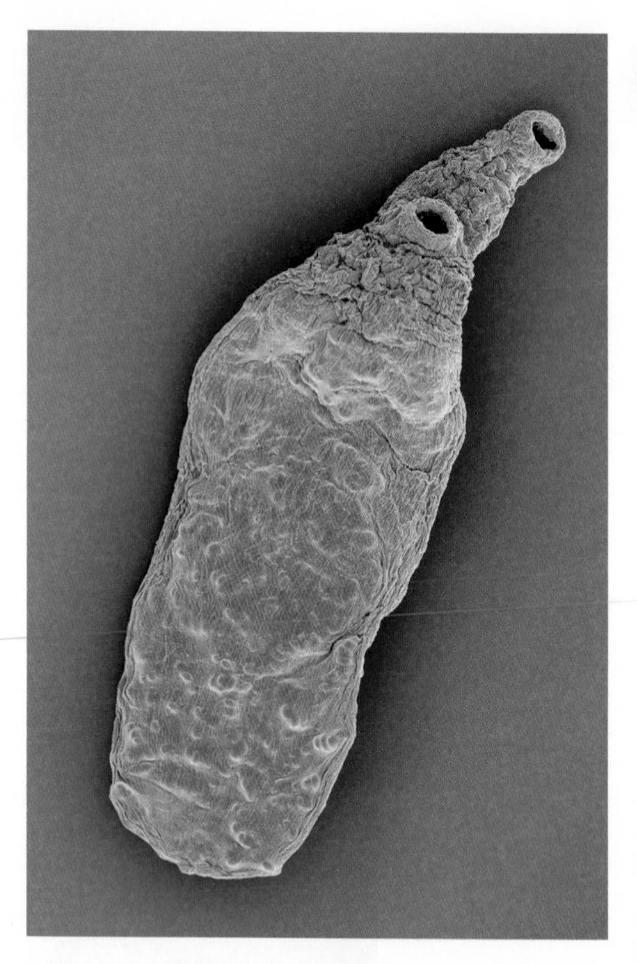

Flukes are parasitic flatworms that require a host to survive. Fluke eggs typically leave the host's body in feces and are ingested by other animals. Most flukes spend part of their life cycle in an intermediate host species.

Free-Living Flatworms

Dugesia is hermaphroditic: Each individual produces both eggs and sperm for sexual reproduction. However, a flatworm cannot fertilize its own eggs. *Dugesia* can also reproduce asexually by regeneration.

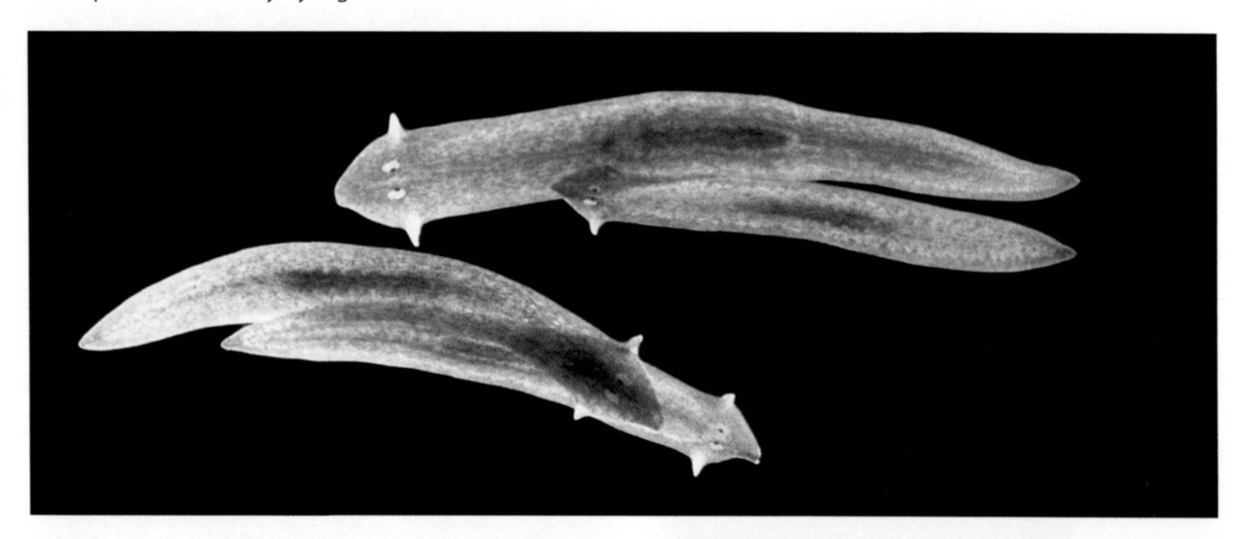

There are many kinds of free-living flatworms. All of them have body systems that are simple, yet represent intriguing solutions to life's challenges.

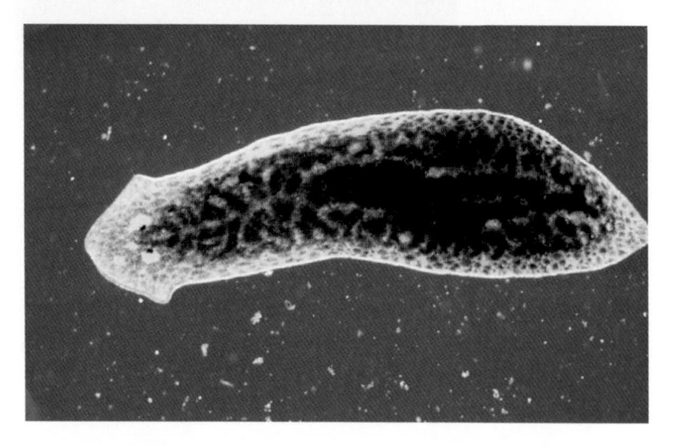

Dugesia belongs to the class of free-living flatworms. This planarian is found in freshwater environments. It eats by sucking small organisms into its tubelike pharynx. *Dugesia* has two eyespots that can detect light and a pair of auricles (ear-shaped appendages) that sense chemicals in the water.

Ferns are vascular plants that do not have seeds. About 12,000 species of fern exist today.

Ferns first appear in the fossil record as far back as the Carboniferous period. Today's coal reserves formed from the compressed remains of buried Carboniferous forests. Modern ferns appear in the fossil record about 160 million years ago.

Division Pteridophyta

Most ferns are small and grow relatively close to the ground. Some, however, can grow to more than 20 m tall. These **tree ferns** may take more than 100 years to reach full height.

Maidenhair ferns (genus *Adiantum*) are characterized by their bright green, delicately shaped leaves. They grow in very damp environments, often near waterfalls.

Individuals in the genus ***Azolla*** look more like mosses than ferns. These tiny plants grow on the surface of ponds and lakes. Many *Azolla* are green in shady environments, but when exposed to direct sun for long periods, they produce a pigment that causes them to turn red.

Pteridium aquilinum

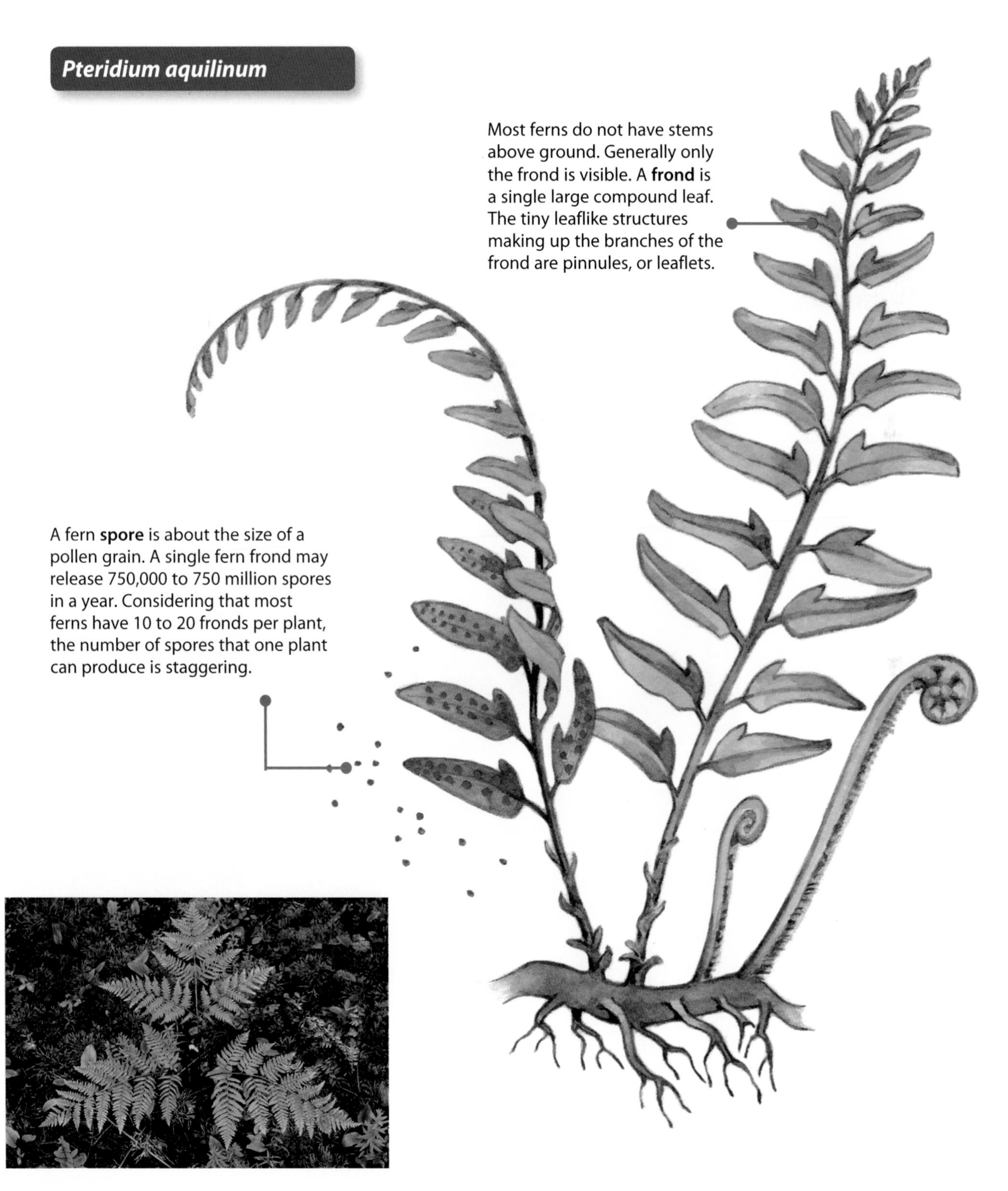

Most ferns do not have stems above ground. Generally only the frond is visible. A **frond** is a single large compound leaf. The tiny leaflike structures making up the branches of the frond are pinnules, or leaflets.
A fern **spore** is about the size of a pollen grain. A single fern frond may release 750,000 to 750 million spores in a year. Considering that most ferns have 10 to 20 fronds per plant, the number of spores that one plant can produce is staggering.

Pteridium aquilinum is the common **bracken fern**.

Monkeys, apes, lemurs, and humans all belong to the mammalian order Primates.

Primates evolved from the earliest primate ancestor in two main lineages: prosimians (lemurs, tarsiers, and lorises) and simians (monkeys and apes). Humans (*Homo sapiens*) are part of the simian lineage. Our closest relatives are the extinct hominids and the great apes.

Order Primates

Lemurs are relatively small primates found in Madagascar. Like all prosimians (and many simians), lemurs are tree dwellers. They have flexible limbs and grasping hands and feet that are necessary for an arboreal lifestyle. Lemurs are among our more distant primate relatives.

The **bonobo** *(Pan paniscus)* is one of two species of chimpanzee that inhabits the forests of central Africa. The hair of bonobos is generally longer than that of common chimpanzees. Bonobos can walk upright for short periods, but they are generally knuckle walkers. Bonobos are among our closest primate relatives.

The **golden lion tamarin** *(Leontopithecus rosalia)* is a small monkey that inhabits the forests of Brazil. Like other New World monkeys, tamarins have grasping tails, a characteristic not found in their Old World cousins.

Homo sapien

Humans are the only primates that habitually walk upright. Adaptations in the **skeleton**—such as the arches in our feet and the curves in our spines—allow us to be bipedal. In relation to body size, human brains are the biggest within the primate order. The cranial capacity of modern humans averages 1,450 cm^2.

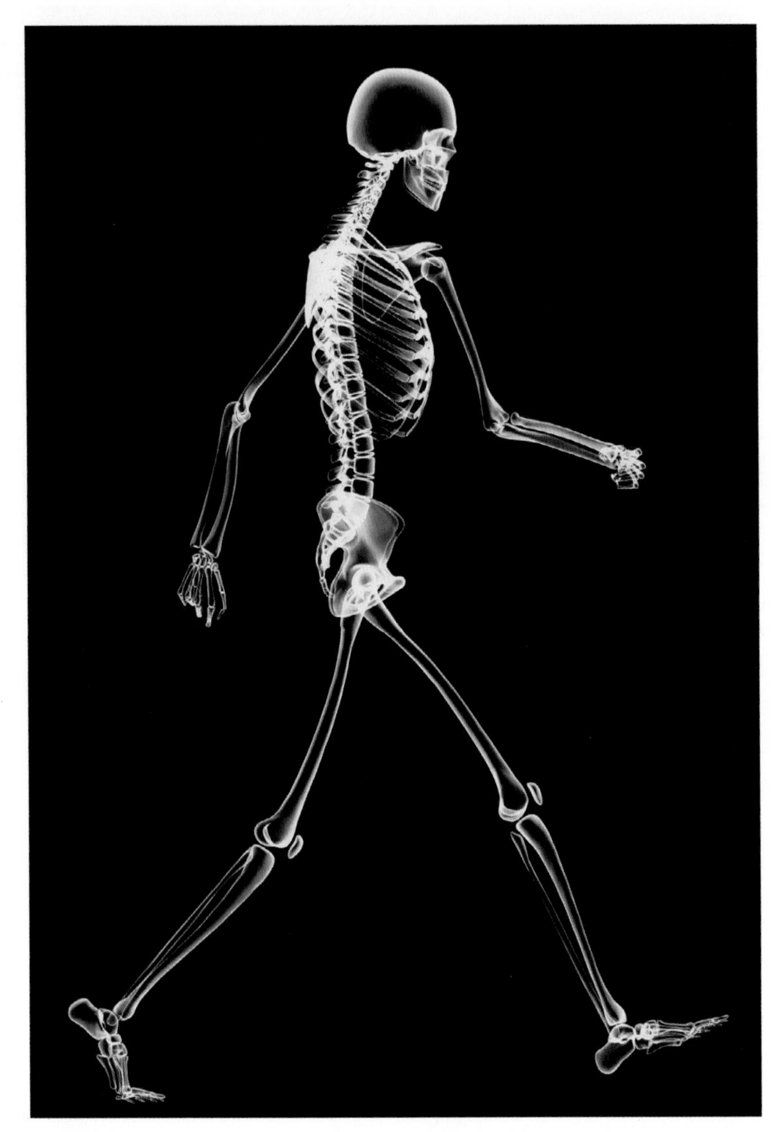

Spoken language is one of the many behaviors that separate humans from other primates. Adaptations in our brains and throat anatomy allow us to produce the complex sounds that create speech.

Elaborate **social rituals** are unique to humans. Celebrations of events such as birthdays and graduations are behaviors that serve no direct physical evolutionary purpose. However, they allow us to create and maintain important social relationships.

An organ system is a group of organs working together to perform a function.

The functions of organ systems are generally the same in all animals, even though the structures may be different. For example, the function of all animal respiratory systems is to bring oxygen into the animal's body and get rid of carbon dioxide.

ORGAN SYSTEMS

SYSTEM	*MAJOR STRUCTURES*	*FUNCTIONS*
Circulatory	Heart, arteries, veins, red blood cells	Transports oxygen and nutrients throughout body; carries wastes away from cells
Digestive	Mouth, stomach, intestines	Breaks down food and absorbs nutrients; expels solid wastes from body
Endocrine	Glands, hypothalamus, specialized brain structures	Regulates metabolism, growth and development, and behavior
Excretory	Kidneys, bladder, skin, lungs	Rids body of metabolic wastes; regulates fluid balance
Immune	T and B cells, lymph nodes	Protects against disease and infection
Integumentary	Hair, skin, nails	Defends body against pathogens; helps regulate body temperature
Muscular	Skeletal, smooth, and cardiac muscles	Skeletal: moves the body and provides structure; smooth: moves substances throughout the body; cardiac: makes up the heart
Nervous	Brain, spinal cord, nerves	Controls conscious thought and cognitive abilities; interprets sensory information; monitors other organ systems
Reproductive	Ovaries and uterus in females, testes in males	Produces gametes (eggs and sperm)
Respiratory	Lungs, bronchi, alveoli	Brings air into the lungs for the exchange of oxygen and carbon dioxide
Skeletal	Bones	Provides support and structure to the body; protects internal organs

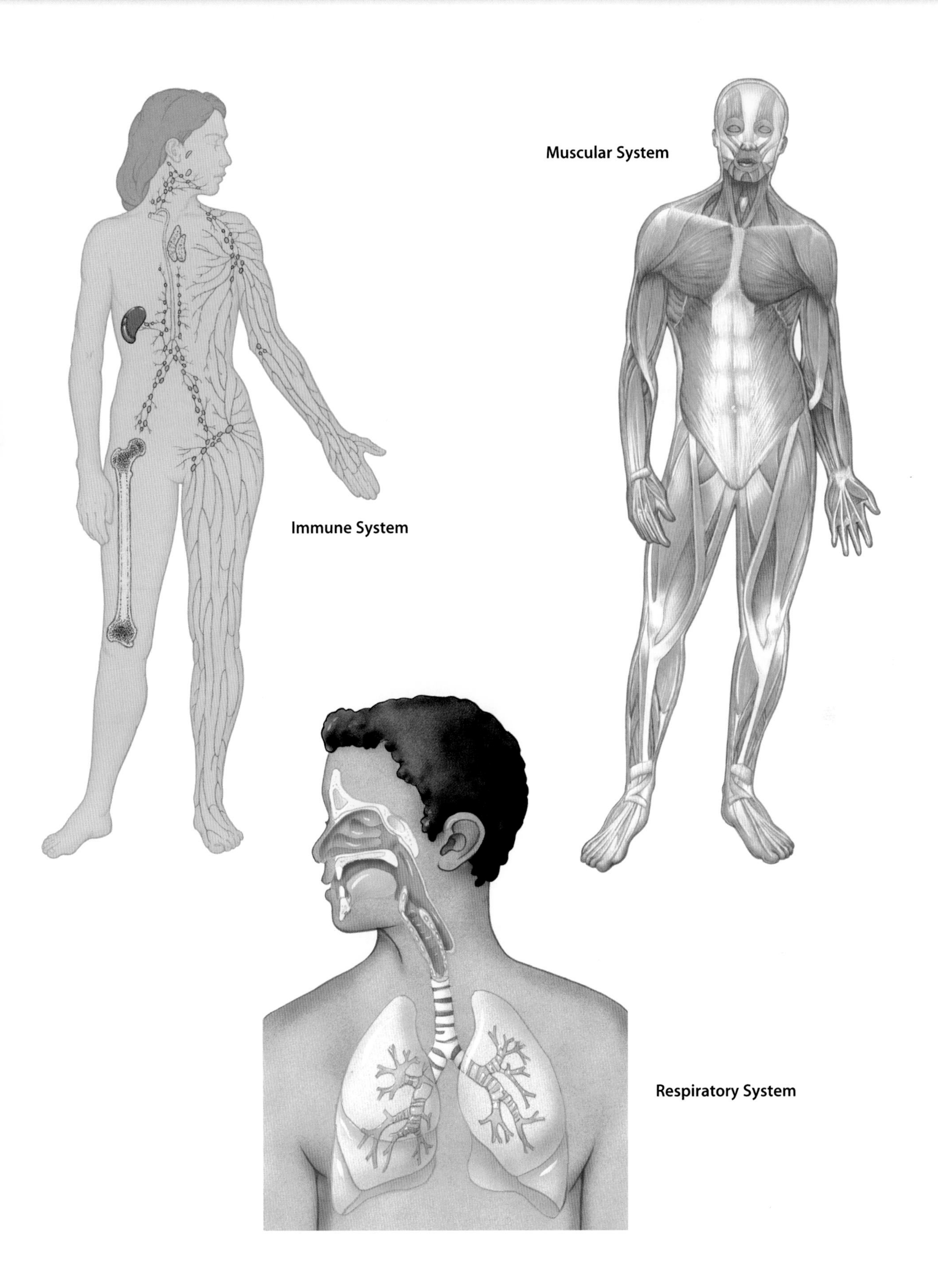
Muscular System
Immune System
Respiratory System

Most animals digest their food inside their bodies, but some animals have much more complex digestive systems than others.

For example, the digestive system of a planarian is a tube with one opening. In contrast, the digestive system of a human has two openings and many organs with different functions.

Flatworm Digestive System

The planarian's digestive system has only one opening, the mouth, which is located at the end of the **pharynx**. Food particles enter the mouth and travel through the pharynx to the gastrovascular cavity to be digested. Solid waste materials travel from the gastrovascular cavity through the pharynx and are expelled through the mouth.

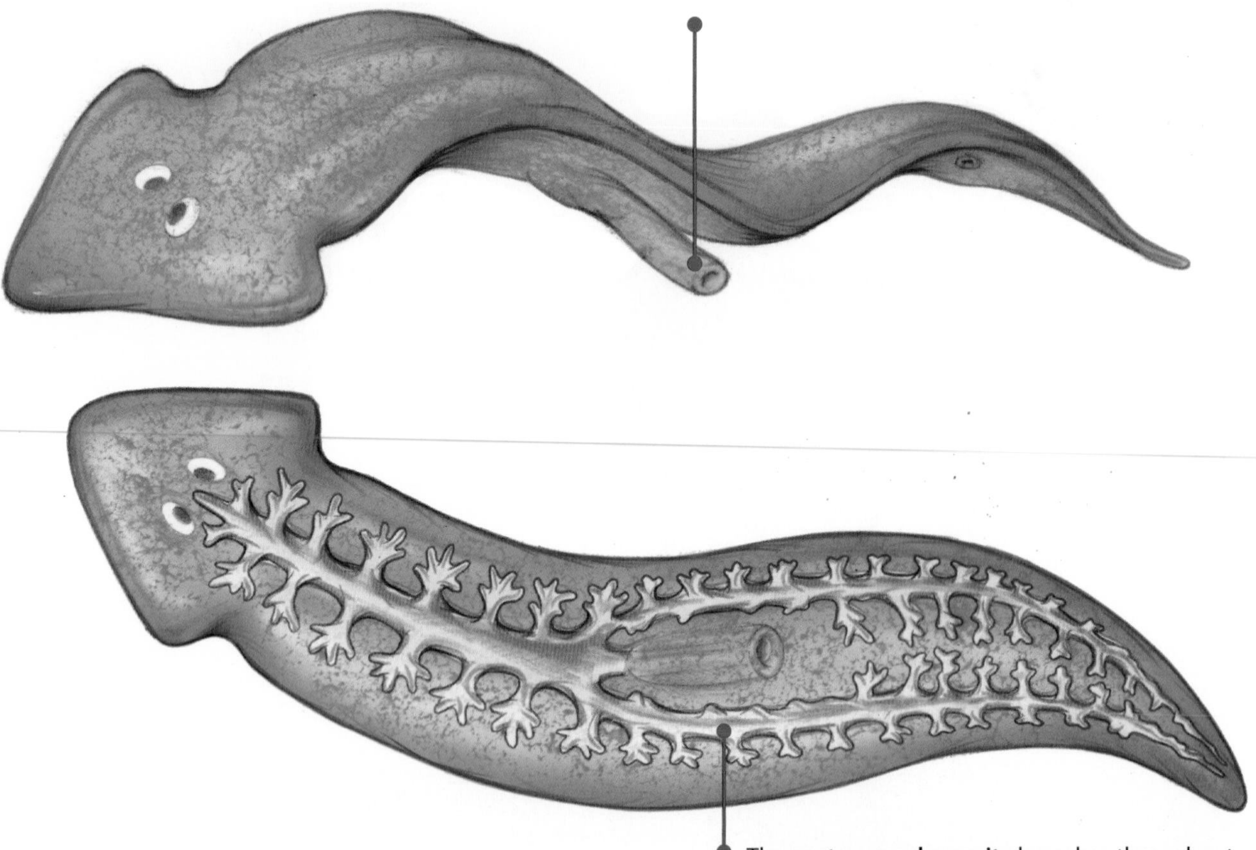

The **gastrovascular cavity** branches throughout the planarian's body. Within the gastrovascular cavity, enzymes break down food into usable molecules, which are absorbed by the animal's tissues. The gastrovascular cavity also stores waste products as they move toward the pharynx for elimination.

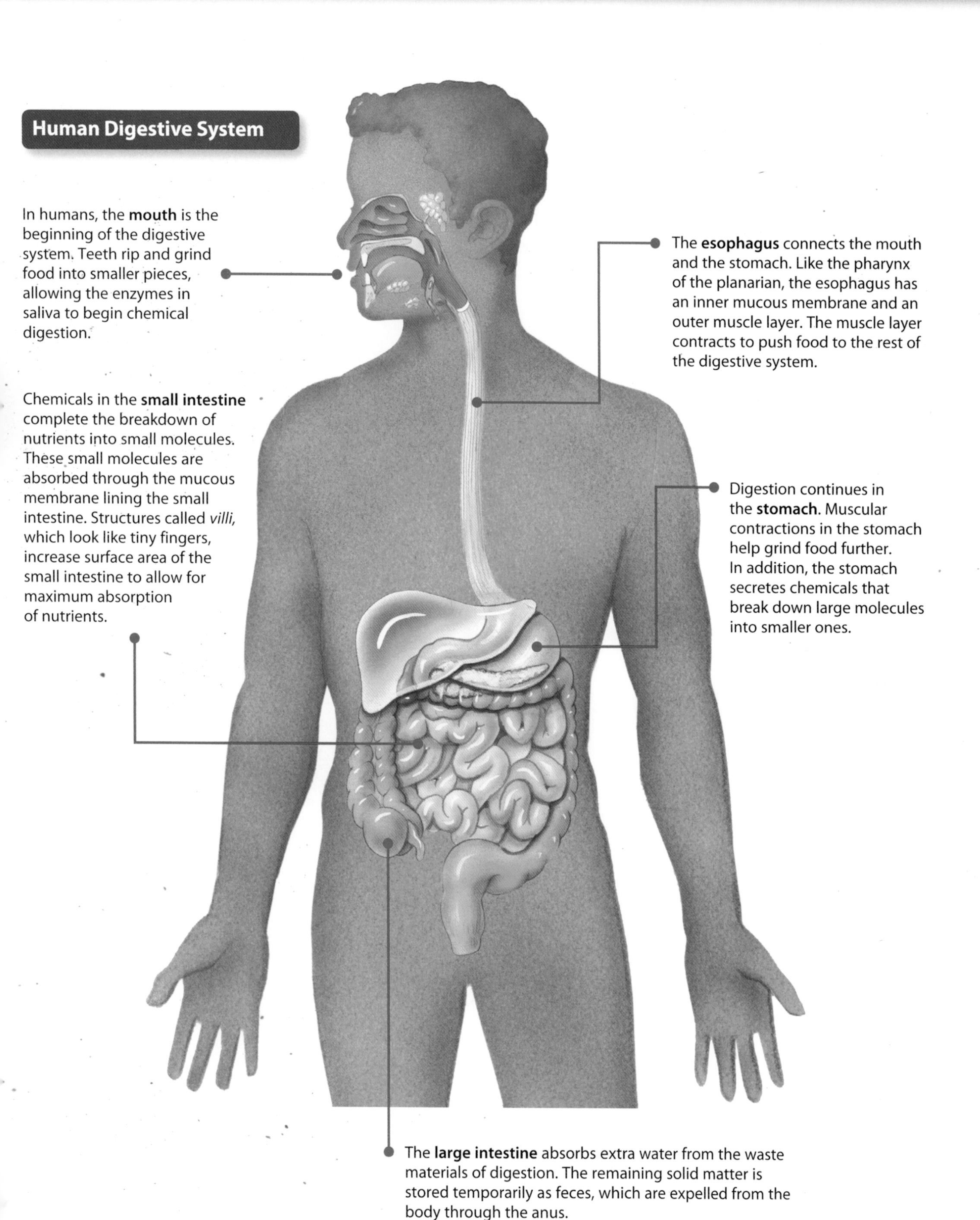

Human Digestive System
In humans, the **mouth** is the beginning of the digestive system. Teeth rip and grind food into smaller pieces, allowing the enzymes in saliva to begin chemical digestion.
The **esophagus** connects the mouth and the stomach. Like the pharynx of the planarian, the esophagus has an inner mucous membrane and an outer muscle layer. The muscle layer contracts to push food to the rest of the digestive system.
Chemicals in the **small intestine** complete the breakdown of nutrients into small molecules. These small molecules are absorbed through the mucous membrane lining the small intestine. Structures called *villi,* which look like tiny fingers, increase surface area of the small intestine to allow for maximum absorption of nutrients.
Digestion continues in the **stomach**. Muscular contractions in the stomach help grind food further. In addition, the stomach secretes chemicals that break down large molecules into smaller ones.

The **large intestine** absorbs extra water from the waste materials of digestion. The remaining solid matter is stored temporarily as feces, which are expelled from the body through the anus.

Enzymes play a key role in breaking down food for use by cells.

Without these important proteins, digestion would proceed so slowly that your cells would all die before getting the energy they needed. Different enzymes help break down specific types of food molecules.

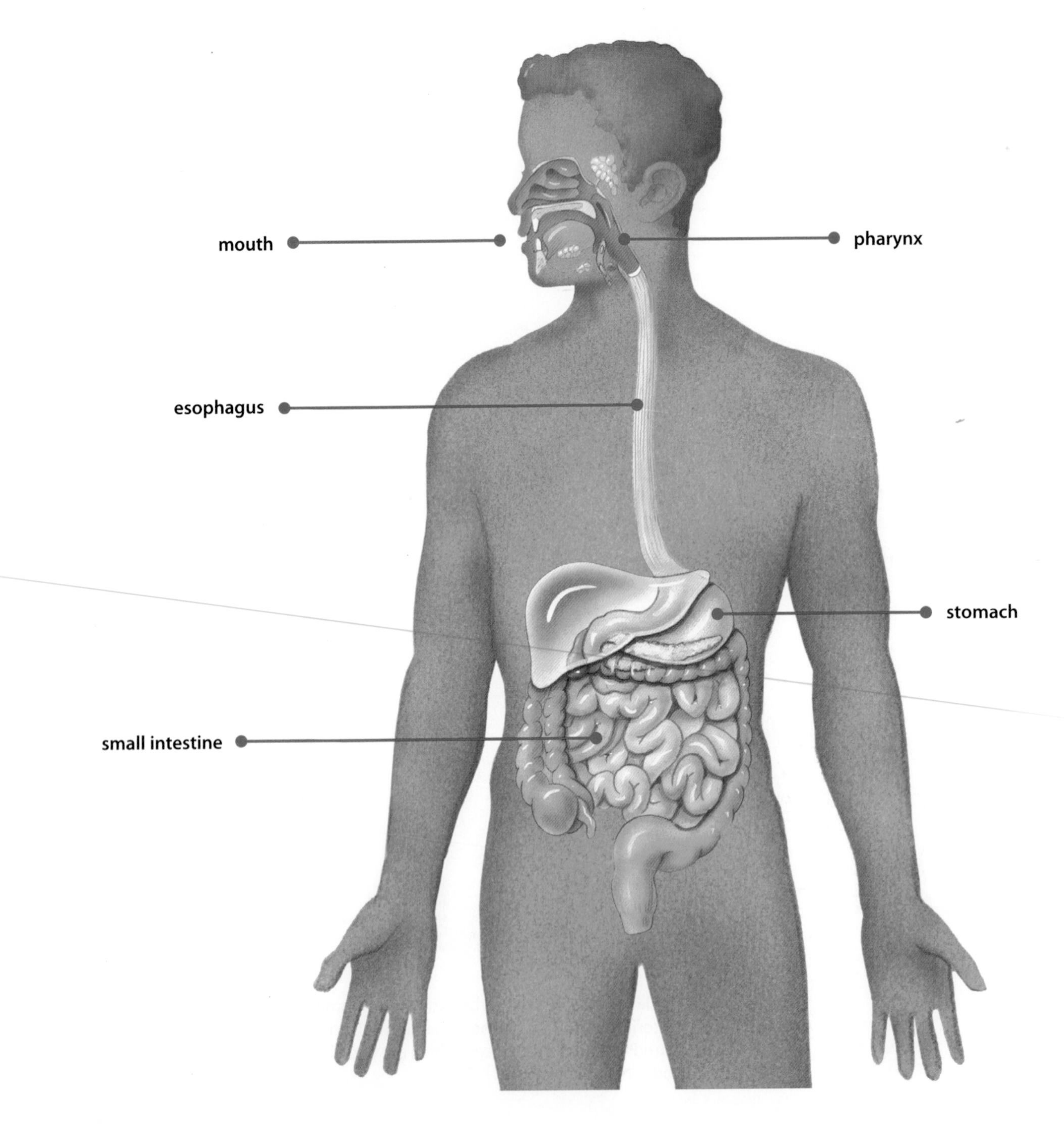

	Carbohydrate Digestion	Protein Digestion	Fat Digestion	Nucleic Acid Digestion
Mouth, Pharynx, Esophagus	polysaccharides (starch, glycogen) → saliva (amylase) → smaller polysaccharides; disaccharides (sucrose) ↓			
Stomach		proteins → pepsin → small polypeptides		
Small Intestine	polysaccharides → pancreatic fluid (amylase) → disaccharides	pancreatic fluid (proteases) → amino acids	fat globules → bile salts → fat droplets → pancreatic fluid (lipases) → glycerol, glycerides, fatty acids	DNA, RNA → pancreatic fluid (nucleases) → nucleotides
Epithelium of Small Intestine	disaccharidases → monosaccharides (glucose)	small peptides → proteases → amino acids		nucleotidases → nucleosides → nucleosidases and phosphatases → sugars, phosphates, nitrogenous bases

The digestive enzymes are shown in tan boxes in this table. The final products of digestion are in red.

An excretory system maintains an organism's water balance and gets rid of metabolic wastes.

In most animals, the excretory system filters the blood or other body fluid and concentrates toxins into a fluid waste product.

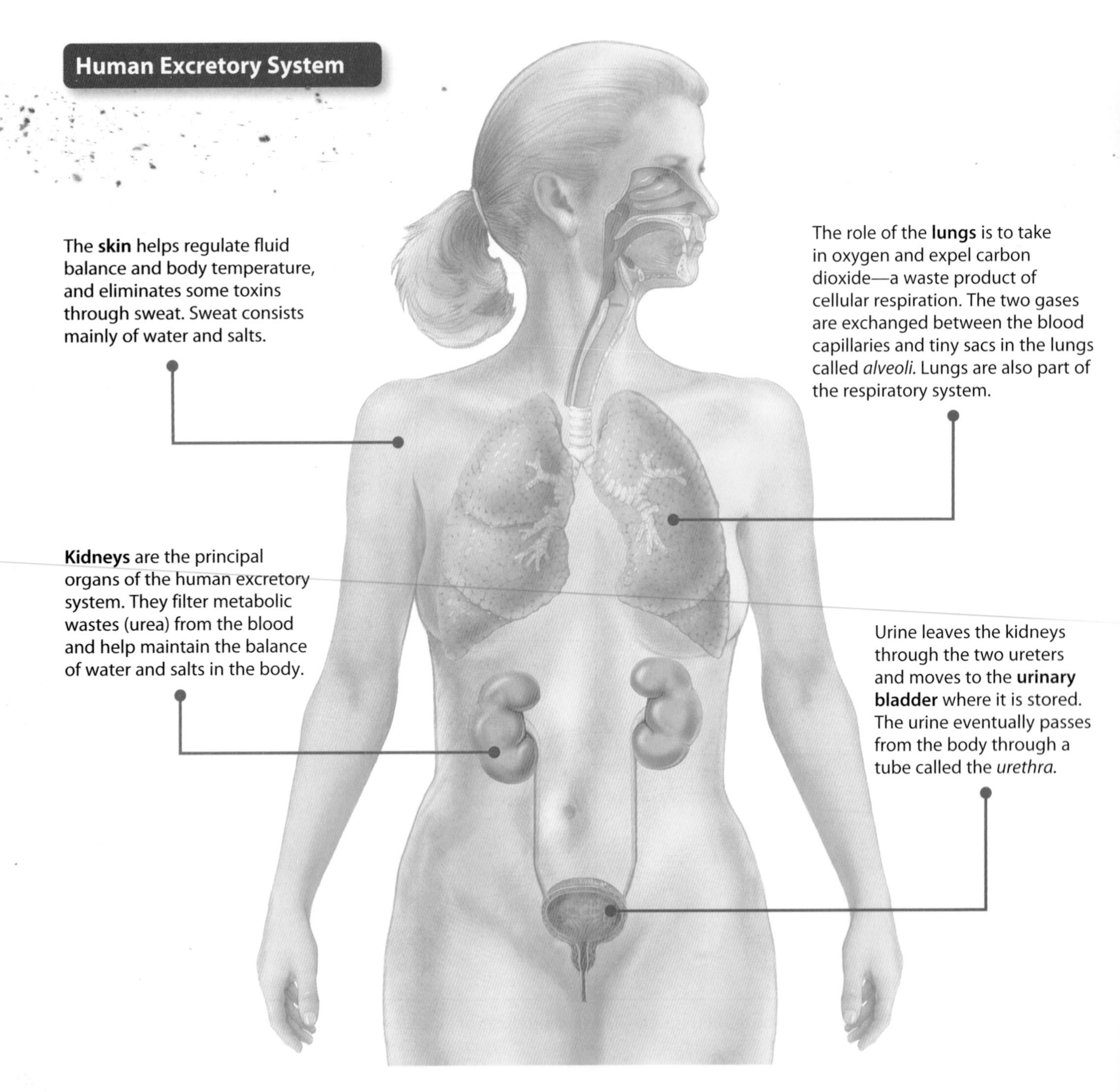

Human Excretory System
The **skin** helps regulate fluid balance and body temperature, and eliminates some toxins through sweat. Sweat consists mainly of water and salts.
The role of the **lungs** is to take in oxygen and expel carbon dioxide—a waste product of cellular respiration. The two gases are exchanged between the blood capillaries and tiny sacs in the lungs called *alveoli.* Lungs are also part of the respiratory system.
Kidneys are the principal organs of the human excretory system. They filter metabolic wastes (urea) from the blood and help maintain the balance of water and salts in the body.
Urine leaves the kidneys through the two ureters and moves to the **urinary bladder** where it is stored. The urine eventually passes from the body through a tube called the *urethra.*

Flatworm Excretory System

In a freshwater flatworm such as *Dugesia*, the **excretory system** functions mainly for water balance. Parasitic flatworms rely more heavily on their excretory systems for filtering wastes.

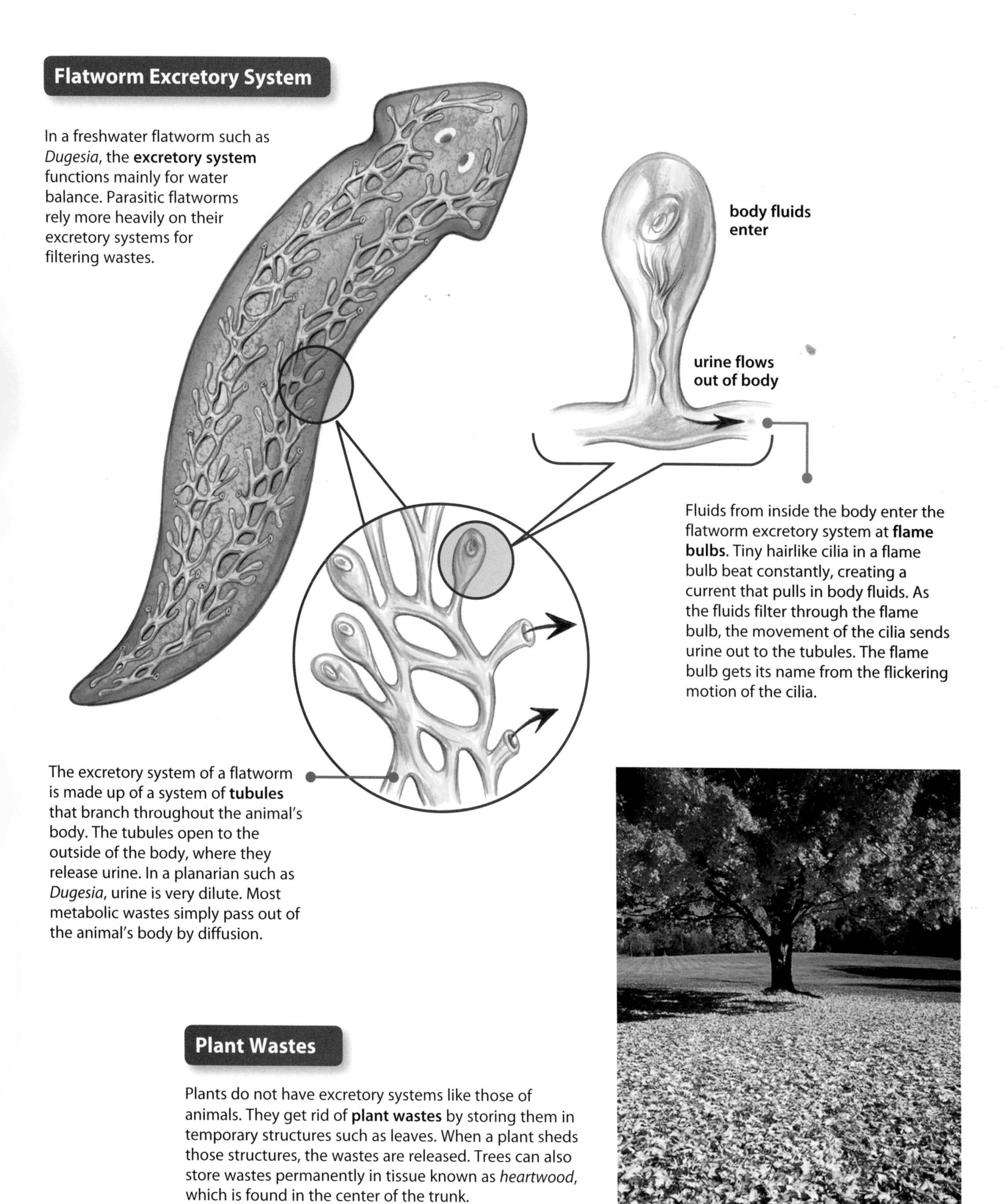

Fluids from inside the body enter the flatworm excretory system at **flame bulbs**. Tiny hairlike cilia in a flame bulb beat constantly, creating a current that pulls in body fluids. As the fluids filter through the flame bulb, the movement of the cilia sends urine out to the tubules. The flame bulb gets its name from the flickering motion of the cilia.

The excretory system of a flatworm is made up of a system of **tubules** that branch throughout the animal's body. The tubules open to the outside of the body, where they release urine. In a planarian such as *Dugesia*, urine is very dilute. Most metabolic wastes simply pass out of the animal's body by diffusion.

Plant Wastes

Plants do not have excretory systems like those of animals. They get rid of **plant wastes** by storing them in temporary structures such as leaves. When a plant sheds those structures, the wastes are released. Trees can also store wastes permanently in tissue known as *heartwood*, which is found in the center of the trunk.

Your kidneys filter your blood to remove wastes and help your body maintain its water balance.

Each kidney contains millions of nephrons, where blood filtration takes place. The wastes that the nephrons remove from the blood become urine.

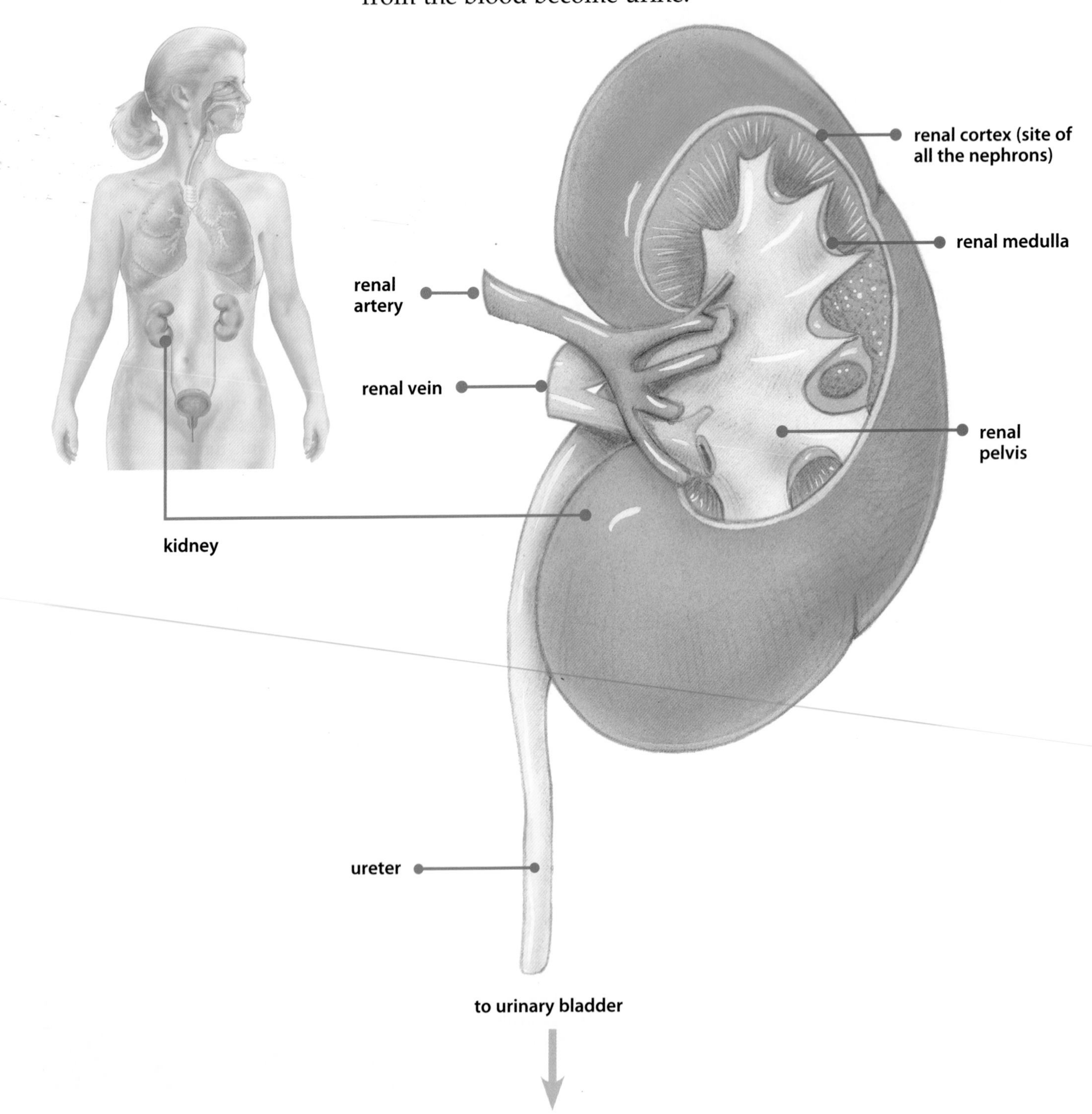

Nephron

In a kidney, blood flows through a network of capillaries called the *glomerulus* in the upper part of the nephron. Materials such as salts, sugars, water, and vitamins diffuse from the blood in the glomerulus into the Bowman's capsule during **filtration**. The fluid that is filtered out of the blood (the filtrate) flows through the nephron.

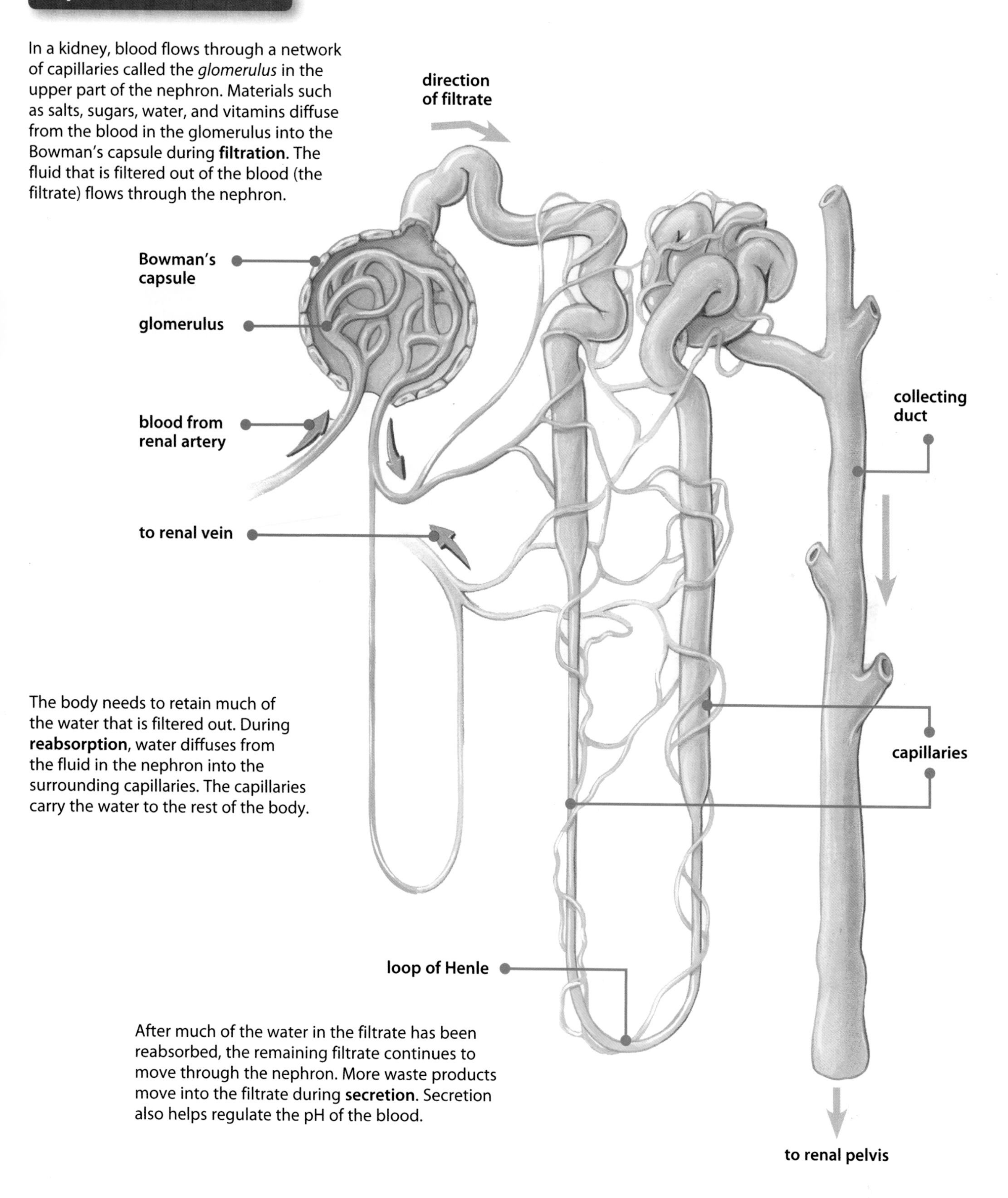

The body needs to retain much of the water that is filtered out. During **reabsorption**, water diffuses from the fluid in the nephron into the surrounding capillaries. The capillaries carry the water to the rest of the body.

After much of the water in the filtrate has been reabsorbed, the remaining filtrate continues to move through the nephron. More waste products move into the filtrate during **secretion**. Secretion also helps regulate the pH of the blood.

Living things exchange gases such as oxygen and carbon dioxide with their environment.

Most organisms—including all plants and animals—use oxygen to break down food molecules for energy. Plants and other photosynthetic organisms also need to take in carbon dioxide to use in photosynthesis.

Gas Exchange in Planarians

Planarians have relatively simple circulatory systems. Gas exchange occurs only on a cellular level. Oxygen gas (O_2) diffuses through the animal's skin and moves from cell to cell. Waste in the form of carbon dioxide (CO_2) diffuses from the cells to the outside environment. Only very small organisms can rely on diffusion alone for gas exchange. Larger organisms cannot rely on diffusion alone to take in enough oxygen or get rid of carbon dioxide quickly enough to survive.

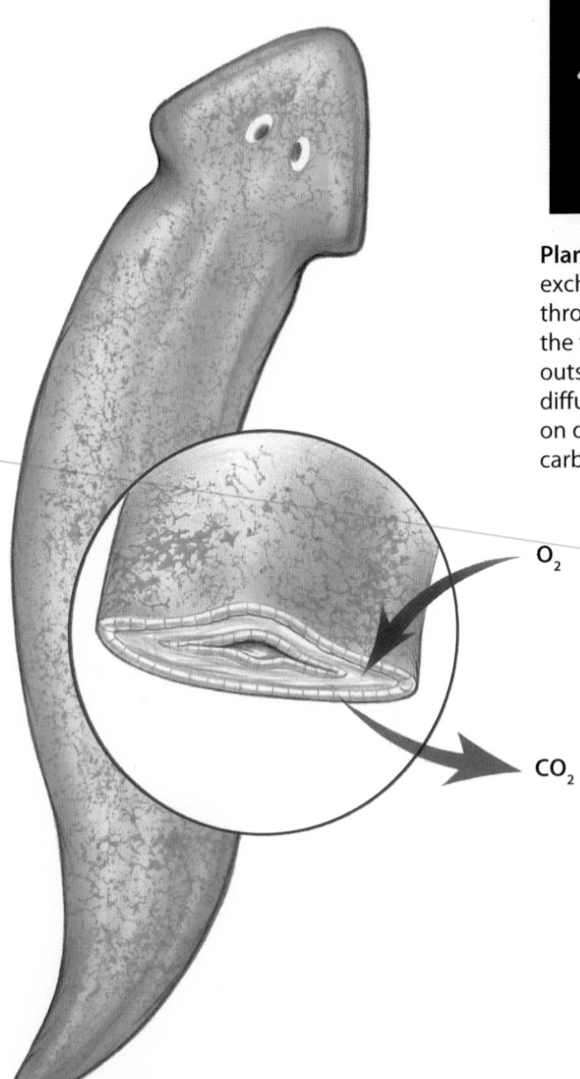

Gas Exchange in Ferns

The leaves of most plants, such as this **fern**, have microscopic pores called *stomata* (singular, *stoma*). Oxygen and carbon dioxide can move into and out of the leaf through an open stoma. The upper surfaces of most leaves have relatively few stomata, while the lower surfaces have many, reducing evaporation of water while the stomata are open.

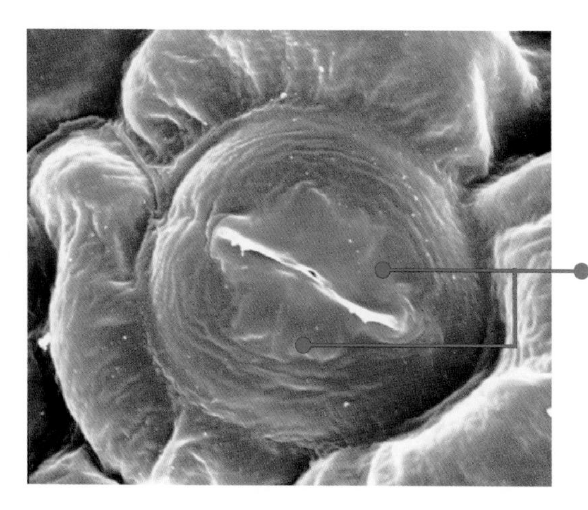

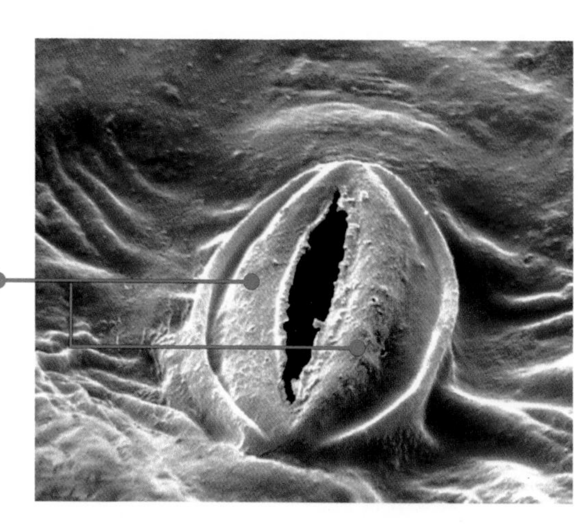

When the guard cells on either side of the stoma relax, the **stoma closes.** This closure prevents constant loss of water molecules through evaporation from the plant surface. Generally, no gas exchange occurs when the stoma is closed.

The guard cells on either side of the stoma expand by taking in water. When the guard cells expand, the **stoma opens**. This opening allows oxygen and carbon dioxide to move into and out of the leaf.

The respiratory system's function is to take in oxygen and expel carbon dioxide.

Every cell in your body requires oxygen and must get rid of waste gases such as carbon dioxide. Your respiratory system allows the cells in your body to exchange those gases with the environment. The main parts of the human respiratory system are the nose, pharynx, larynx, trachea, bronchi, and lungs.

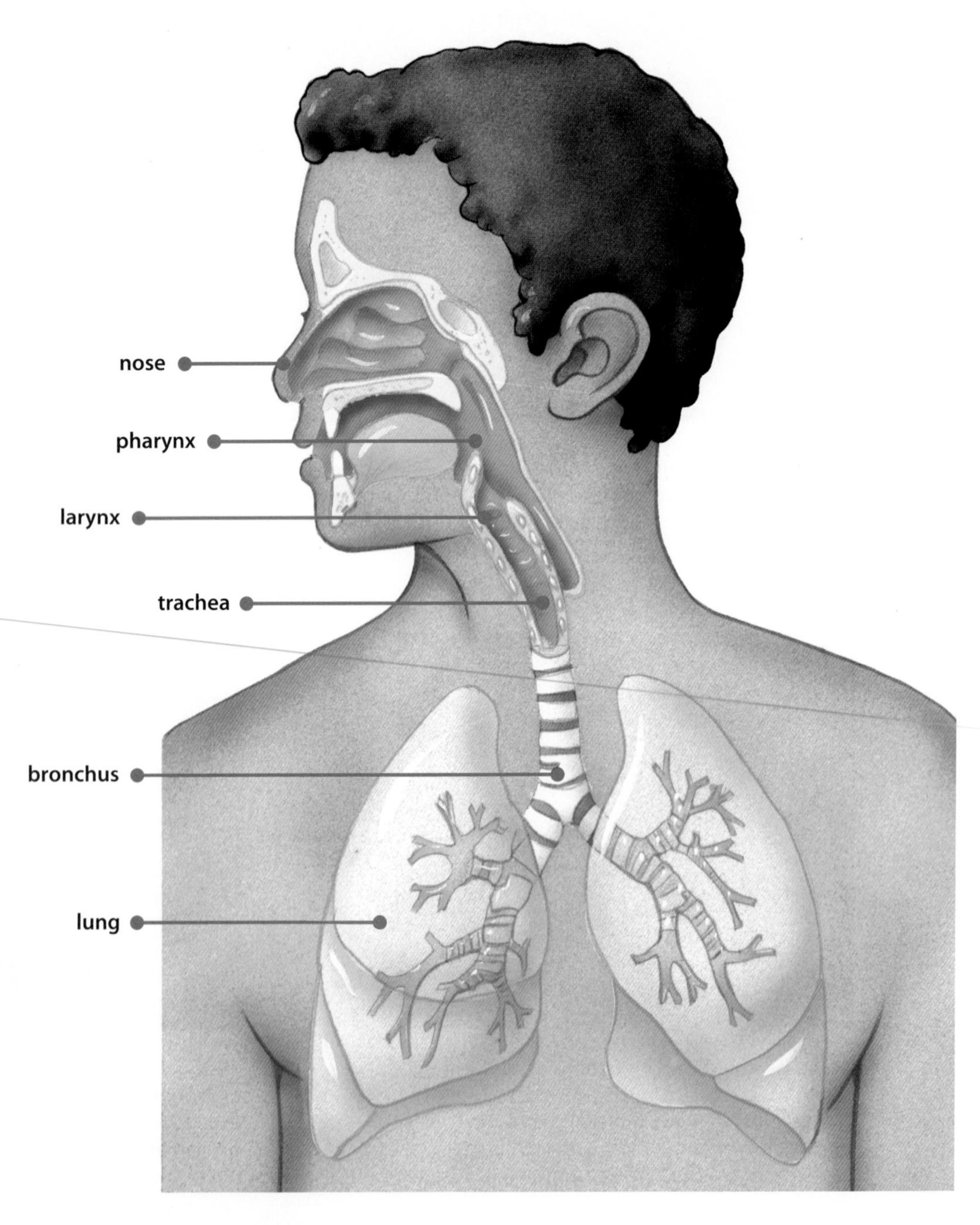

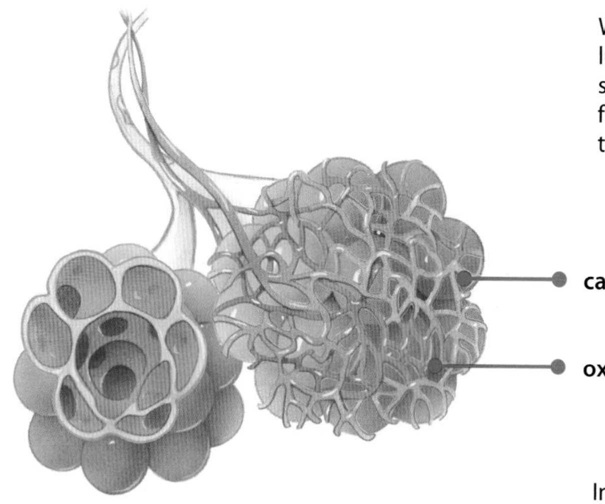

When you **inhale**, air rushes into your lungs. Within your lungs are millions of tiny sacs called *alveoli*. They are surrounded by tiny blood vessels called *capillaries*. Oxygen from the air diffuses into the blood vessels, where it binds to the hemoglobin in red blood cells.

In the lungs, carbon dioxide diffuses out of the blood and into the alveoli. When you **exhale**, the carbon dioxide moves out of your body and into the air.

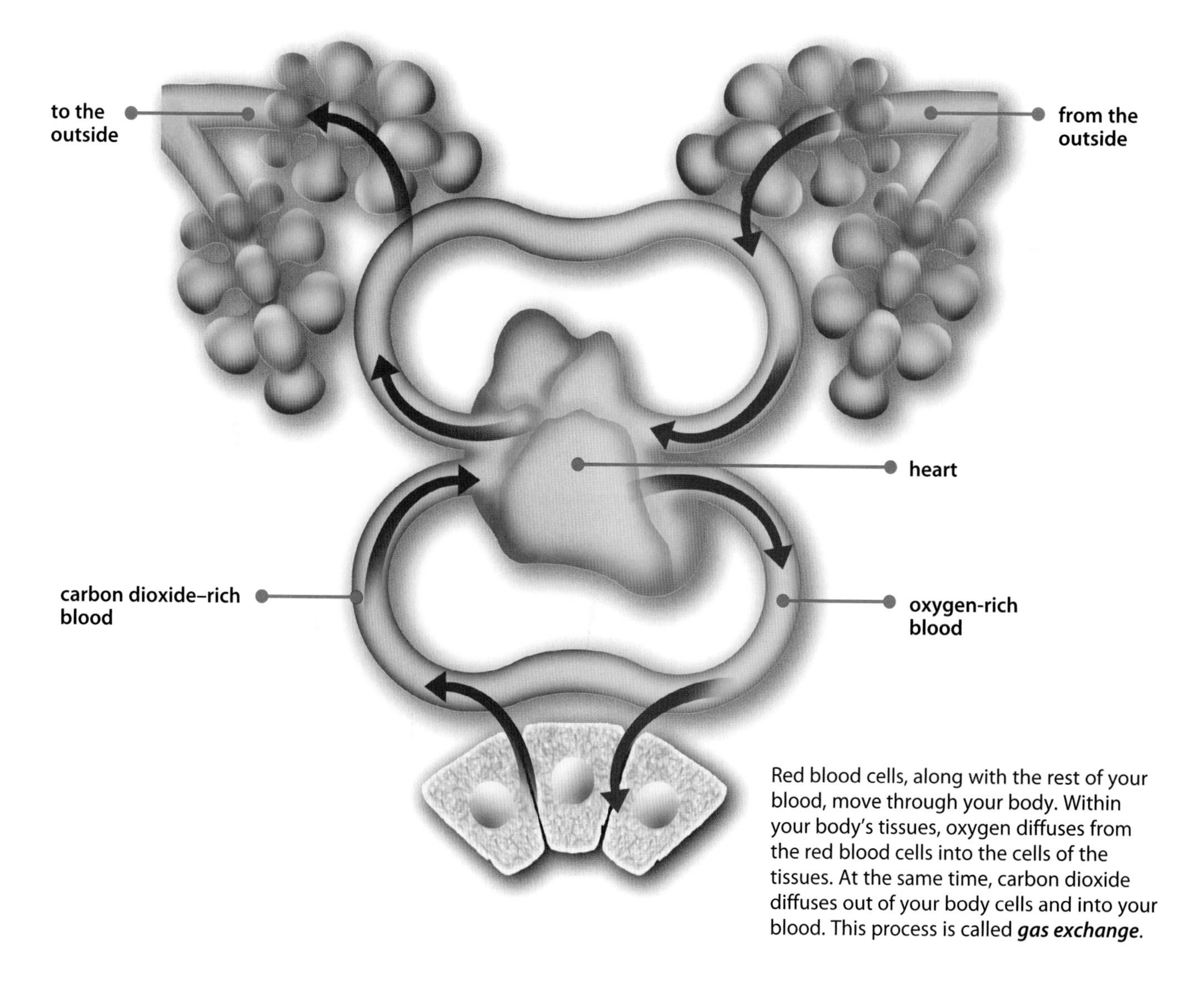

Red blood cells, along with the rest of your blood, move through your body. Within your body's tissues, oxygen diffuses from the red blood cells into the cells of the tissues. At the same time, carbon dioxide diffuses out of your body cells and into your blood. This process is called ***gas exchange***.

An animal's nervous system controls body processes and allows the organism to react to stimuli.

The nervous systems of flatworms and humans are vastly different, but both systems coordinate muscles, regulate organs, and sense and respond to input from sensory structures.

Flatworm Nervous System

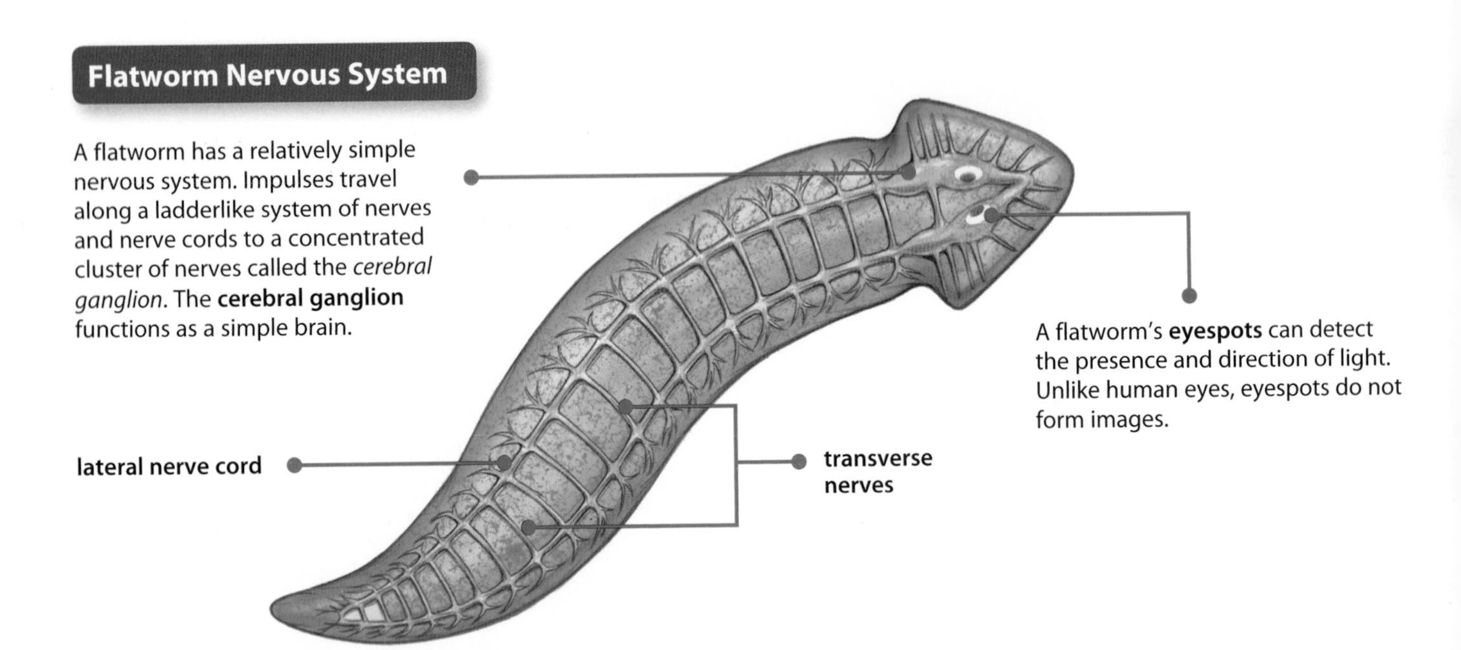

A flatworm has a relatively simple nervous system. Impulses travel along a ladderlike system of nerves and nerve cords to a concentrated cluster of nerves called the *cerebral ganglion*. The **cerebral ganglion** functions as a simple brain.
A flatworm's **eyespots** can detect the presence and direction of light. Unlike human eyes, eyespots do not form images.
lateral nerve cord
transverse nerves

Plant Rapid Movement

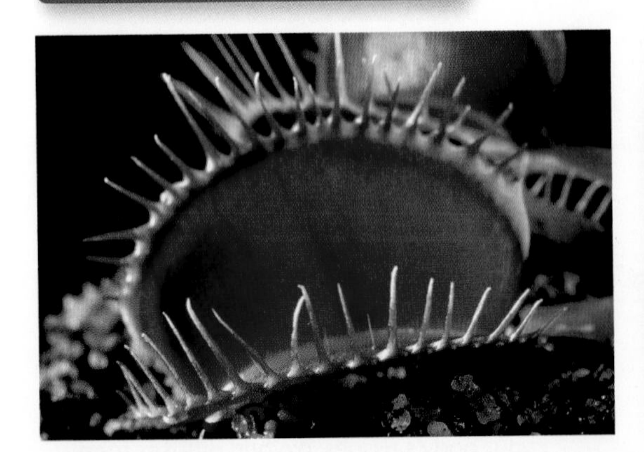

Plants do not have a nervous system or nerves, but plants, such as the **Venus flytrap** *(Dionaea muscipula)*, receive and respond to stimuli. The plant has trigger hairs on the flat surface of its leaves. When an insect touches two trigger hairs or touches one hair twice in quick succession, the leaf snaps shut and traps the insect.

Human Brain

Humans have complex nervous systems. The **human brain** is responsible for increased motor function and sensory perception, as well as cognitive thought and emotion.

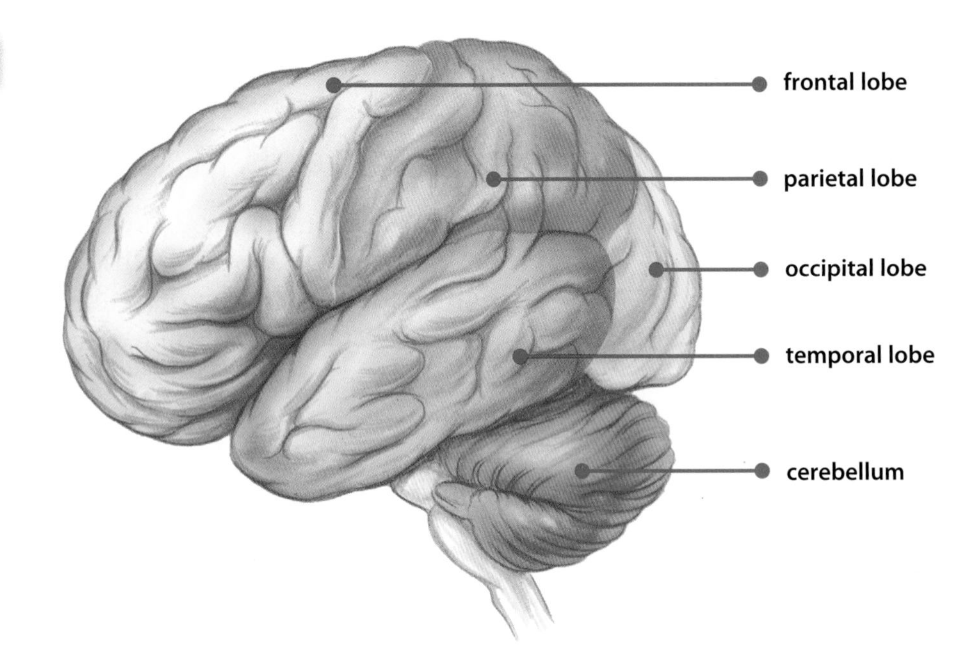

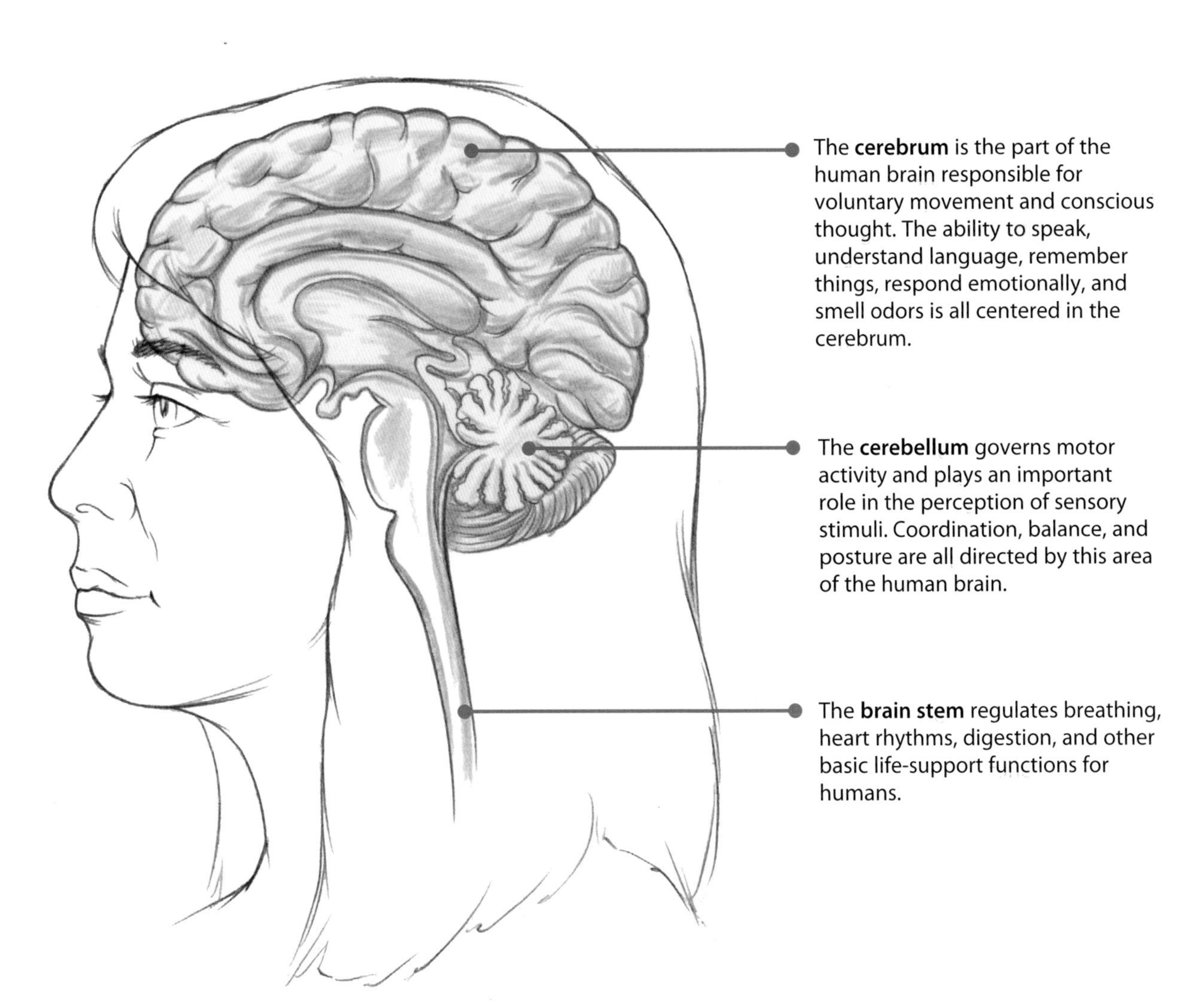

The **cerebrum** is the part of the human brain responsible for voluntary movement and conscious thought. The ability to speak, understand language, remember things, respond emotionally, and smell odors is all centered in the cerebrum.

The **cerebellum** governs motor activity and plays an important role in the perception of sensory stimuli. Coordination, balance, and posture are all directed by this area of the human brain.

The **brain stem** regulates breathing, heart rhythms, digestion, and other basic life-support functions for humans.

Your nervous system allows you to detect and respond to stimuli in the environment.

For example, your nervous system allows you to feel a sting when an insect bites you. At the same time, your nervous system sends signals to your hand and arm, causing them to move to brush the insect away.

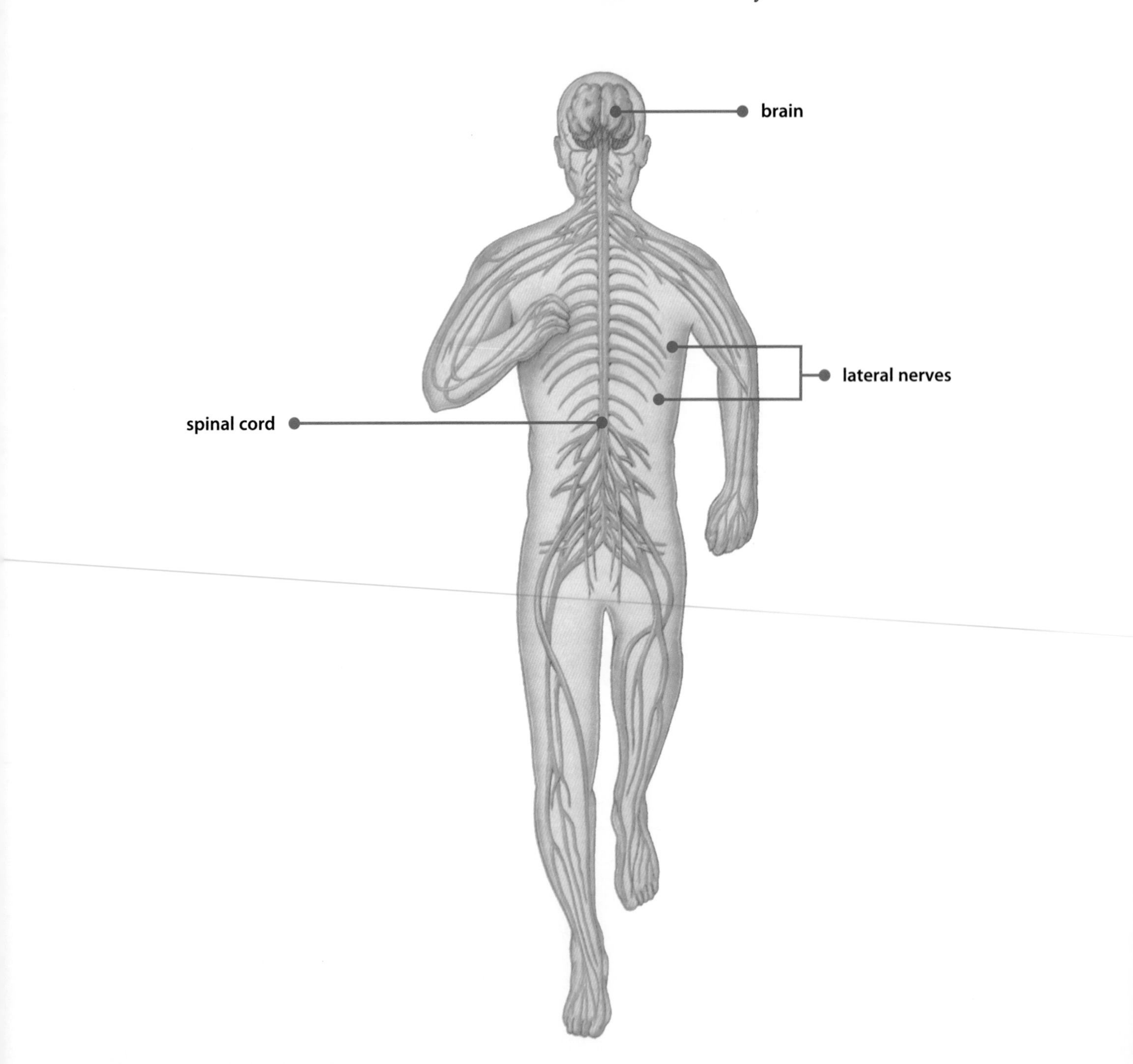

Neurons are the cells that carry information through the nervous system. That information is carried in the form of electrical and chemical signals. There are two main kinds of neurons in your body: motor neurons and sensory neurons.

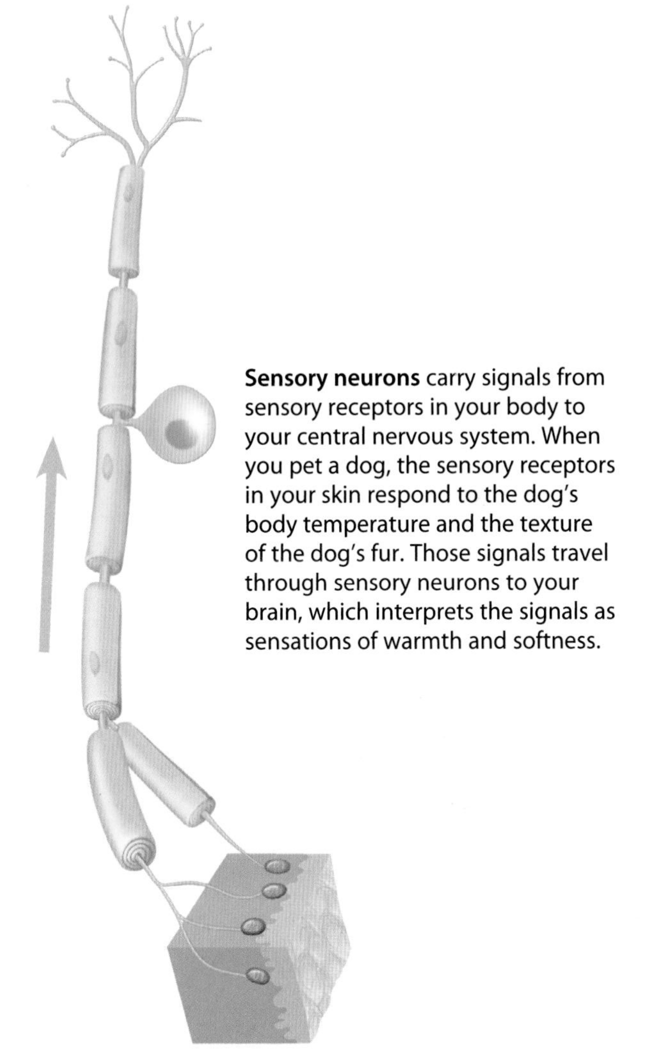

Sensory neurons carry signals from sensory receptors in your body to your central nervous system. When you pet a dog, the sensory receptors in your skin respond to the dog's body temperature and the texture of the dog's fur. Those signals travel through sensory neurons to your brain, which interprets the signals as sensations of warmth and softness.

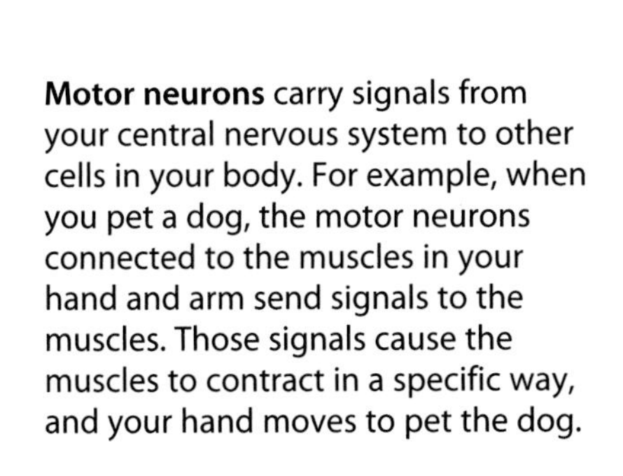

Motor neurons carry signals from your central nervous system to other cells in your body. For example, when you pet a dog, the motor neurons connected to the muscles in your hand and arm send signals to the muscles. Those signals cause the muscles to contract in a specific way, and your hand moves to pet the dog.

Information travels through the nervous system in the form of electrical and chemical signals.

Electrical discharges called *action potentials* move along the membrane of specialized nerve cells called *neurons*. When information passes between neurons, it is carried by chemicals.

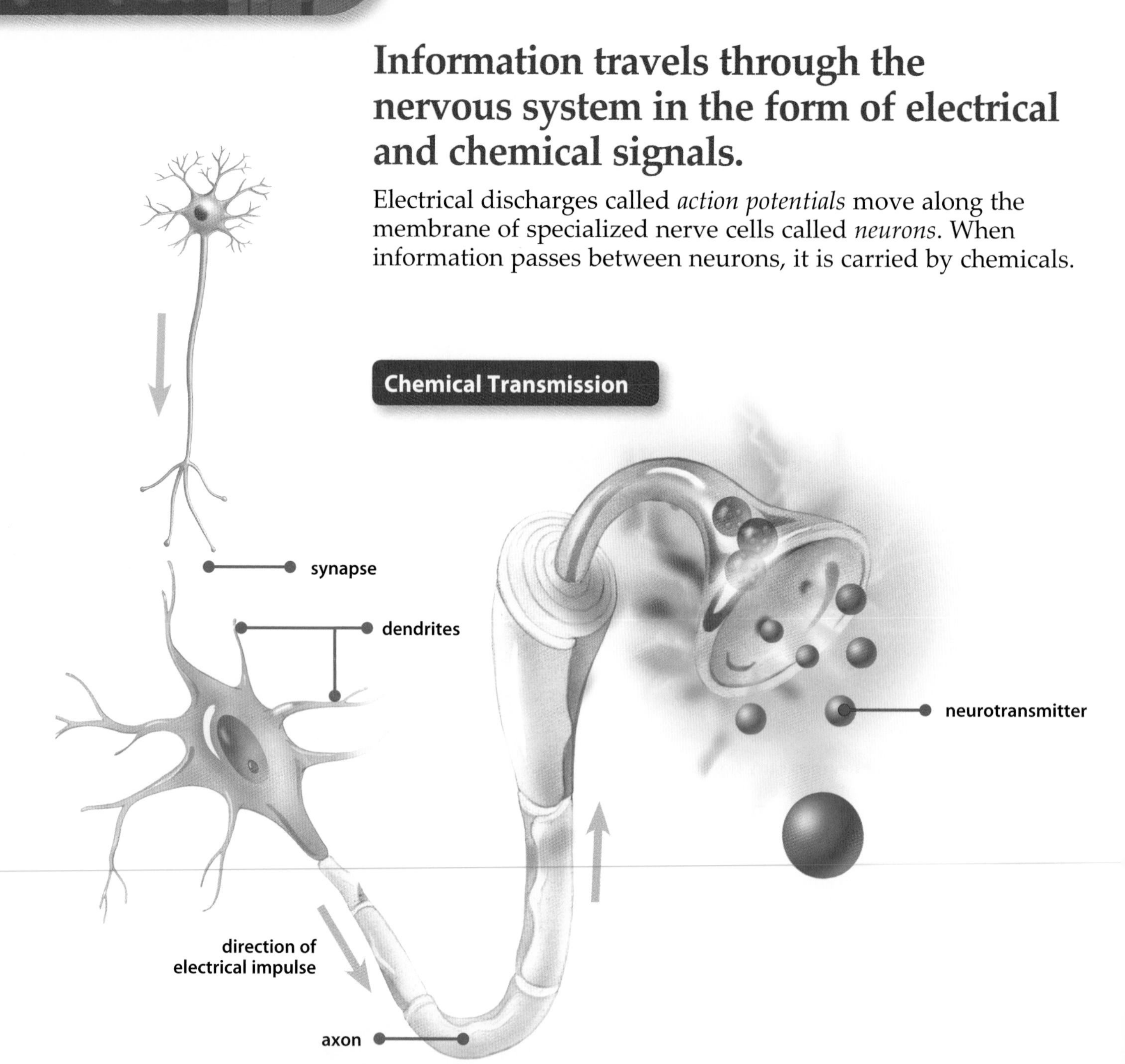

The space between neurons is called a *synapse*. When a traveling electrical impulse reaches the end of a neuron, it triggers the **release of chemicals** called *neurotransmitters*. Neurotransmitters diffuse across the synapse to a receptor in the corresponding neuron called a *dendrite*. When the dendrite detects the neurotransmitters, the cell produces an electrical impulse that travels in the same manner to the next synapse.

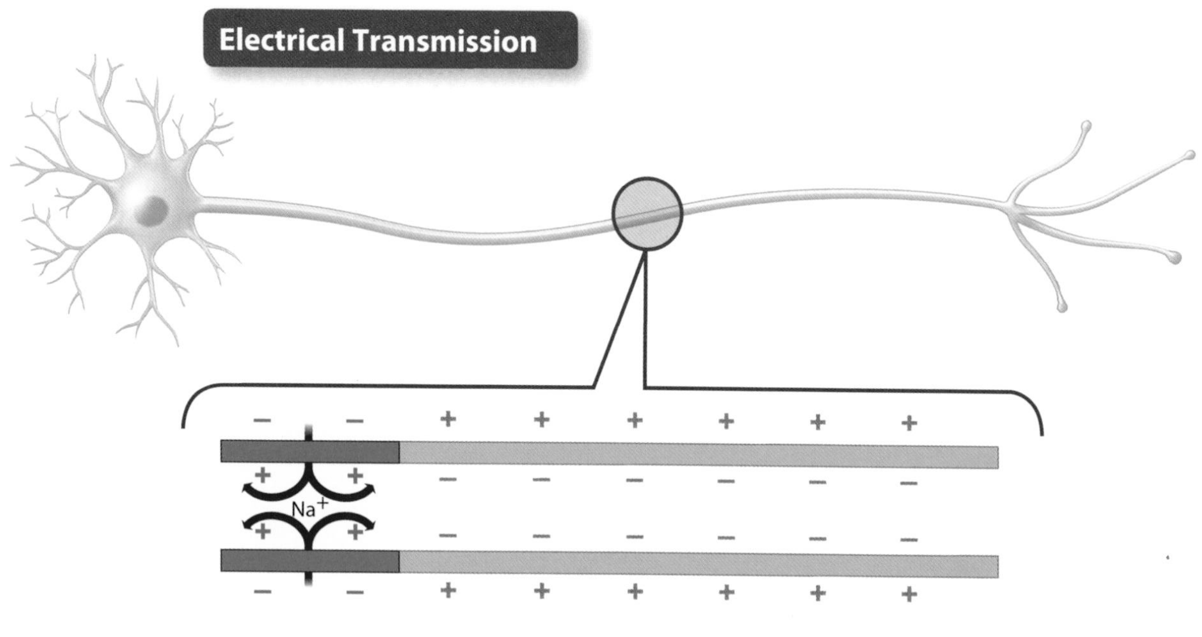

An electrical signal begins as sodium ions (Na^+) flow into an axon, and the total electrical charge on that section of the axon's membrane changes.

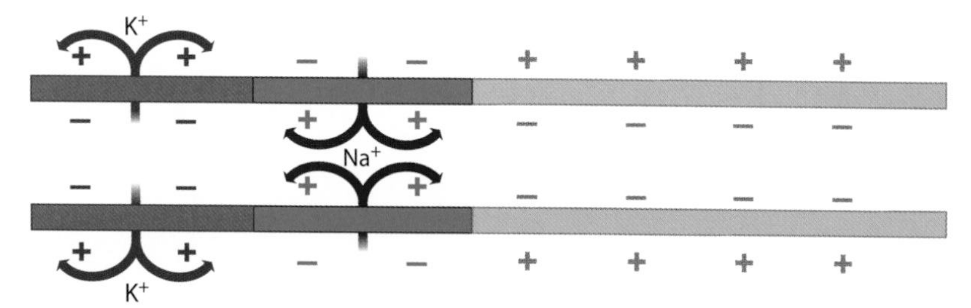

The change in the electrical charge of the axon membrane moves to the next section of the membrane. There, sodium ions again flow into the axon and change the membrane's total charge. At the same time, potassium ions (K^+) flow out of the axon along the first part of the membrane.

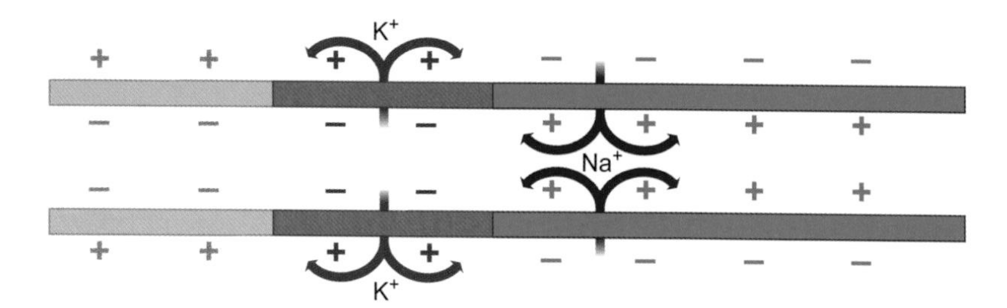

This sequence of sodium ions flowing in and potassium ions flowing out continues along the length of the axon. Eventually, the change in the axon membrane charge (the electrical signal) reaches the end of the axon, where it triggers the release of neurotransmitters.

Human and Flatworm Muscular Systems

Every move you make occurs because of the contraction of muscles.

The muscular and skeletal systems work together to allow that movement. Muscles are held to bones by elastic tissues called *tendons*. As muscles contract, the tendons pull on the bones and move them.

Flatworm Muscular System

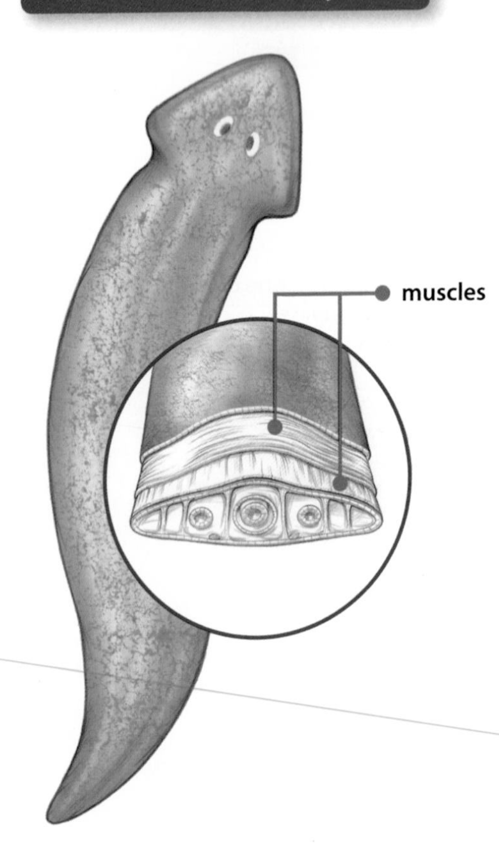

A flatworm does not have a bony skeleton like that of a human. Instead, fluids in the flatworm's body are under pressure, creating a **hydrostatic skeleton**. Muscles in the flatworm's body work against the pressure to create movement.

Antagonistic Pairs

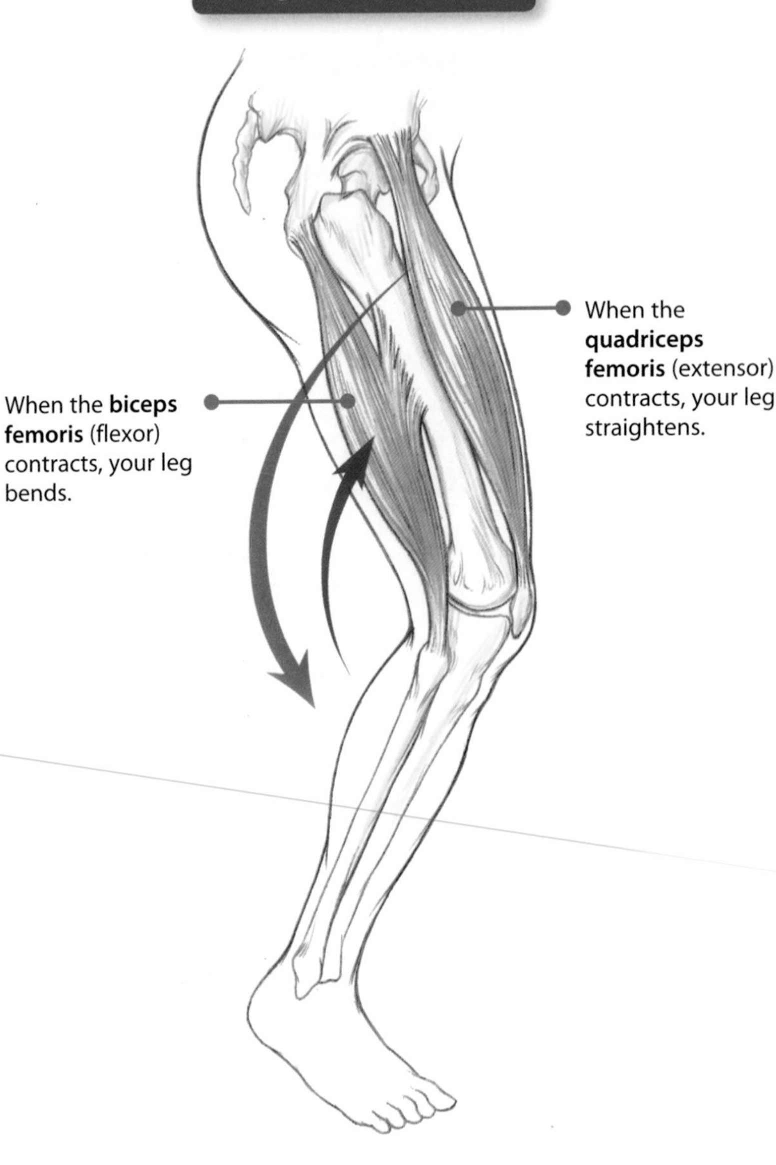

When the **biceps femoris** (flexor) contracts, your leg bends.
When the **quadriceps femoris** (extensor) contracts, your leg straightens.

Skeletal muscles can pull but cannot push, so most muscles work in pairs. For example, flexors bend a limb and extensors straighten the limb. These muscles are **antagonistic pairs**—they work in opposite directions.

Human Muscular System

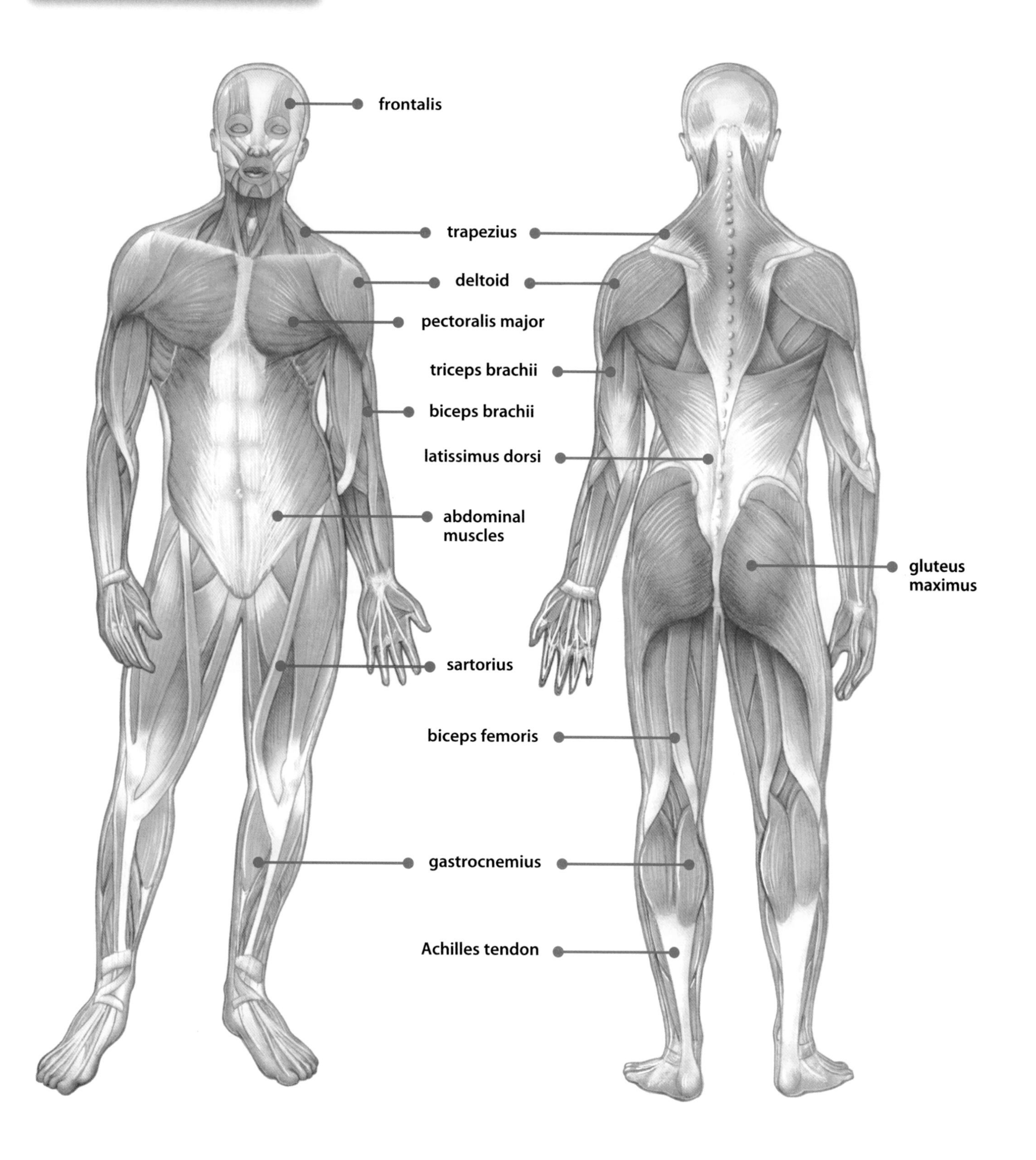

Muscle fibers contract by the sliding movement of specialized protein filaments called *myosin* and *actin*.

All cells require ATP to carry out their functions, but muscle cells need exceptionally large amounts of ATP to power the many chemical and physical changes involved in muscle contraction.

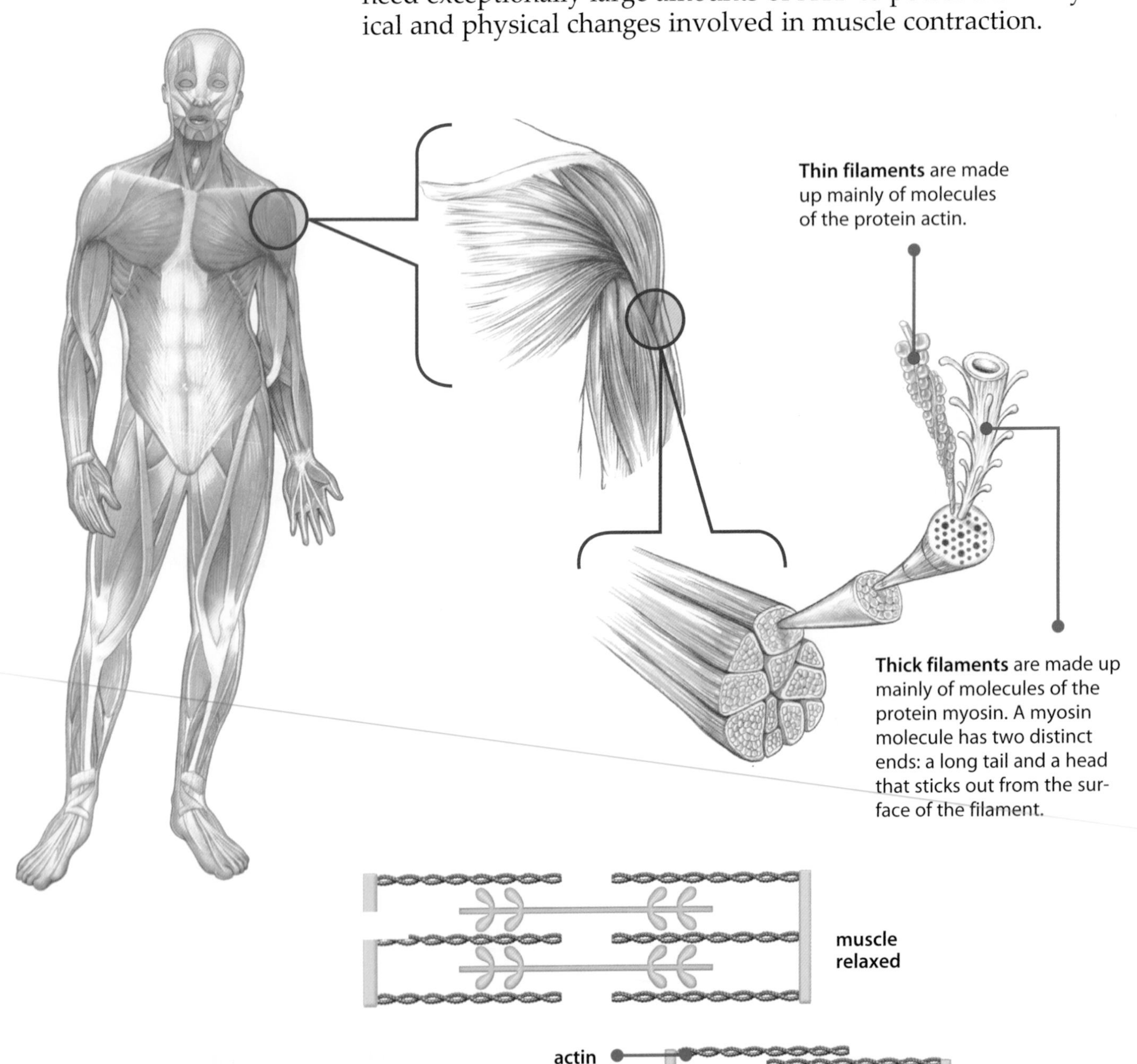

Thin filaments are made up mainly of molecules of the protein actin.
Thick filaments are made up mainly of molecules of the protein myosin. A myosin molecule has two distinct ends: a long tail and a head that sticks out from the surface of the filament.
muscle relaxed

During a **muscle contraction**, the thin and thick filaments slide past each other, causing the muscle fiber to contract or shorten.

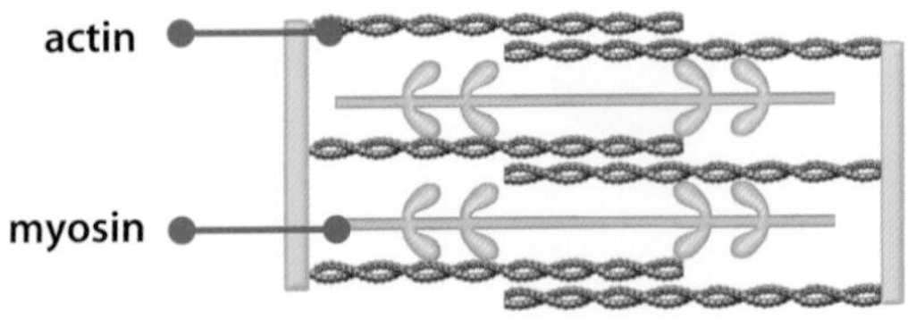

For muscle to contract, myosin heads must be able to bind to particular sites on actin molecules. When a muscle fiber is resting, the binding sites are blocked. To unblock the sites, calcium ions (Ca^{2+}) in the cytoplasm of the muscle cell must bind to a strand of proteins along the thin filament. When calcium ions bind, the myosin-binding sites are exposed and the muscle can contract.

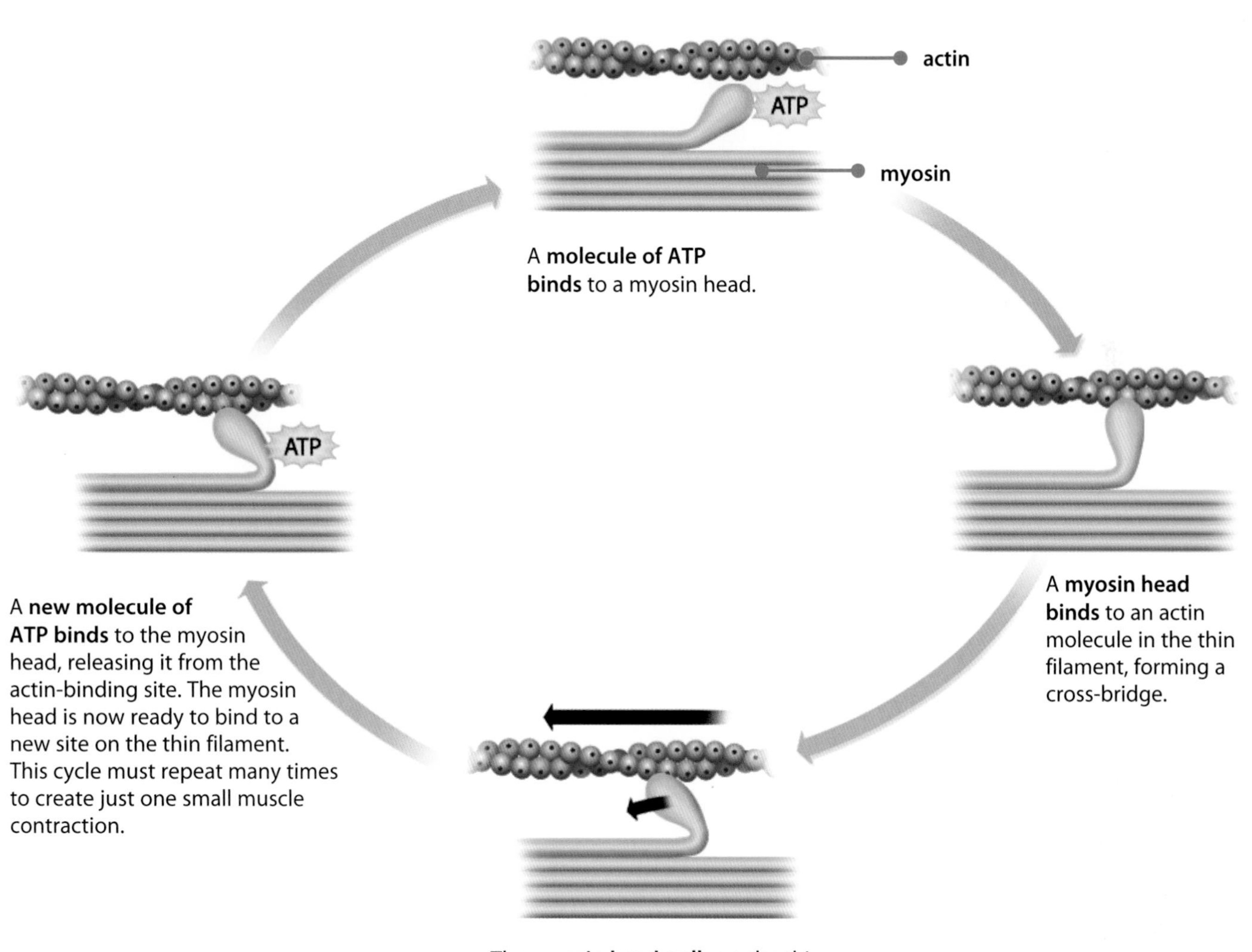

A **molecule of ATP binds** to a myosin head.

A **myosin head binds** to an actin molecule in the thin filament, forming a cross-bridge.

The **myosin head pulls** on the thin filament, causing the thick and thin filaments to slide past one another.

A **new molecule of ATP binds** to the myosin head, releasing it from the actin-binding site. The myosin head is now ready to bind to a new site on the thin filament. This cycle must repeat many times to create just one small muscle contraction.

The endocrine system is the chemical control system of the human body.

The endocrine system controls many cycles and processes, from sleep patterns to childbirth, by sending chemical signals called *hormones* to the cells in various body systems. Without hormones, few of the functions that sustain life could take place.

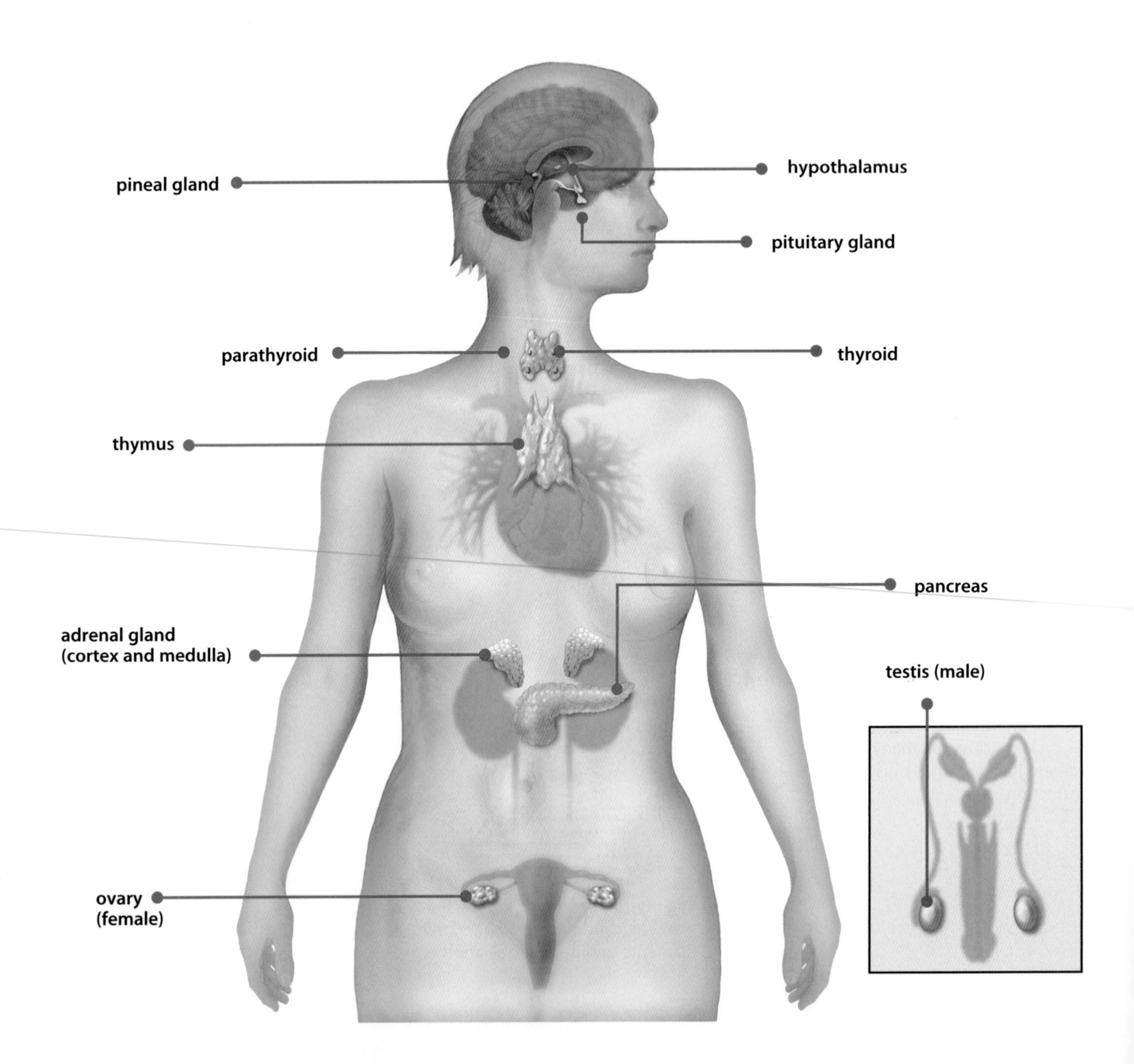

ENDOCRINE GLANDS, HORMONES, AND EFFECTS

THE GLAND ...	SECRETES THE HORMONE(S) ...	AND CAUSES THE FOLLOWING EFFECT(S) ...
Hypothalamus	Releasing hormones Inhibiting hormones Pituitary hormones	Stimulate the pituitary gland to release other hormones Cause the pituitary gland to stop releasing other hormones Produce some hormones secreted by the pituitary gland
Pineal	Melatonin	Regulates sleep patterns and other biological rhythms
Pituitary	See table below	See table below
Parathyroid	Parathyroid hormone	Increases blood calcium levels
Thyroid	Thyroxine and triiodothyronine Calcitonin	Regulate metabolism Reduces blood calcium levels
Thymus	Thymosin	Stimulates maturation of T cells
Adrenal cortex	Glucocorticoids (such as cortisol) Mineralocorticoids (such as aldosterone)	Increase blood glucose levels Regulate salt and water levels in the body
Adrenal medulla	Epinephrine and norepinephrine	Increase blood glucose level; increase metabolic rate; cause some blood vessels to contract; regulate fight-or-flight response
Pancreas	Insulin Glucagon	Stimulates cells to absorb glucose Stimulates release of glucose
Ovary	Estrogen Progesterone	Causes lining of uterus to grow; controls some female secondary sex characteristics such as the growth of breasts Causes lining of the uterus to grow
Testis	Androgens (such as testosterone)	Stimulate formation of sperm; control some male secondary sex characteristics such as facial hair

PITUITARY HORMONES AND EFFECTS

THE HORMONE ...	TARGETS THE ...	AND CAUSES THE FOLLOWING EFFECT(S) ...
Antidiuretic hormone (ADH)	Kidney tubules	Promotes water retention by the kidneys
Oxytocin	Uterine muscles and mammary glands	Stimulates contractions of the uterine muscles; causes mammary glands to secrete milk
Follicle-stimulating hormone (FSH)	Ovaries or testes	Stimulates egg or sperm production
Luteinizing hormone (LH)	Ovaries or testes	Causes the production of estrogen and progesterone; stimulates ovulation; stimulates the production of androgens such as testosterone
Thyroid-stimulating hormone (TSH)	Thyroid	Regulates the release of thyroid hormones
Adrenocorticotropic hormone (ACTH)	Adrenal cortex	Stimulates the production and secretion of glucocorticoids and mineralocorticoids
Prolactin	Mammary glands	Stimulates the growth of mammary glands and milk production
Melanocyte-stimulating hormone (MSH)	Melanocytes	Regulates the activity of pigment-containing cells
Endorphins	Pain receptors of the brain	Inhibit pain perception
Growth hormone (GH)	Bones, muscles, liver	Stimulates growth and metabolism

Plant hormones control processes at every stage of a plant's growth and development.

Hormones are chemical messengers produced in one part of the plant's body that influence or control the function of cells elsewhere in the plant. Different hormones are produced in different parts of the plant.

PLANT HORMONES

HORMONE	WHERE PRODUCED	HOW TRANSPORTED	EFFECT ON PLANT
Auxin	Developing seeds, shoots, and young leaves	From cell to cell	Influences tropisms; stimulates the development of fruits; stimulates the production of ethylene
Cytokinins	Root caps	Through xylem from roots to shoots	Promote cell division; influence cell growth and differentiation
Ethylene	Most tissues	By diffusion	Causes fruits to ripen and mature
Abscisic acid	Mature leaves and roots in response to water stress	From leaves through phloem	Causes stomata to close; inhibits seed germination and the ripening of fruits
Gibberellins	Developing seeds and tissues of young shoots	Through phloem and xylem	Cause cell elongation and division; stimulate the germination of seeds

Auxin

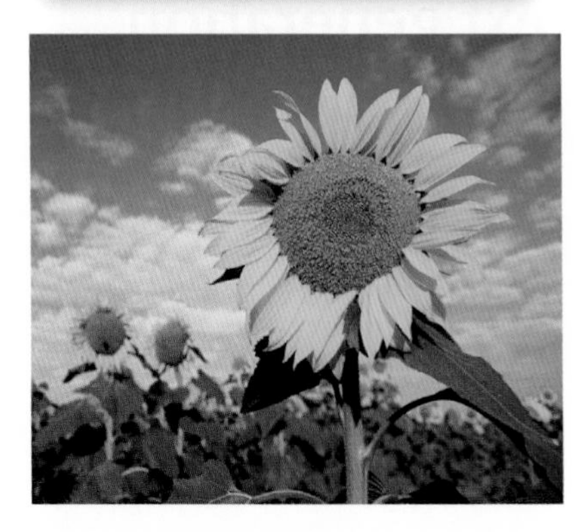

Plant stems grow toward light—a phenomenon known as *phototropism*. This phenomenon occurs because of the hormone **auxin**. When light comes at a plant from one direction, auxin accumulates in the cells on the shaded side of the stem. The cells begin to elongate in the area where auxin is concentrated. The uneven elongation of cells causes the stem to bend in the direction of the light.

Abscisic Acid

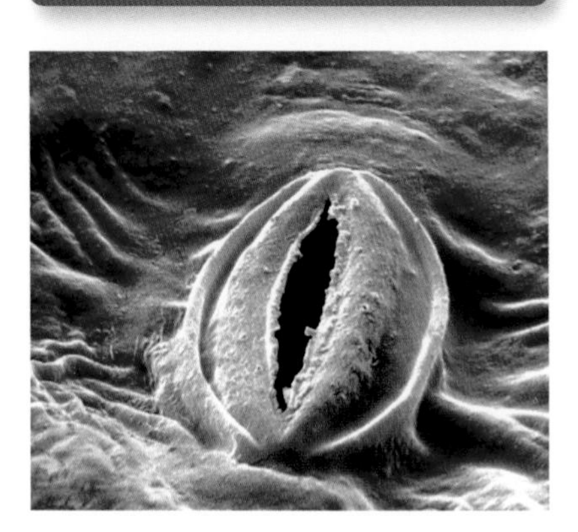

Shortages of water can stimulate a plant to secrete **abscisic acid**. This hormone makes the stomata of the plant close, so the plant loses less water.

Ethylene

Ethylene causes fruits to mature and ripen. Plants produce this hormone naturally. Many commercial fruit growers use ethylene as part of their production process. They often pick and ship fruit before it has fully ripened to prevent it from spoiling before it reaches the consumer. They then treat the fruit with ethylene gas to help it ripen quickly.

Cytokinins

Cytokinins promote cell division. These onion roots are growing because of the influence of cytokinins on growth and differentiation of the cells in the roots.

Gibberellins

Gibberellins are produced in germinating seeds and young tissue. These hormones stimulate cell division and cell elongation.

During reproduction, organisms pass genetic material to the next generation.

Sexual reproduction generally requires two parents. In asexual reproduction, one parent provides all the genetic material for the offspring.

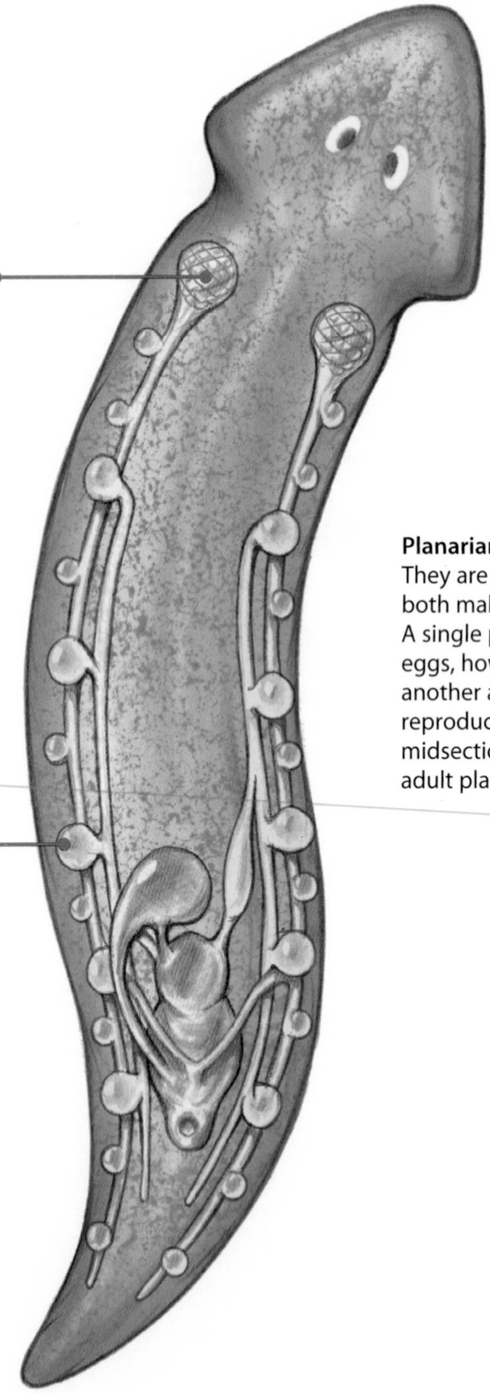

Ovaries, the female reproductive organs, produce eggs by meiosis. Egg cells are haploid (1*n*)—meaning they have one copy of each chromosome. Haploid cells have half as many chromosomes as a normal body cell.

Planarians can reproduce sexually and asexually. They are hermaphroditic—that is, they possess both male and female reproductive organs. A single planarian's sperm cannot fertilize its own eggs, however. Instead, planarians mate with one another and exchange sperm. When planarians reproduce asexually, they split in half across their midsection, and each half regenerates into an adult planarian.

Testes, the male reproductive organs, produce sperm by meiosis. Like egg cells, sperm cells are haploid.

Like all plants, **ferns** have a two-stage life cycle described as an *alternation of generations.* The two fern generations, one whose cells are haploid (1*n*) and one whose cells are diploid (2*n*), exist as individual plants. In more complex plants, such as seed plants, the 1*n* generation remains on the larger 2*n* plant.

The spores of the fern germinate to form **gametophytes**. Every cell of a gametophyte's body is haploid. Gametophytes produce both eggs and sperm by mitosis. The eggs and sperm are thus haploid.

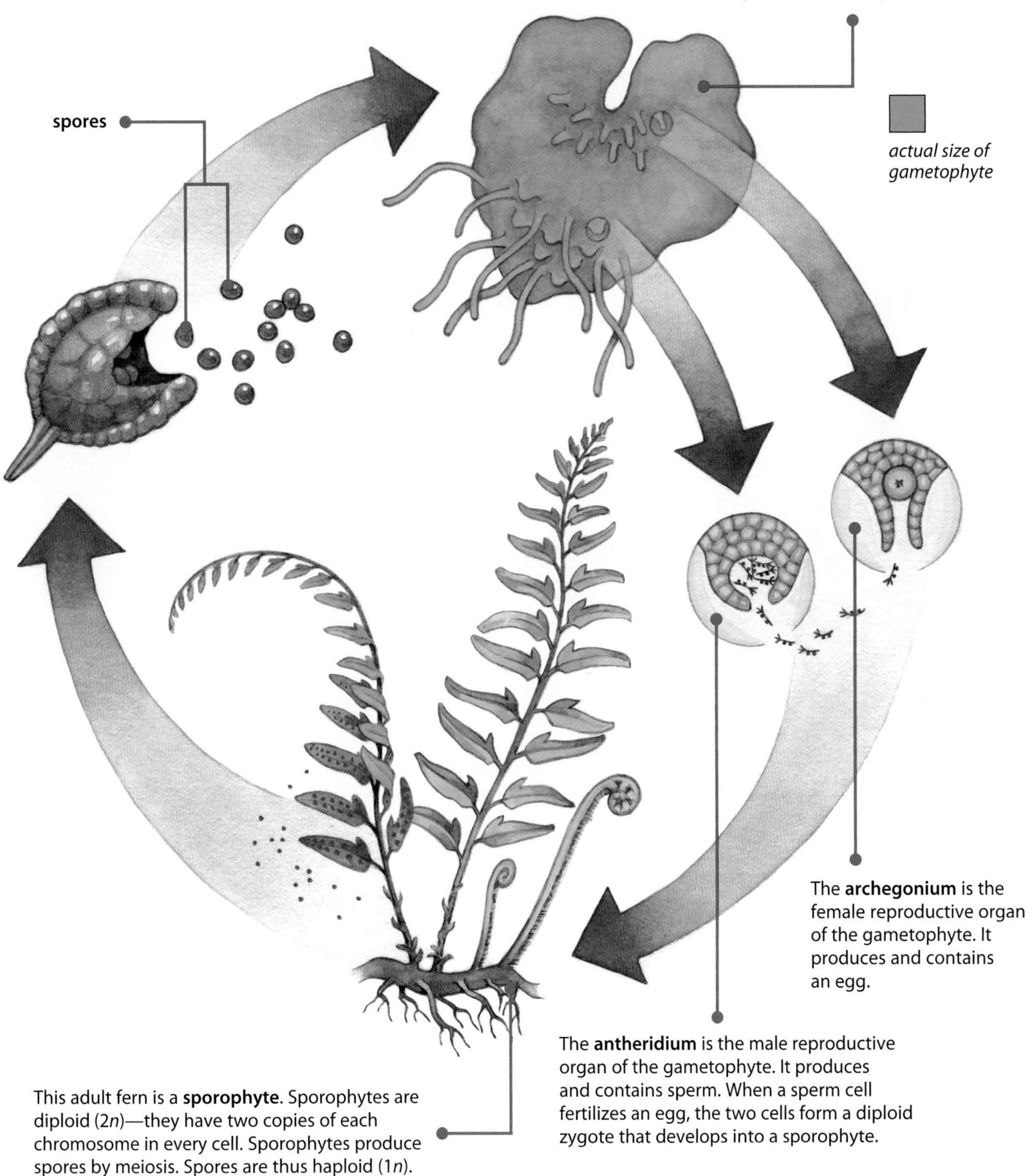

The **archegonium** is the female reproductive organ of the gametophyte. It produces and contains an egg.

The **antheridium** is the male reproductive organ of the gametophyte. It produces and contains sperm. When a sperm cell fertilizes an egg, the two cells form a diploid zygote that develops into a sporophyte.

This adult fern is a **sporophyte.** Sporophytes are diploid (2*n*)—they have two copies of each chromosome in every cell. Sporophytes produce spores by meiosis. Spores are thus haploid (1*n*).

After fertilization, a human embryo grows inside its mother.

A special organ called a *placenta,* a remarkable adaptation of most mammals, maintains a separation between the blood circulation of the mother and embryo. The placenta allows the embryo to receive food from the mother's blood and allows the removal of waste products from the embryo.

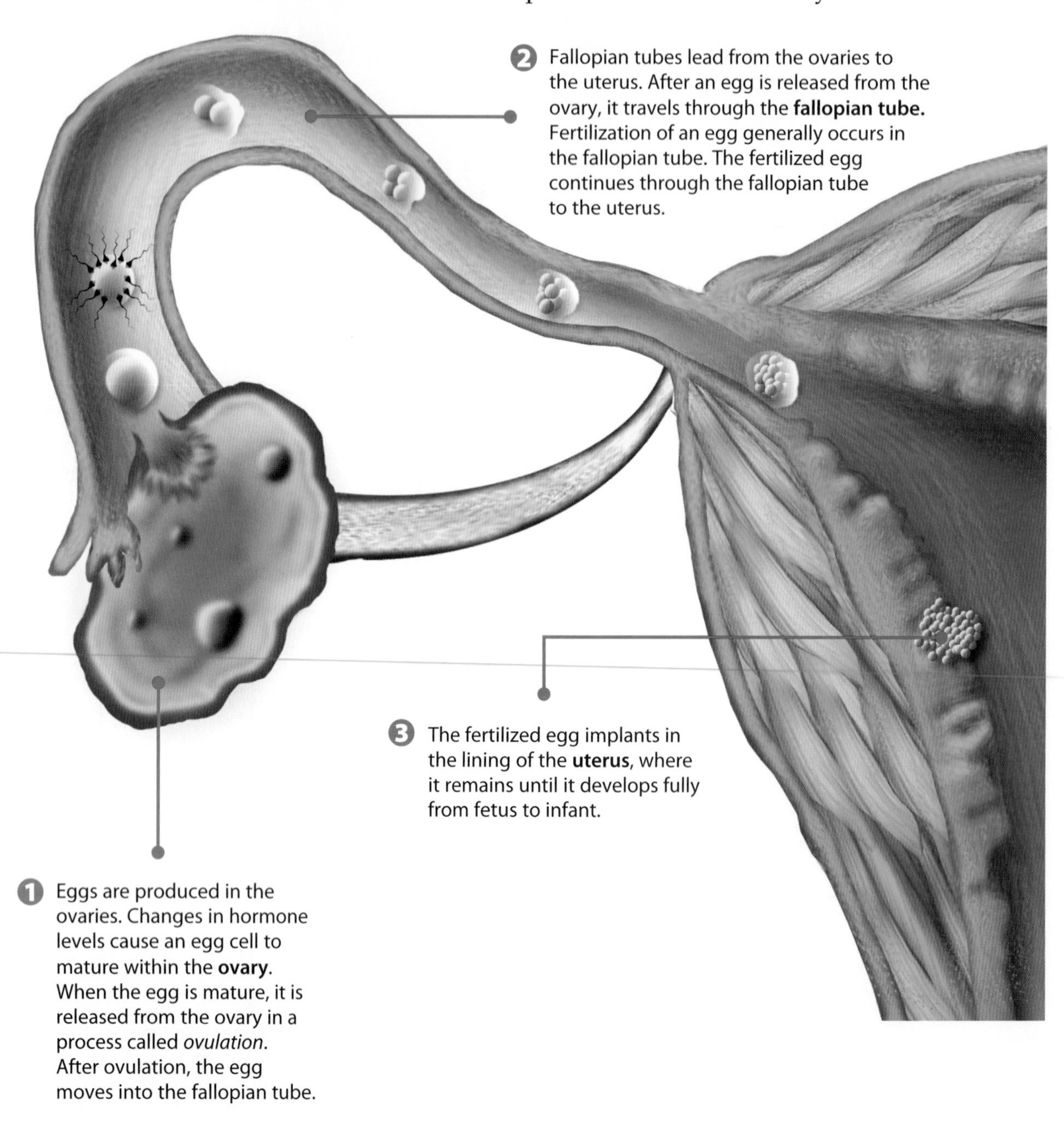

2 Fallopian tubes lead from the ovaries to the uterus. After an egg is released from the ovary, it travels through the **fallopian tube.** Fertilization of an egg generally occurs in the fallopian tube. The fertilized egg continues through the fallopian tube to the uterus.
3 The fertilized egg implants in the lining of the **uterus**, where it remains until it develops fully from fetus to infant.
1 Eggs are produced in the ovaries. Changes in hormone levels cause an egg cell to mature within the **ovary**. When the egg is mature, it is released from the ovary in a process called *ovulation*. After ovulation, the egg moves into the fallopian tube.

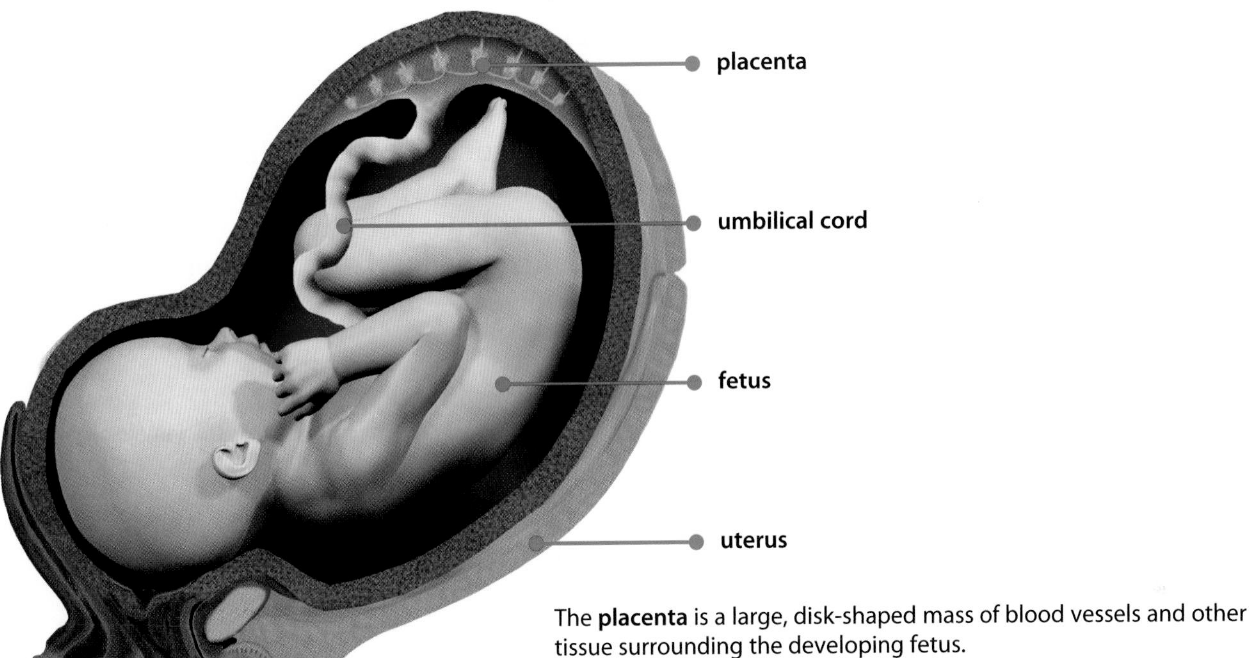

The **placenta** is a large, disk-shaped mass of blood vessels and other tissue surrounding the developing fetus.

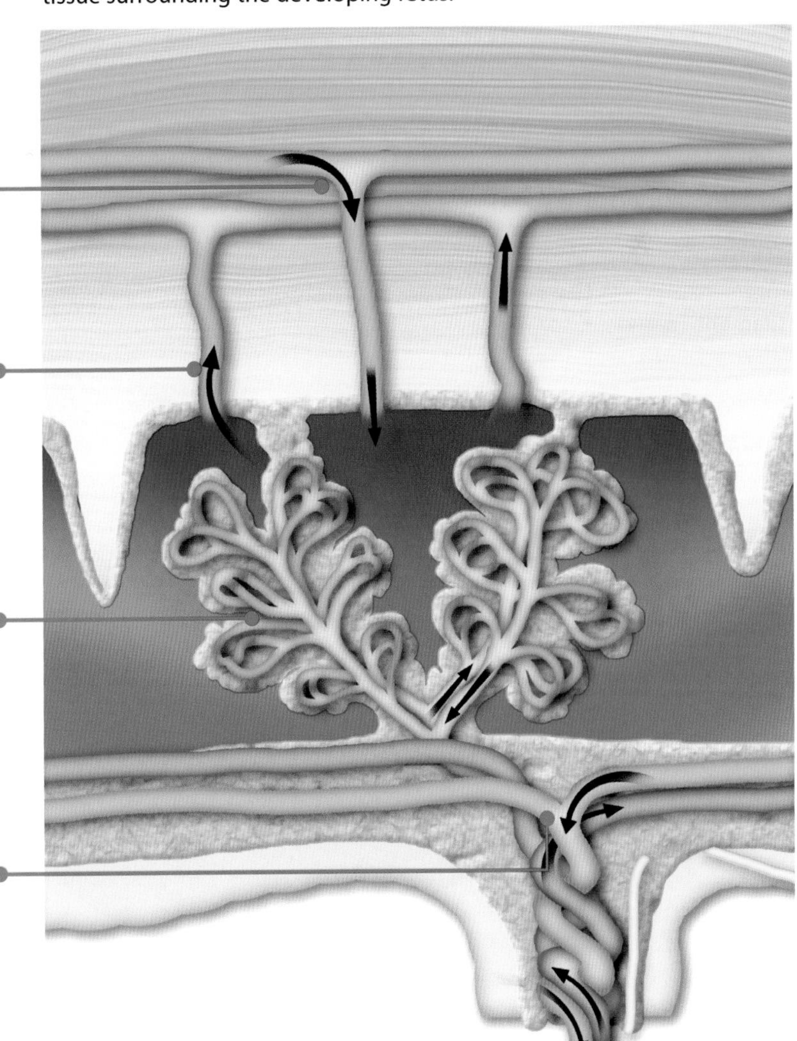

Blood from the mother enters the placenta through the **maternal arteries**.
Blood containing fetal waste products flows back to the mother through the **maternal veins**.
Maternal blood within the placenta flows around the **fetal capillaries**. Materials such as oxygen and nutrients diffuse from the maternal blood into the blood in the fetal capillaries. Waste products such as carbon dioxide diffuse from the fetal capillaries into the maternal blood.
Fetal arteries carry oxygenated blood to the fetus. Fetal veins carry waste to the mother. Both are located in the **umbilical cord**.

Most plants on earth are angiosperms, or flowering plants.

Flowers are reproductive structures. Depending on the species of plant, a flower may contain only male reproductive organs, only female reproductive organs, or both male and female reproductive organs. Fruits develop from a flower's female structures after fertilization takes place.

The **stamen** is the male organ of a flower. This structure usually consists of the anther, where pollen grains are produced, and a stalk called the *filament*. Not all flowers have stamens. Many flowers have more than one stamen.

The **pistil** is the female organ of a flower. This structure is made up of the stigma, style, ovary, and ovules. This flower contains only one pistil. Some flowers, however, have more than one pistil or none at all.

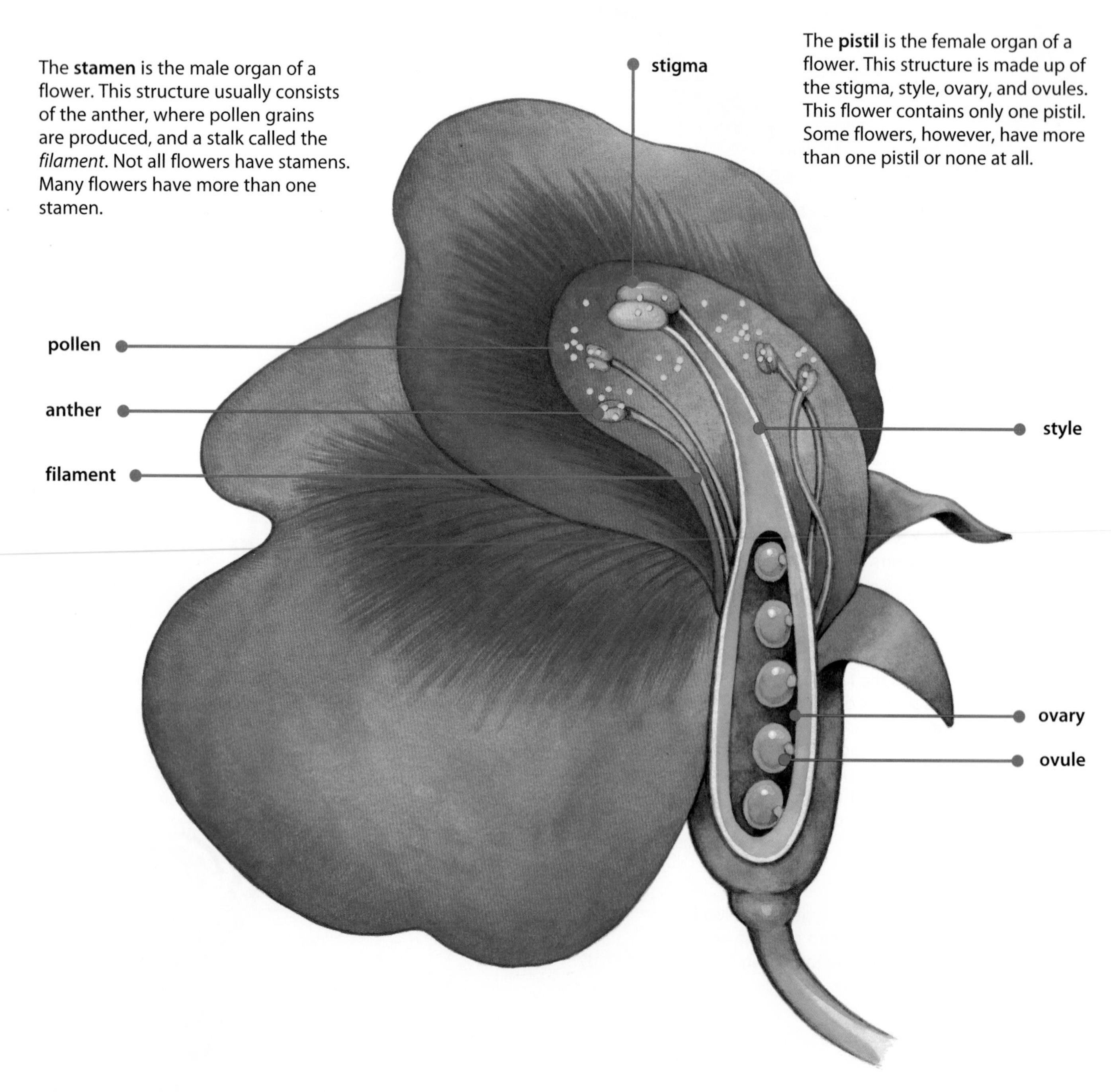

Mature flowers produce **gametes**. Male gametes are carried within pollen grains to a stigma on the same plant or, more commonly, another plant. This process is known as *pollination.* After pollination, a tube from the pollen grain grows down through the style and into the ovary. Sperm cells move through the tube to the egg cells within the ovules. The fusion of a sperm cell and an egg cell is called *fertilization.*

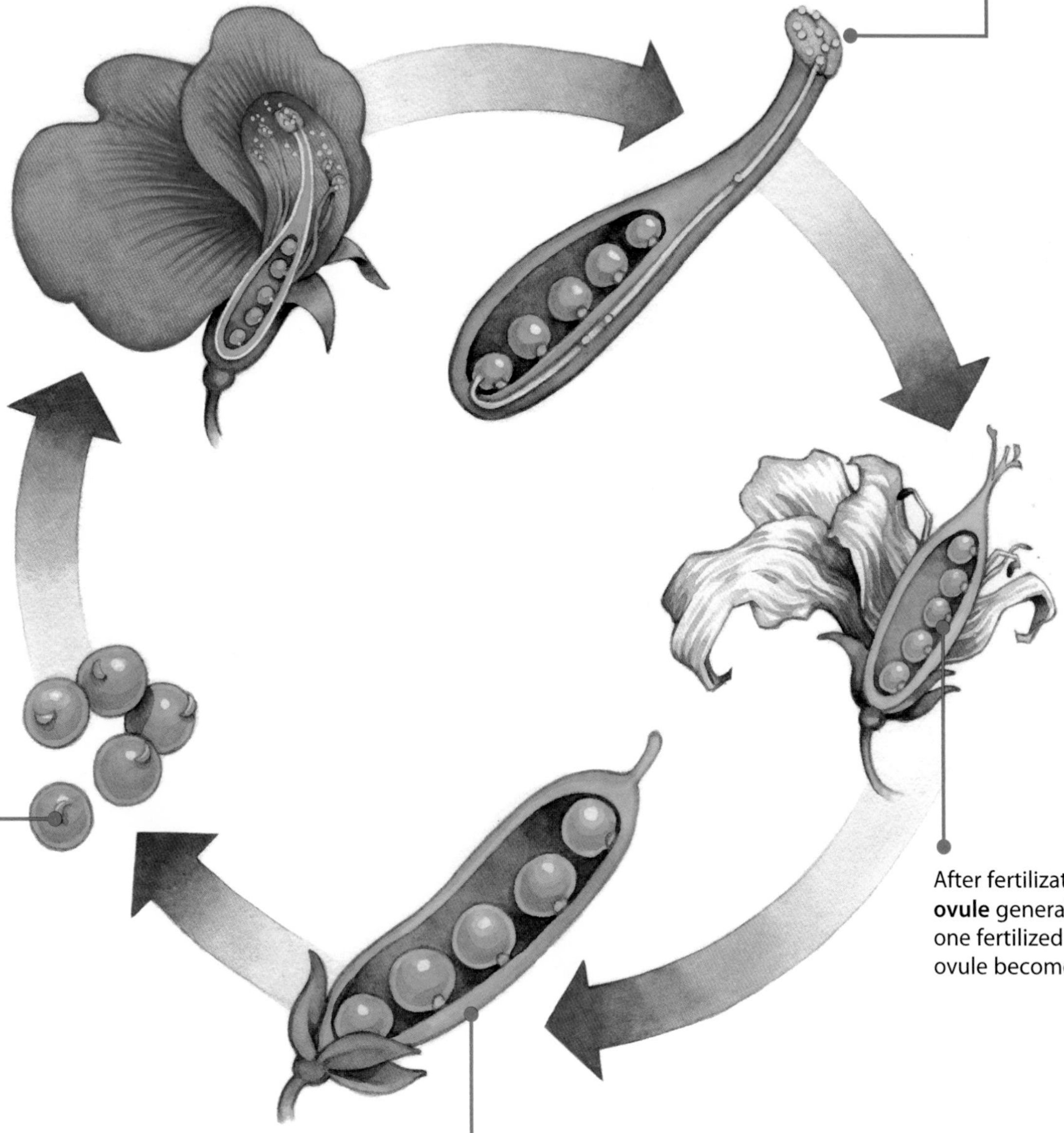

After fertilization, each **ovule** generally contains one fertilized egg. Each ovule becomes a seed.

Each **seed** contains a tiny embryo. Under favorable conditions, a seed can germinate. If conditions remain favorable, the seed can develop into a mature plant, and the cycle of reproduction can begin again.

The mature **ovary** containing fertilized eggs becomes a fruit. Many plant materials that we call vegetables, such as this pea pod, are actually fruits.

Your immune system helps protect you from harmful pathogens such as viruses, bacteria, and fungi.

Each organ in the immune system performs a specific function to help keep you healthy and fight off the pathogens that you are exposed to every day.

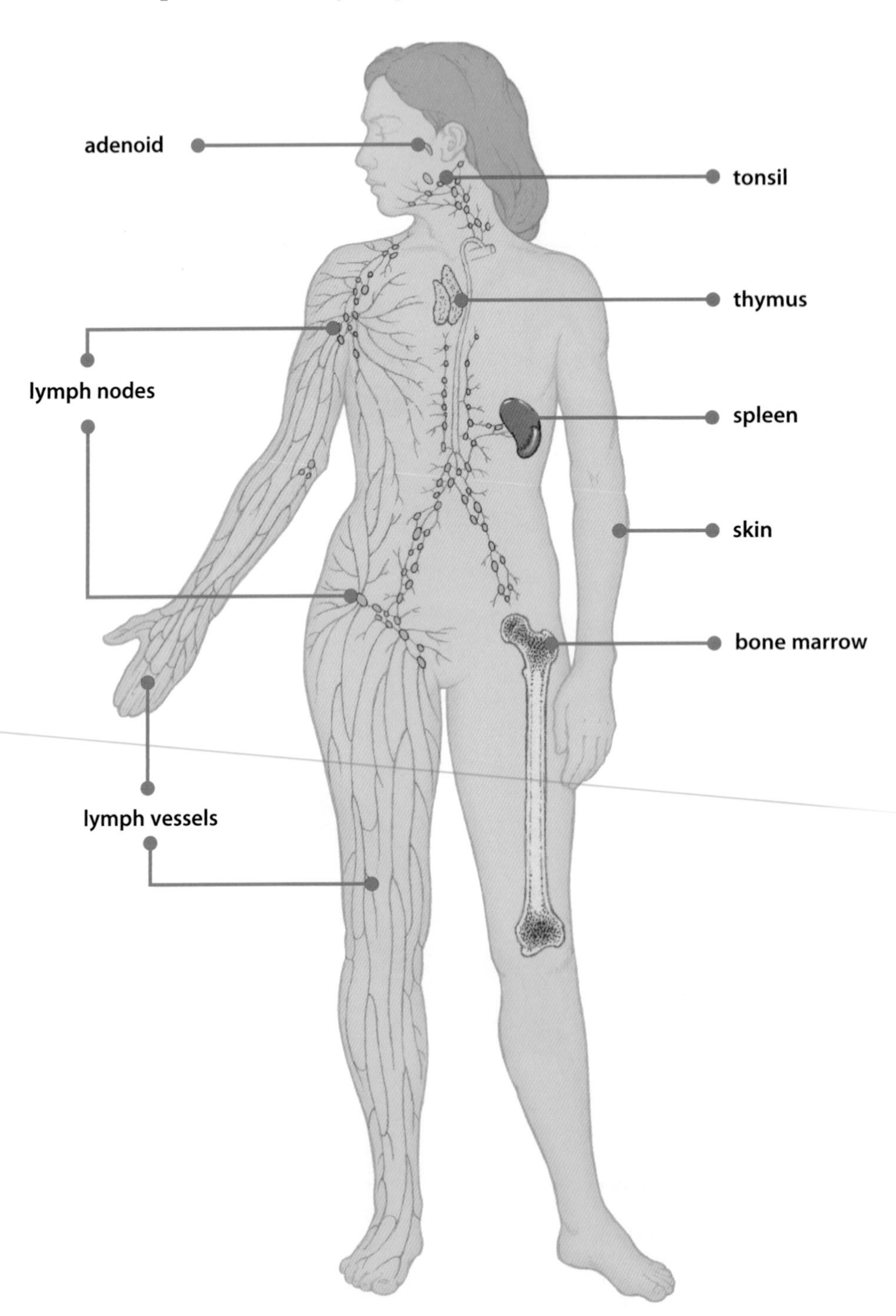

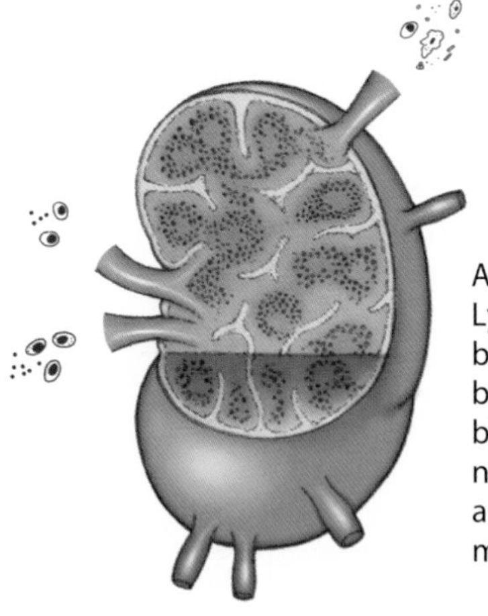

A **lymph node** helps filter blood and lymph. Lymph is a clear fluid that contains white blood cells and circulates throughout the body. Lymph nodes also help produce white blood cells. When you are sick, your lymph nodes—located mainly in your neck, armpits, and groin—may swell because they contain more white blood cells.

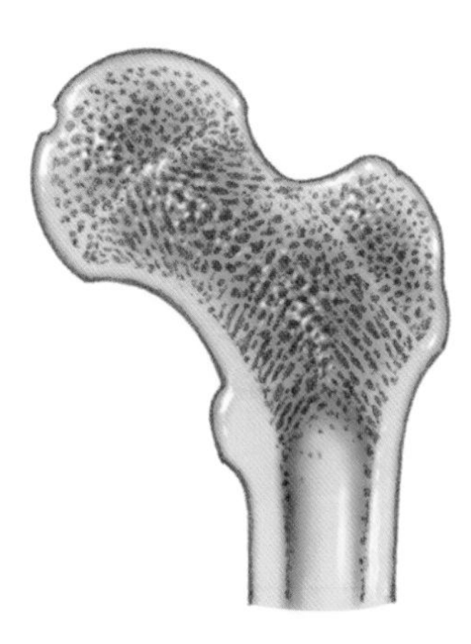

Many white blood cells, which attack and destroy pathogens, form in **bone marrow**. This soft, spongy tissue contains millions of cells that can develop into different kinds of blood cells.

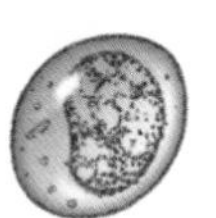

Lymphocytes produce antibodies, which can destroy viruses and other pathogens.

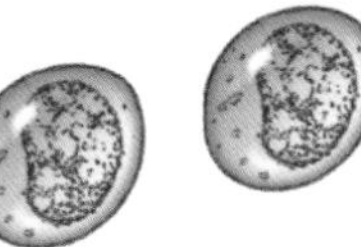

The **thymus** is a small organ in the neck behind the upper part of the breastbone. Some lymphocytes mature in the thymus. Lymphocytes help recognize and destroy viruses and other pathogens. Your thymus was most active when you were a baby. By the time you are an adult, it will have become much smaller and less active.

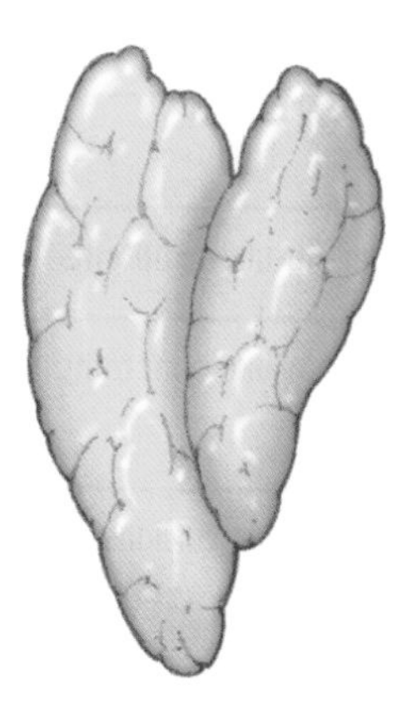

One type of white blood cell, the lymphocyte, is produced in the **spleen**. Your spleen also helps filter your blood and remove dead blood cells.

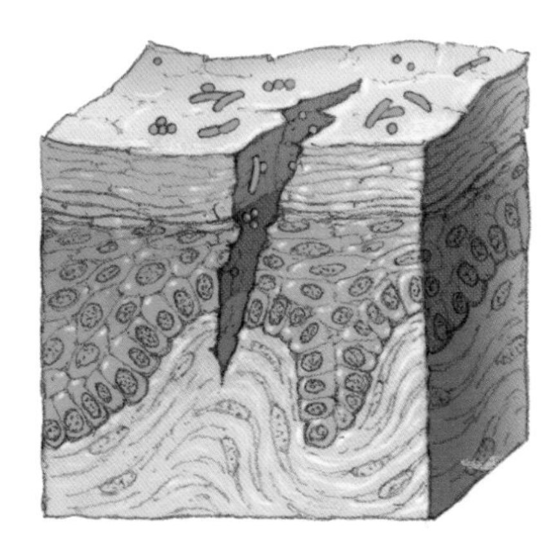

The **skin** is one of the most important organs in the immune system. The skin acts as a defensive barrier against pathogens. Unless there is a break in your skin, such as a cut or a scrape, most pathogens cannot pass through your skin and into your body.

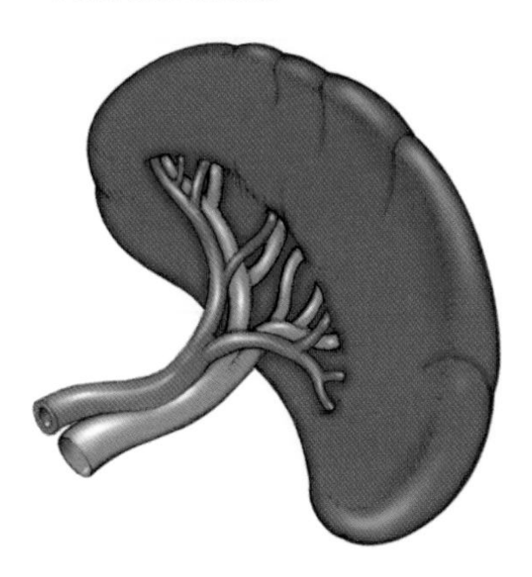

Most human infectious diseases are caused by bacteria or viruses.

Bacteria are living organisms. Although viruses are not alive, they reproduce within host cells and can cause some of our most common—and some of our most dreaded—diseases. Many bacterial diseases can be treated with antibiotics. However, antibiotics are not effective against viral diseases.

VIRAL DISEASES

DISEASE	DESCRIPTION	MEANS OF TRANSMISSION
Common cold	Cough, sinus congestion, muscle aches	Direct contact with infected materials, inhalation
Influenza (flu)	Fever, cough, sore throat, chills, fatigue, headache, muscle aches	Inhalation
Chicken pox	Red, blistering rash	Coughs and sneezes of infected individual, direct contact with fluid from sores
AIDS	Failure of the immune system	Contact with contaminated blood or needles, sexual contact
Hepatitis A	Yellow skin, joint pain, swollen liver, flu-like symptoms	Through contaminated food, water, or blood
Hepatitis B	Yellow skin, joint pain, swollen liver, flu-like symptoms (can also cause liver cancer)	Contact with contaminated blood or needles, sexual contact
Rabies	Fever, depression, difficulty swallowing, convulsions, paralysis (fatal)	Bite from an infected animal
SARS	Headache, cough, high fever (potentially fatal)	Direct contact with infected materials, inhalation
Yellow fever	Yellow skin, weakness, fever (potentially fatal)	Bite from an infected mosquito
Ebola	Uncontrollable bleeding, fever	Through body fluids

BACTERIAL DISEASES			
DISEASE	***BACTERIUM CAUSING DISEASE***	***DESCRIPTION***	***CAUSE OR MEANS OF TRANSMISSION***
Dental cavities	*Streptococcus mutans*	Tooth decay	Overabundant bacteria in the mouth
Strep throat	*Streptococcus pyogenes*	Sore throat, fever	Direct contact with fluids from an infected individual
Lyme disease	*Borrelia burgdorferi*	Swelling in joints, rash, pain	Bite from an infected tick
Cholera	*Vibrio cholerae*	Vomiting and diarrhea (often fatal)	Through contaminated water
Tuberculosis	*Mycobacterium tuberculosis*	Breathing difficulties, fever, cough	Inhalation
Typhus	*Rickettsia prowazekii*	Headache, fever	Bite from an infected louse or flea
Anthrax	*Bacillus anthracis*	Breathing difficulties, fever	Inhalation
Bubonic plague	*Yersinia pestis*	Fever, swollen lymph nodes, bleeding (often fatal)	Bite from an infected flea

Your body has defenses to reduce the number of pathogens that can enter or thrive in your body.

Your skin provides a first line of defense against pathogens. Germs can enter your body, however, through breaks in your skin such as cuts and scrapes. Other defenses can destroy the pathogens that do enter your body.

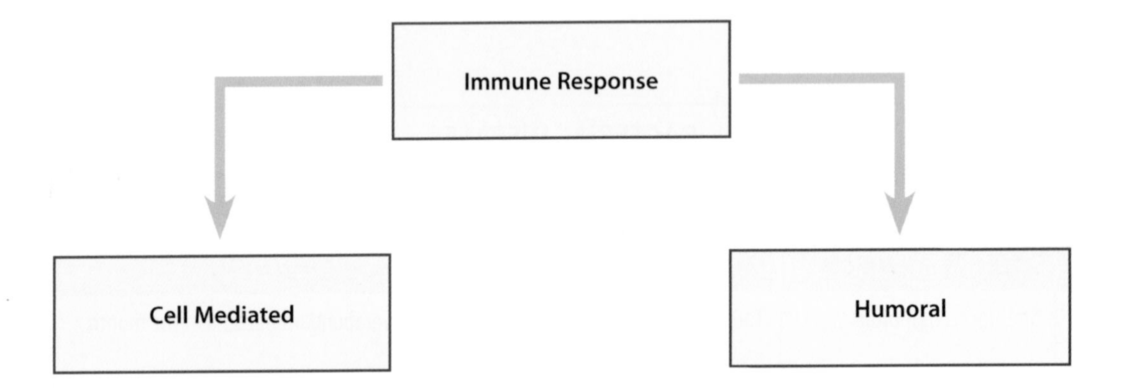

Your body's immune system can respond to pathogens in different ways. **Cell-mediated immune response** involves a kind of lymphocyte called a *T cell*. T cells can destroy infected body cells. **Humoral immune response** involves another kind of lymphocyte called a *B cell*. B cells can become plasma cells, which produce antibodies. Antibodies bind to specific pathogens and can act as markers on infected cells. The markers allow other immune cells to recognize infected body cells.

TYPES OF CELLS IN THE IMMUNE SYSTEM

TYPE OF CELL	FUNCTION
B cell	Marks infected body cells for destruction
Cytotoxic T cell	Destroys infected body cells marked by B cells
Helper T cell	Stimulates cytotoxic T cells and B cells
Macrophage	Consumes and destroys pathogens
Memory cell	Stores information about a specific pathogen so the body can recognize it in the future
Natural killer cell	Destroys infected body cells
Neutrophil	Consumes and destroys pathogens
Plasma cell	Produces antibodies

A Cut Heals

1. Injured cells at the cut release compounds called *histamines*. These chemical messengers cause the blood vessels around the cut to dilate (widen), allowing more blood to flow to the site of the cut. The increased blood flow allows more of your body's immune system cells to get to the cut and help destroy any pathogens that have entered your body. It also may make the skin near the cut look red or slightly swollen.

2. Specialized white blood cells called *monocytes* and *neutrophils* accumulate near the cut. These cells can consume and destroy many bacteria, viruses, and other pathogens that may have entered your bloodstream through the cut.

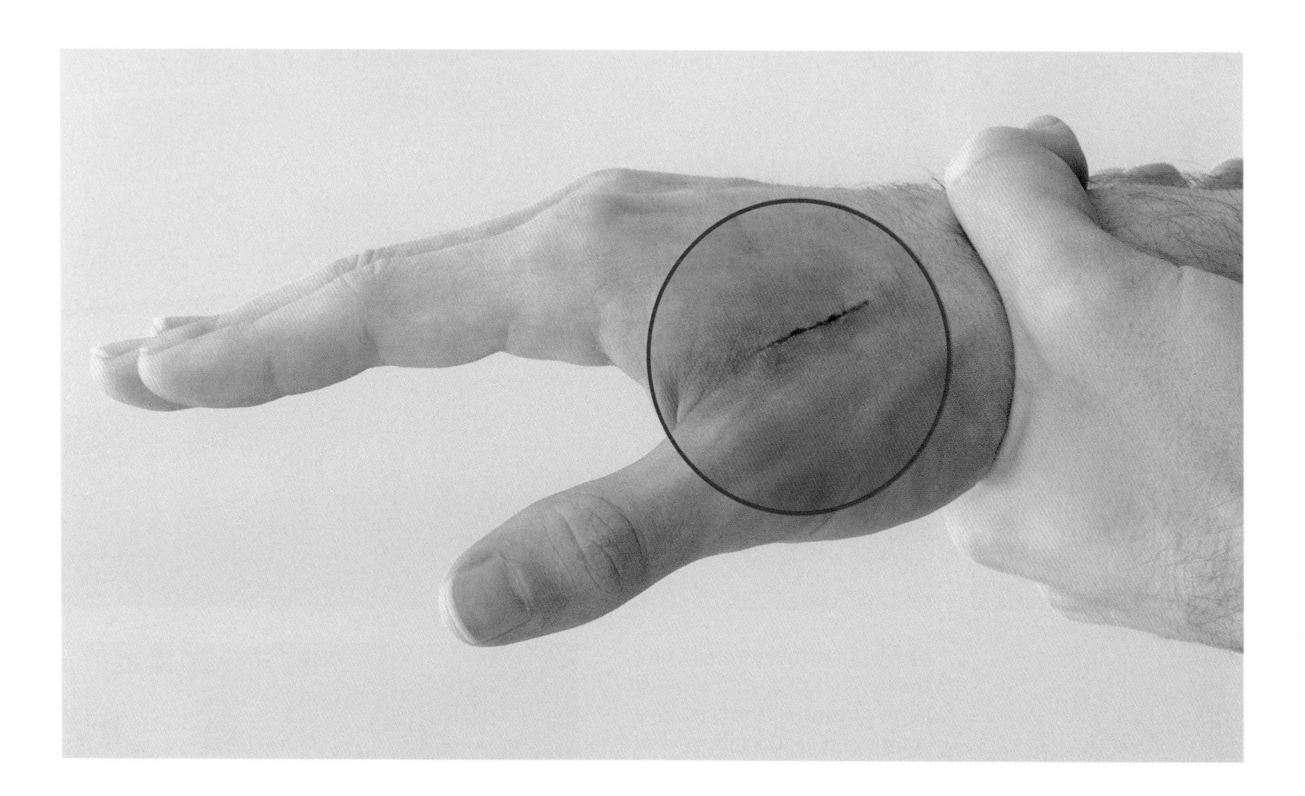

3. Some of the monocytes may move out of the blood vessels and into the surrounding tissue to become macrophages. Like monocytes, macrophages can ingest and destroy pathogens.

4. The clot that formed on the cut begins to dry out and harden, forming a scab. The scab helps prevent more pathogens from entering your body through the break in your skin. Below the scab, skin cells begin to divide more rapidly to produce new skin. After new skin has formed, the scab falls off.

Plants have evolved many kinds of defenses against other organisms.

Most plant defense adaptations involve structures or substances that deter herbivores.

Many plants have **spines** or **thorns** that protect them from large grazing herbivores. The spines of a cactus (above right) and a spurge (above left) are modified leaves that most likely evolved as an adaptation to prevent excessive water loss. The thorns of a rose are modified trichomes or hairs that grow from the epidermis covering the plant stem.

The **dense hairs** on a pussy willow bud make it difficult for small herbivores such as insects to feed on the plant.

The milky **sap** of a poppy contains powerful chemical compounds that discourage herbivores from feeding on the plant. These chemicals, known as *alkaloids*, can be highly addictive to humans.

Many plants, such as this poison ivy, produce **chemical compounds** that are irritating to humans and other animals.

This large growth on the tree is called a *burl*. A **burl** forms a protective covering on a wound. This burl contains clusters of buds that are clones of the parent tree. If the tree becomes severely damaged, the buds can grow to replace the parent tree.

Every living thing is part of the biosphere.

Nested within the biosphere are five additional ecological levels of organization. Each level is influenced by the interactions of components in the levels above and below it. Ultimately, all living and nonliving things are connected.

Ecological Levels of Organization

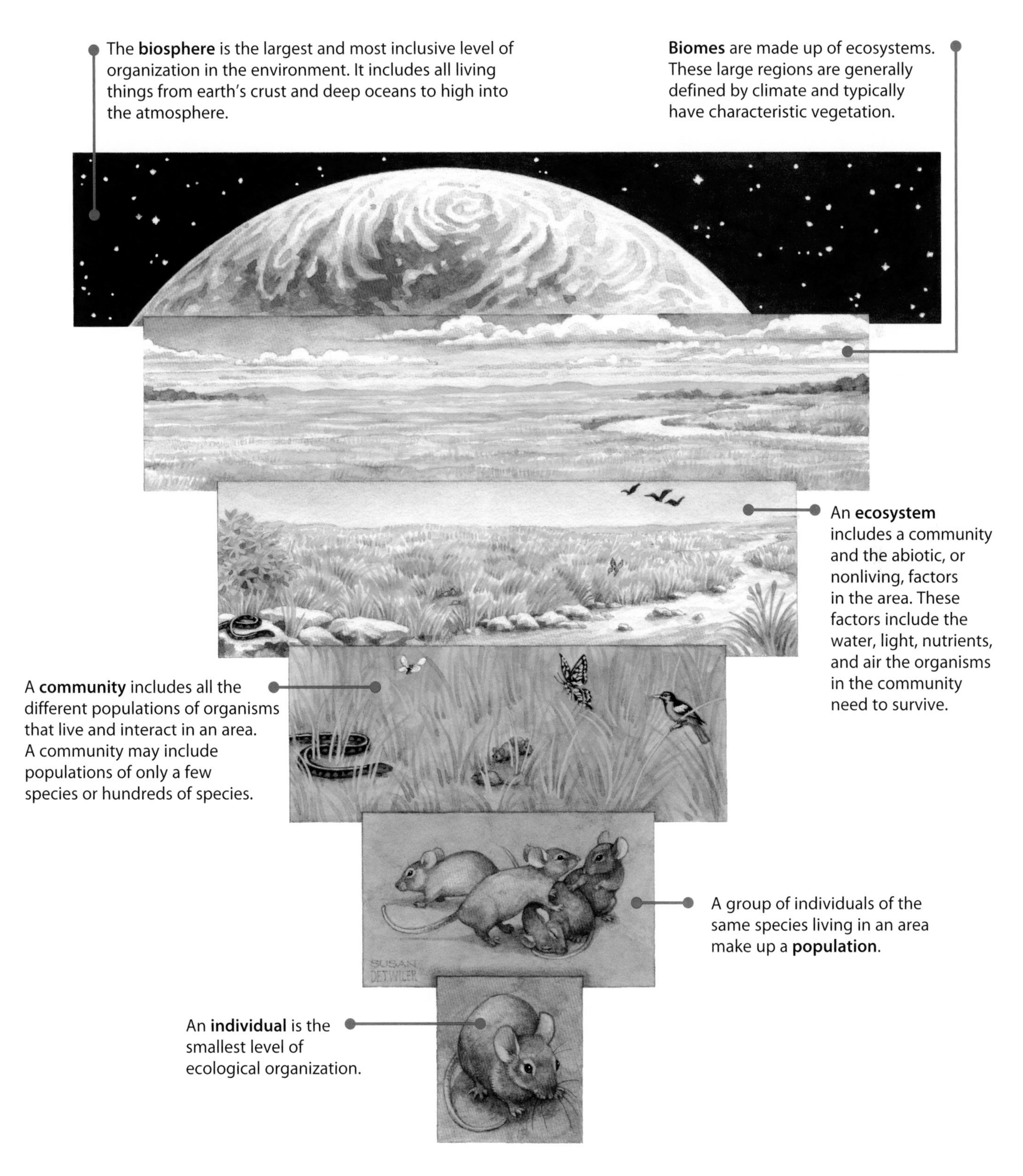

The **biosphere** is the largest and most inclusive level of organization in the environment. It includes all living things from earth's crust and deep oceans to high into the atmosphere.
Biomes are made up of ecosystems. These large regions are generally defined by climate and typically have characteristic vegetation.
An **ecosystem** includes a community and the abiotic, or nonliving, factors in the area. These factors include the water, light, nutrients, and air the organisms in the community need to survive.
A **community** includes all the different populations of organisms that live and interact in an area. A community may include populations of only a few species or hundreds of species.
A group of individuals of the same species living in an area make up a **population**.
An **individual** is the smallest level of ecological organization.

Populations increase until some environmental factor limits the increase.

In the 1800s, Charles Darwin noted that a single pair of organisms could, hypothetically, overrun the earth with its descendants in a relatively short time. We do not see this happen, however, because population growth is eventually limited by the availability of resources.

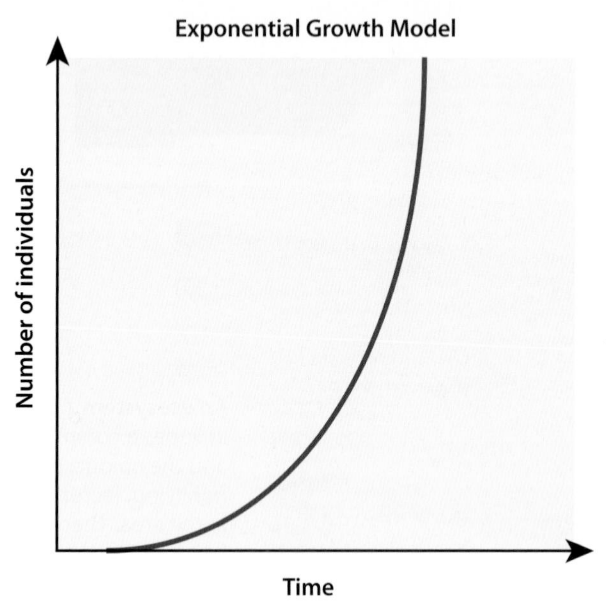

In an **exponential growth model**, population growth (an increase in the number of individuals) continues indefinitely. Though many populations show the characteristic J-shaped exponential growth curve for a particular period of time, no population can keep growing exponentially.

In a **logistic growth model**, a population's numbers increase until the population reaches its carrying capacity (*K*). Carrying capacity is the largest population that a particular environment can support at a particular time. If a population exceeds its carrying capacity, there will not be enough resources for every individual. Some individuals will die or have to leave.

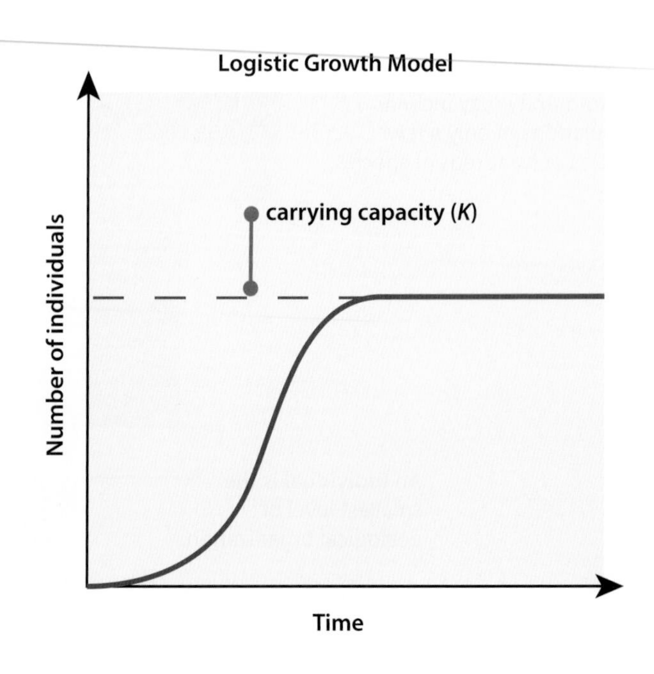

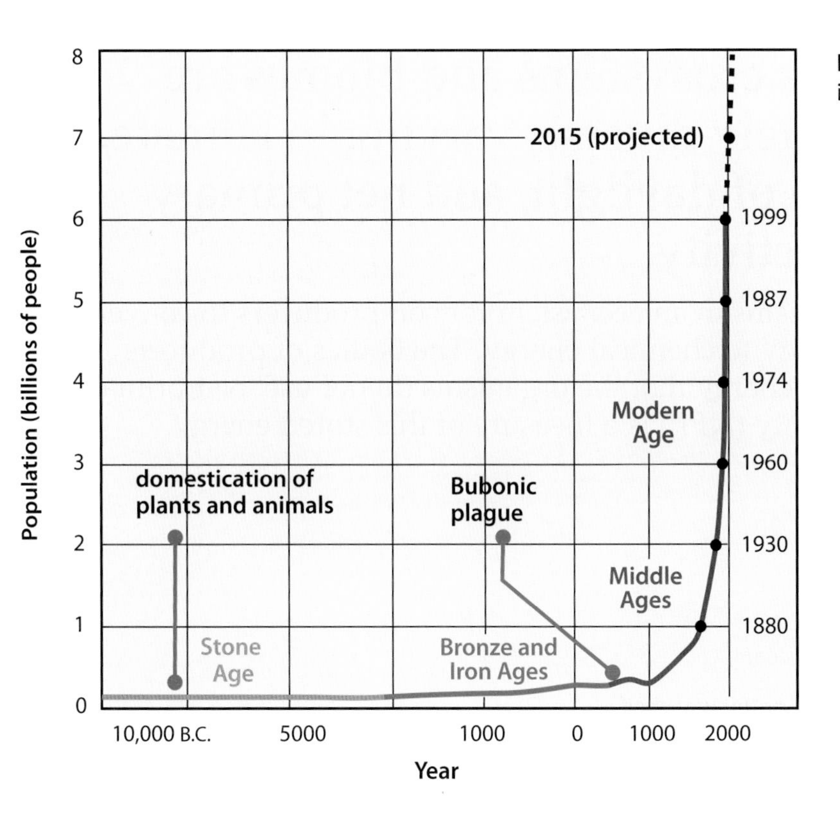

Human population growth is currently in an exponential phase.

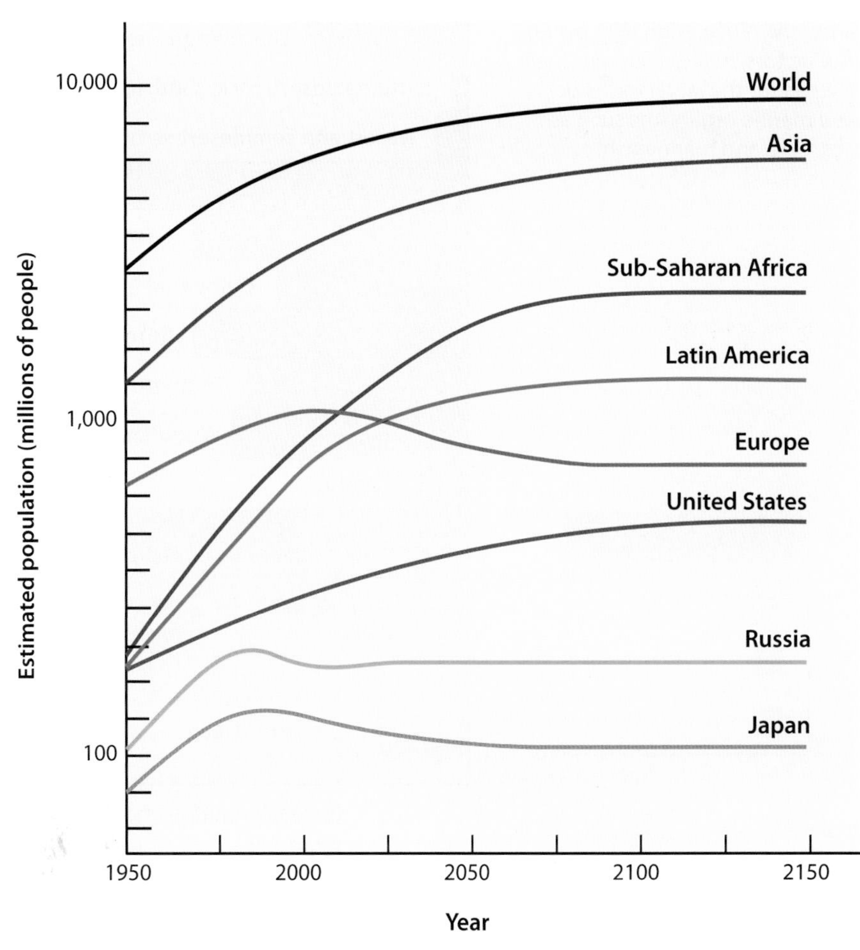

Estuaries are partially enclosed bodies of water where freshwater from rivers and streams mixes with seawater. Healthy estuaries are highly productive ecosystems. The main producers in estuaries are phytoplankton, salt-tolerant coastal plants, and algae. High NPP, among other factors, makes estuaries ideal nurseries for the larval forms of many marine organisms such as crabs, eels, and marine fish.

Earth's ecosystems and biomes are extremely diverse, varying in climate, length of daylight, and net primary productivity.

All organisms in an ecosystem rely on producers to convert light energy to chemical energy. The bodies of producers store any energy that the organisms do not use. Net primary productivity (NPP) is a measure of this stored energy.

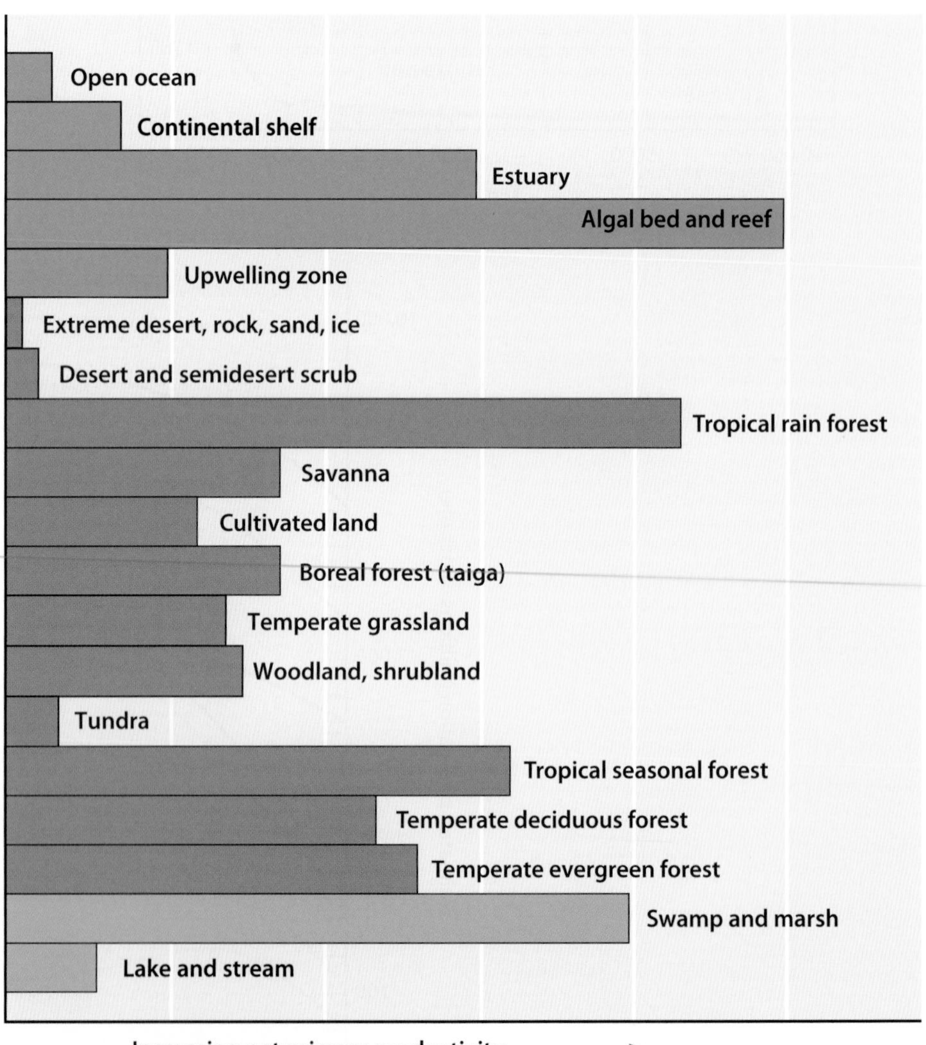

Tropical rain forests are highly productive and contain an incredible diversity of life. They make up only a tiny percentage of earth's surface, but they account for the second highest percentage of earth's NPP. Rain forests are characterized by regular heavy rainfall (up to 200 cm per year) and an average year-round temperature of 25°C. Because conditions for growth are generally favorable throughout the year, tropical rain forest trees carry out photosynthesis all year long.

Temperatures in the treeless plains of the arctic **tundra** are cool in summer and below freezing in winter. Little precipitation falls in the tundra. Most moisture is locked away in a permanently frozen soil layer called *permafrost*. In the summer, small plants take advantage of long daylight hours and a thin layer of thawed soil to grow for a few short months. Nutrient cycling is slow in the tundra, and NPP is low.

Most people think of deserts as hot places, but a **desert** is any area that receives less than 10 cm of rainfall each year. Some deserts are actually quite cold, regularly experiencing temperatures below freezing. Compared to most other ecosystems, deserts are relatively unproductive. When rain does fall, it usually comes in quick bursts that wash away topsoil. Despite low NPP, some deserts have a surprisingly high amount of biodiversity.

Lakes are bodies of freshwater. NPP in lakes is generally tied to the seasons. Photosynthesis rates are highest in spring as daylight hours increase. Nutrient shortages may occur in late summer as plants and their producers die and the nutrients stored in their bodies sink to the bottom of the lake. Productivity increases slightly again in the fall when changing temperatures cause cooling waters to mix and bring the nutrients back to the surface.

A biome is a large area of earth defined by its climate and by the organisms that live there.

Latitude, topography, temperature, and precipitation all affect the climate that defines each biome. The organisms that live in each biome have specific adaptations that allow them to survive there.

The **polar ice** biome includes the areas around earth's poles that are always covered in snow and ice. Almost no producers live at the top of the polar ice biome, though many producers are found in the waters here. Consumers in this biome, such as polar bears, rely on organisms that live in the oceans beneath the ice for their food.

Tundra is located in areas that are cold all year and receive little precipitation. Beneath the ground is a layer of soil called *permafrost,* which remains frozen all year. During the summer, the top layer of soil may thaw, allowing a few plants to grow. A limited number of animal species and microorganisms live in the tundra, so it is one of the least diverse biomes on earth.

The **taiga**, or boreal forest, is characterized by long, cold winters and short, cool summers. Large numbers of coniferous trees, such as pines and cedars, are common in taiga biomes. Various consumers, such as mice, hares, finches, mink, and wolverines, also make their homes in the taiga.

Mountains are characterized by many different climates and organisms.

Chaparral is a biome with woody shrubs found in temperate climates that experiences periodic wildfires.

Temperate grasslands are located in areas that receive a fairly small amount of rainfall and have distinct seasons. Because there is limited rainfall, few trees grow in temperate grasslands. Grasses and shrubs are abundant, however, and the soil is very fertile. Many temperate grasslands have become centers of agriculture because of their highly fertile soil.

The **tropical rain forest** receives a large amount of precipitation and is fairly warm all year. Many tropical forests experience two seasons: wet and dry. Tropical forests are some of the most diverse biomes on earth—they are home to thousands of species of plants, animals, and other organisms.

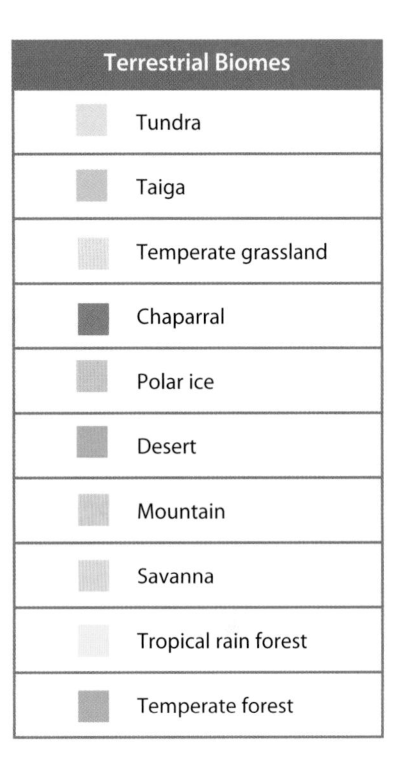

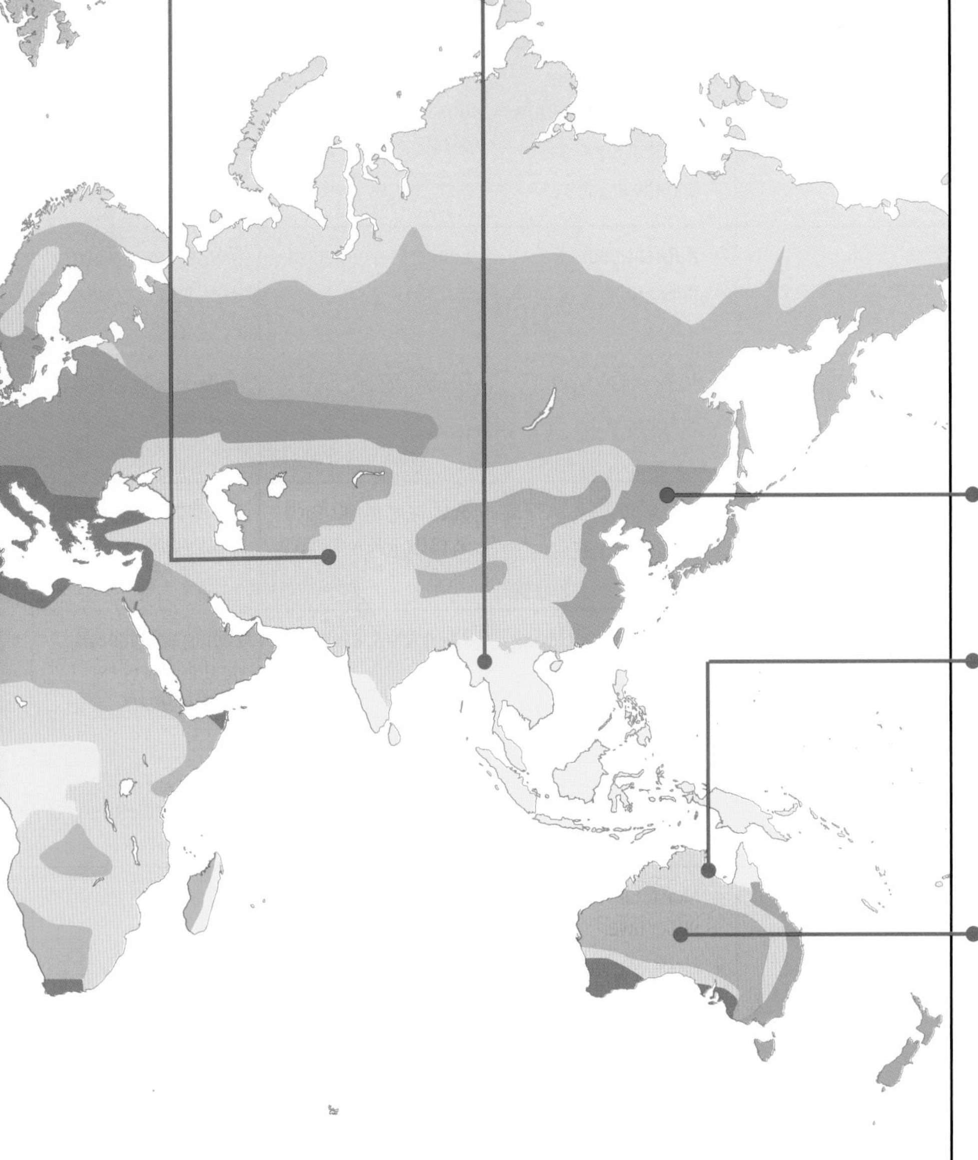

Deciduous trees, such as maple, oak, and birch, as well as many smaller plants such as ferns, are common in the **temperate forest**. Deer, moose, mice, bears, owls, and foxes are typical consumers here.

Regions in the tropics that receive a moderate amount of rainfall are generally part of the **savanna.** Tall grasses and shrubs are the most common plants, but some trees grow here as well.

Deserts cover about one-fifth of earth's surface. Deserts receive very little precipitation, and most have very high temperatures during the day and lower temperatures at night. Some regions of earth at high latitudes can also be classified as deserts because of their low rainfall, even though temperatures there are low most of the time.

Each biome has a distinct set of temperature, precipitation, and soil characteristics.

These features affect the types of organisms that can live in a given biome. The organisms in a specific biome are adapted to that biome's characteristics.

BIOME CHARACTERISTICS

BIOME	AVERAGE YEARLY TEMPERATURE	AVERAGE YEARLY PRECIPITATION	SOIL CHARACTERISTICS	REPRESENTATIVE VEGETATION	REPRESENTATIVE ANIMAL LIFE
Tundra	–26ºC to 12ºC	Less than 25 cm	• Thin, moist upper layer over permafrost • Nutrient poor • Slightly acidic	Mosses, lichens, grasses, small woody plants	Caribou, arctic foxes, lemmings, snowshoe hares
Taiga	–10ºC to 14ºC	35 to 75 cm	• Nutrient poor • Very acidic	Conifers (evergreens)	Moose, bears, wolves, lynxes
Temperate grassland	0ºC to 25ºC	25 to 75 cm	• Thick upper layer • Nutrient rich	Dense grasses	Buffalo, prairie dogs, coyotes
Desert	7ºC to 38ºC	Less than 25 cm	• Dry, sandy • Nutrient poor	Succulent plants such as cacti, a few grasses	Lizards, snakes, foxes
Savanna	16ºC to 34ºC	75 to 150 cm	• Dry, thin upper layer • Nutrient poor	Tall grasses, a few trees	Zebras, wildebeests, giraffes, gazelles, lions, leopards
Tropical rain forest	20ºC to 34ºC	200 to 400 cm	• Moist, thin upper layer • Nutrient poor	Broadleaf trees, shrubs, vines, mosses	Monkeys, snakes, lizards, birds, insects
Temperate forest	6ºC to 28ºC	75 to 125 cm	• Moist, fairly thick upper layer • Moderate levels of nutrients	Deciduous trees, shrubs, evergreens	Bears, wolves, deer, foxes, raccoons, squirrels

Temperature and Moisture in Biomes

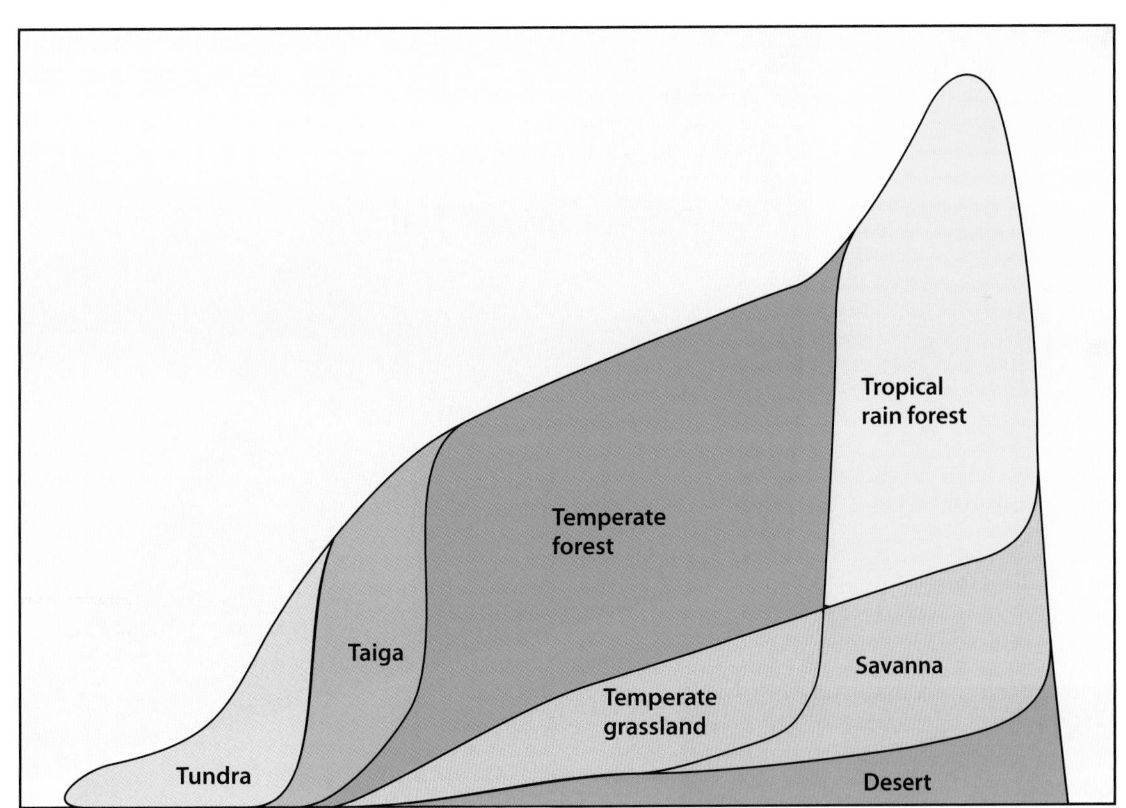

Refer to Biome Characteristics chart opposite page.

Marine organisms have adaptations that help them survive the conditions that exist where they live.

For example, organisms that live in the intertidal zone have adaptations that allow them to survive crashing waves. Organisms that live in the abyssal zone are adapted to extremely dark, cold, high-pressure conditions.

Intertidal zone: ghost crab

Sublittoral zone: coral reef

Bathyl zone: octopus

Oceanic zone (shallow): manatee

Oceanic zone (shallow): plankton

Oceanic zone (moderate depth): sperm whale

Oceanic zone (deep): anglerfish

Abyssal zone: tube worm

Species extinction is a natural process, but humans have greatly accelerated the rate of extinction.

Humans have caused extinctions through destruction of habitat, overhunting and overfishing, introduction of exotic species, and pollution. The loss of any species can affect an entire ecosystem and may have negative consequences for humans.

Green sea turtles (*Chelonia mydas*) are just one of many endangered sea turtles. Though adult sea turtles spend their lives in the sea, females lay their eggs on land, generally returning to the same beach on which they hatched. Destruction of beach habitat for tourism and real estate development has left sea turtles with fewer places to lay their eggs. Hatchlings, which look to the light of the horizon to guide them out to sea, become disoriented by lights from human dwellings. As they wander in the wrong direction, they are more vulnerable to predators and drying out. Sea turtle numbers are also declining as a result of egg gathering, hunting, and accidental death in fishing nets.

Sea otters (*Enhydra lutris*) are a keystone species. A keystone species is one whose impact on or importance to an ecosystem is greater than its numbers would predict. As a keystone species, sea otters help maintain stability in the kelp bed communities in which they live. When sea otter numbers decline, urchins—a favorite prey of sea otters—flourish. With their numbers unchecked, urchins overfeed on the kelp beds, thus destroying the community. In the eighteenth and nineteenth centuries, hunters killed these playful, intelligent animals in staggering numbers for their fur. Today, sea otters are endangered.

Bluefin tuna (*Thunnus* spp.) are the largest living bony fish. They can live 30 years or more and may reach sizes up to almost 2 m (6.5 ft). Bluefin are prized as sushi: A single animal can sell for up to $180,000 in Japan. For decades, these animals have been overfished, leading to declining numbers. Conservation organizations currently list bluefin tuna as threatened.

An endemic species is one that is native to a specific area and found nowhere else. Hawaii is home to many endemic species, including a wide variety of brilliantly colored **honeycreepers**. Many species of honeycreeper have gone extinct, and many others are critically endangered, such as this one, known as the Hawaii creeper (*Oreomystis mana*). Some species of honeycreepers have only five or fewer individuals left. Habitat destruction is responsible for the decline of many honeycreepers. Introduced species such as rats have preyed directly on many native birds, thereby reducing their numbers.

Golden poison dart frogs (*Phyllobates terribilis*) are the most deadly of the poison dart frogs. Glands in their skin produce a toxin that can kill small animals and even humans. Like many amphibians in tropical regions, golden poison dart frogs are endangered because of habitat destruction. Much of their South American rain forest habitat has been cut down for agriculture and logging. Researchers are currently looking for beneficial uses of the frogs' powerful toxin. The loss of this species and other poison dart frogs could mean a loss of potentially helpful products, such as medicines.

KNOWN THREATENED AND EXTINCT SPECIES WORLDWIDE

GROUP	NUMBER EXTINCT SINCE ABOUT 1800	NUMBER THREATENED OR ENDANGERED
Amphibians	7	146
Birds	132	1,194
Fishes	91	750
Insects	70	553
Mammals	78	1,130
Mollusks	303	967
Other invertebrates	8	439
Plants	106	6,774
Reptiles	22	293

A food chain describes the flow of energy from one species to another in an ecosystem.

An organism uses much of the energy it acquires to carry out its life processes. Energy stored within the organism's body, however, can be passed on to the next organism in the food chain.

WHAT EATS WHAT?

	SOURCE OF ENERGY	*EXAMPLES*
Producers	Make their own food; most carry out photosynthesis; a few carry out chemosynthesis	Algae, grasses, many protists, some bacteria, mosses, ferns, pine trees, flowering plants
Consumers	Eat producers or other consumers; some are decomposers	Rabbits, squid, humans, tarantulas, bullfrogs, ravens, salmon, pythons, many bacteria, mushrooms

Structure of a Prairie Ecosystem

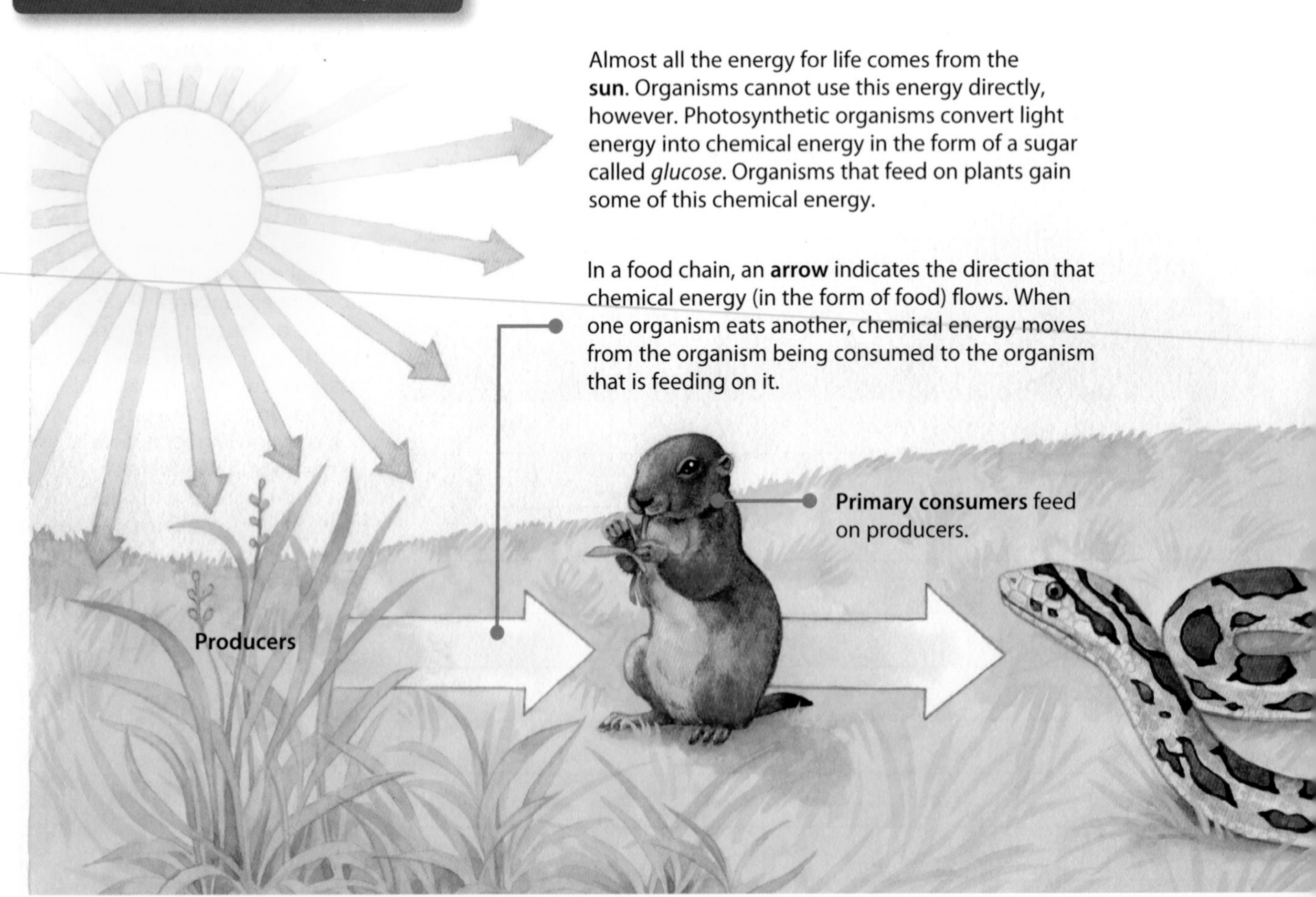

Almost all the energy for life comes from the **sun**. Organisms cannot use this energy directly, however. Photosynthetic organisms convert light energy into chemical energy in the form of a sugar called *glucose*. Organisms that feed on plants gain some of this chemical energy.
In a food chain, an **arrow** indicates the direction that chemical energy (in the form of food) flows. When one organism eats another, chemical energy moves from the organism being consumed to the organism that is feeding on it.
Primary consumers feed on producers.
Producers

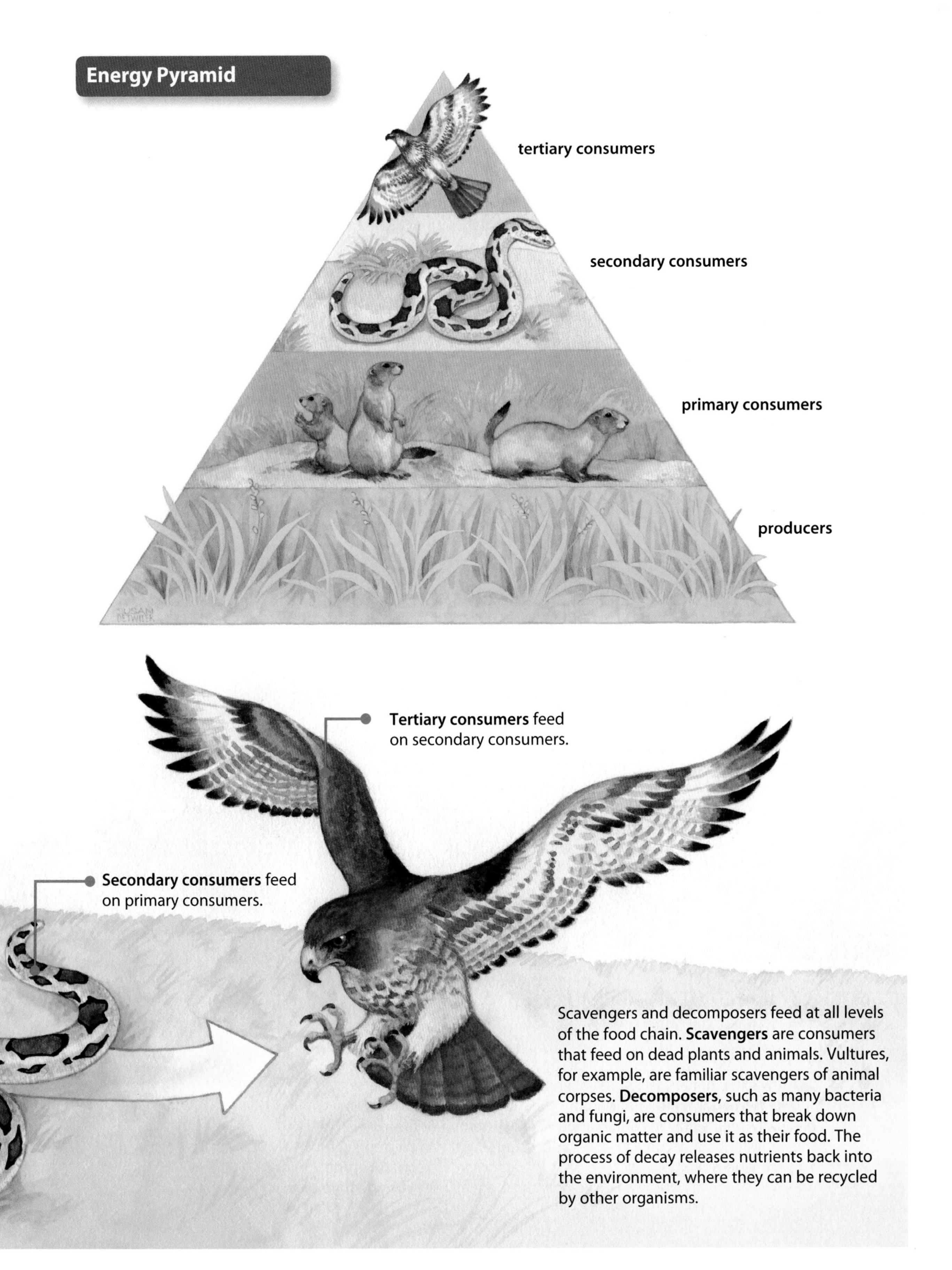

Scavengers and decomposers feed at all levels of the food chain. **Scavengers** are consumers that feed on dead plants and animals. Vultures, for example, are familiar scavengers of animal corpses. **Decomposers**, such as many bacteria and fungi, are consumers that break down organic matter and use it as their food. The process of decay releases nutrients back into the environment, where they can be recycled by other organisms.

Energy flows through an ecosystem as organisms photosynthesize or feed on other organisms.

Various models represent different aspects of this energy flow. A food chain shows the direction of energy flow. An energy pyramid represents the amount of energy available at different trophic levels in the ecosystem. A food web shows the complexity of feeding relationships.

As the **energy** in an ecosystem moves from one trophic level up to the next, much of the energy is converted to heat. Because this energy is not in a usable form, it is considered lost. Only about 10 percent of the energy available at one trophic level is usable by the organisms at the next level.

In general, the top of an **energy pyramid** contains the fewest organisms. The numbers shown here represent a hypothetical prairie ecosystem. This ecosystem can support a very small number of top consumers.

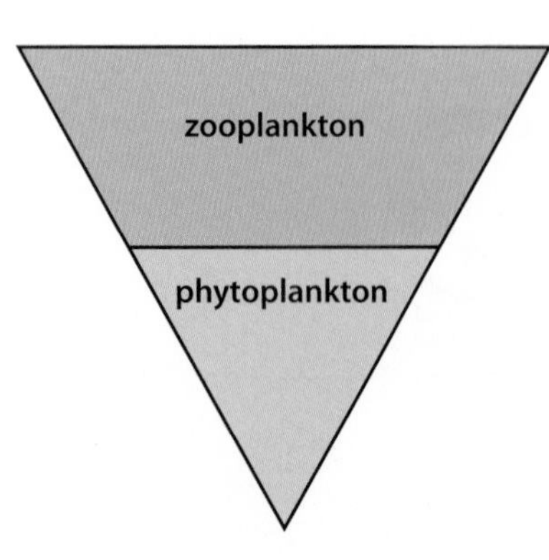

In a few exceptional cases, a relatively small number of producers supports a larger number of primary consumers. This phenomenon generally occurs only in certain **aquatic ecosystems**. For example, in the English Channel zooplankton is more abundant than phytoplankton. This scenario is possible because phytoplankton grow, reproduce, and are consumed very quickly. Fewer individuals are alive at any one time.

Food Webs

Most organisms feed on a variety of organisms or are food for a variety of consumers. A **food web** represents feeding relationships in an ecosystem better than a simple food chain. A snake, for example, may be the secondary consumer in one food chain, but the tertiary consumer in another.

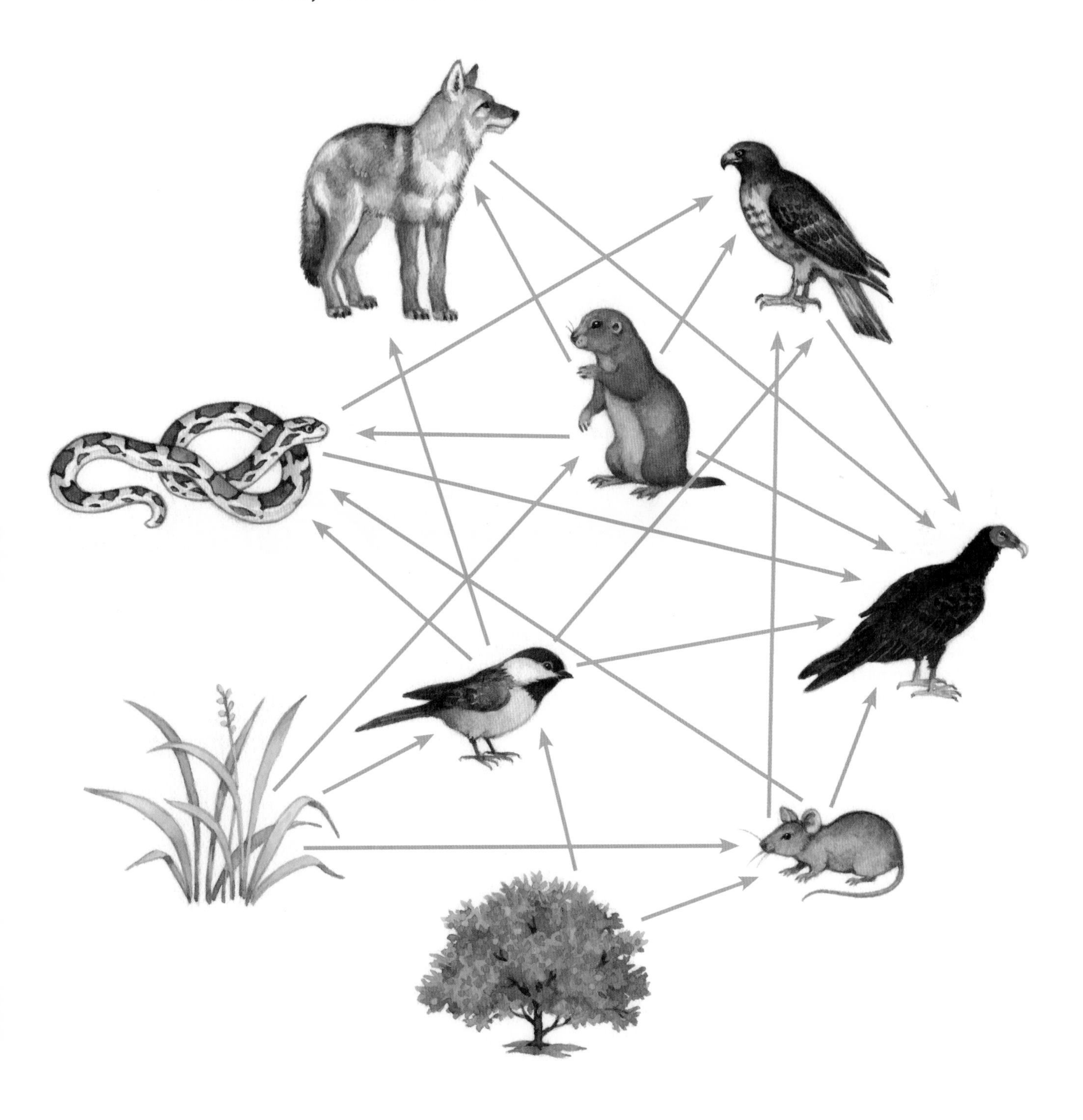

Nitrogen on earth is continuously moving between different reservoirs.

The reservoirs of nitrogen and the processes that cause nitrogen to move between them make up the nitrogen cycle.

The **atmosphere** is the largest nitrogen reservoir on earth. Almost all nitrogen in the atmosphere is in the form of nitrogen gas (N_2).

Some kinds of soil bacteria, called *denitrifying bacteria*, convert nitrate into **nitrogen gas**. This nitrogen gas moves from the soil into the atmosphere.

Although all living things require **nitrogen** to survive, most cannot use nitrogen gas directly from the atmosphere. Nitrogen-fixing bacteria can convert nitrogen gas into other compounds, such as ammonia and nitrates, that plants can use. Animals obtain usable nitrogen by eating plants or other organisms. When organisms decay, the nitrogen in their bodies returns to the soil.

Human activities—such as fertilizer production and the burning of fossil fuels—can change the amount of nitrates and other nitrogen compounds in earth's system. In fact, humans' actions have nearly doubled the amount of atmospheric nitrogen converted into ammonia and nitrate. This increase has a significant impact on the global nitrogen cycle.

Ammonia, nitrates, and other nitrogen compounds dissolve easily in rainwater. **Runoff** can carry these compounds into the oceans.

Marine organisms also rely on nitrogen-fixing bacteria to convert atmospheric nitrogen gas into ammonia and nitrate. Phytoplankton and other producers in the oceans can use these nitrogen compounds. Marine animals obtain nitrogen by feeding on other organisms. Decomposers also help mobilize nitrogen in marine ecosystems. Denitrifying bacteria convert nitrate into nitrogen gas, which flows back into the atmosphere.

Phosphorus is constantly recycled through different processes.

These processes and the reservoirs in which phosphorus is stored make up the phosphorus cycle.

Rocks are an important phosphorus reservoir. They may be uplifted, or brought close to the surface, by geologic processes such as mountain building. Weathering by water and mining by people can break down the rock, allowing phosphorus to be released into the soil. In addition, people can add fertilizers, which may contain phosphorus, to the soil.

Plants and soil microorganisms take up phosphorus from **soil** and from rainwater. Animals obtain phosphorus by eating plants and other organisms. When organisms die, decomposers such as bacteria and fungi break down the remains and return the phosphorus to the soil.

Runoff can carry phosphorus from the land to the oceans.

Sewage treatment plants may release **wastewater** into the oceans. This wastewater may contain significant amounts of phosphorus, which end up in the oceans.

The **oceans** are some of the largest phosphorus reservoirs on earth. Most of this phosphorus is dissolved in the ocean water.

Marine organisms obtain phosphorus from ocean water and by eating other organisms.

When marine organisms die, their **remains** may settle to the ocean floor and become buried in sediment. Phosphorus buried in marine sediment is not available for organisms to use.

Carbon is the basis of all life on earth.

The carbon on earth moves through many different reservoirs, including living things, the atmosphere, the oceans, and even rocks. Carbon can exist in different forms in each reservoir, and various processes act to move carbon between reservoirs. Without these processes, life on earth could not exist.

When **fossil fuels and organic matter** burn, carbon dioxide is released into the atmosphere.

Plants and other photosynthetic organisms remove carbon dioxide from the atmosphere. During **photosynthesis**, the carbon dioxide is converted into glucose and other materials that the organisms use for growth and development.

Plants, animals, and most other organisms on earth release carbon dioxide into the atmosphere as part of cellular respiration. During **cellular respiration**, sugars combine with oxygen to produce carbon dioxide, water, and chemical energy that the organisms can use.

The **organic matter and rock fragments** in soil contain carbon. Rocks below or at earth's surface may contain carbon in the form of minerals or fossil fuels.

The **living things** on earth's surface contain carbon in their cells.

Most of the carbon in the **atmosphere** is in the form of carbon dioxide. Methane and other gaseous hydrocarbons in the atmosphere also contain carbon. These compounds act as greenhouse gases, absorbing reflected light and radiating it back as heat, which helps keep earth warm.

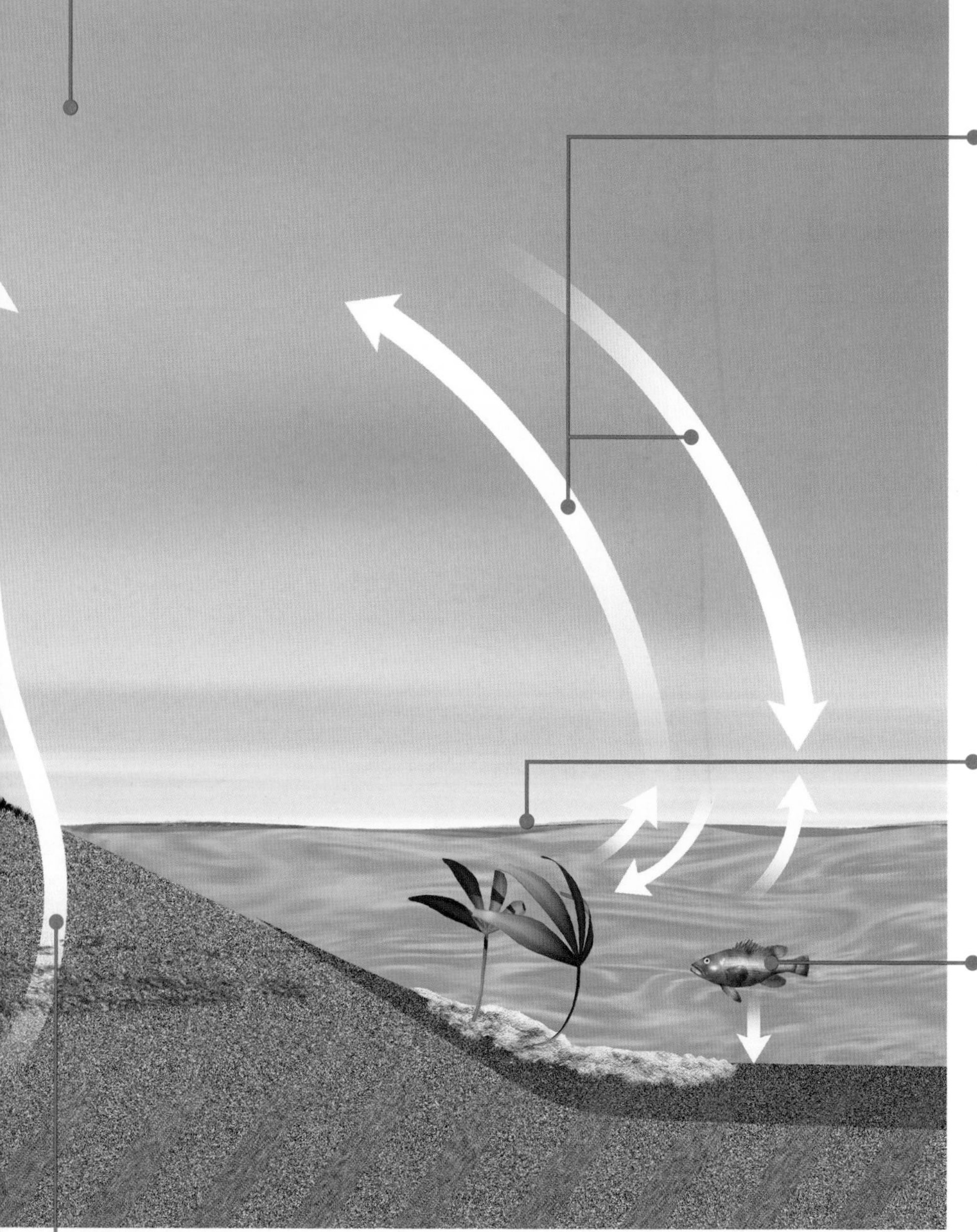

Carbon dioxide dissolved in **water** can diffuse into the atmosphere. In addition, carbon dioxide in the atmosphere can dissolve in surface water.

The **oceans** are the largest carbon reservoir on earth. Ocean-dwelling organisms contain carbon in their cells. Some, such as corals and shellfish, use carbon to build hard skeletons out of carbonate minerals. A smaller amount of carbon dioxide is also dissolved in ocean water.

When organisms in the oceans die, they can decompose. This produces carbon dioxide, which can dissolve in ocean water or move into the atmosphere. The remains of some **ocean organisms** do not completely decay. Instead, they can be buried and compressed. After millions of years, they may turn into fossil fuels such as oil and natural gas.

When **dead organisms** break down, carbon dioxide is released into the atmosphere. Some of the carbon is also incorporated into soil organic matter. The remains of some organisms can be buried and compressed to produce fossil fuels, such as coal.

Almost no water enters or exits the earth system.

However, the water on earth does change forms, moving from one reservoir to another, such as from the oceans to the atmosphere. Water reservoirs and the processes that move water between reservoirs make up the water cycle.

Water that moves over the land into the oceans is **runoff**. Runoff may flow directly into the oceans or it may flow into other water bodies such as ponds, lakes, and rivers, which then drain into the oceans.

Water in the **atmosphere** exists primarily as water vapor, a gas. However, the water in clouds is in the form of tiny, liquid water droplets.

Living things, especially plants, give off water vapor during **respiration and transpiration**. When animals breathe out, they give off water vapor. During transpiration, water vapor passes out of tiny pores in plant leaves.

All **living things** contain water in their cells. Without water, organisms on earth could not survive.

Only a tiny fraction of earth's water is **surface water.** Surface water includes lakes, rivers, ponds, swamps, and streams.

Water moves from earth's surface into the ground through **percolation**. Percolation is the primary way that water enters aquifers (underground rock bodies that store water).

Groundwater is the second largest freshwater reservoir on earth. Groundwater is water that is located below earth's surface, stored in layers of rock.

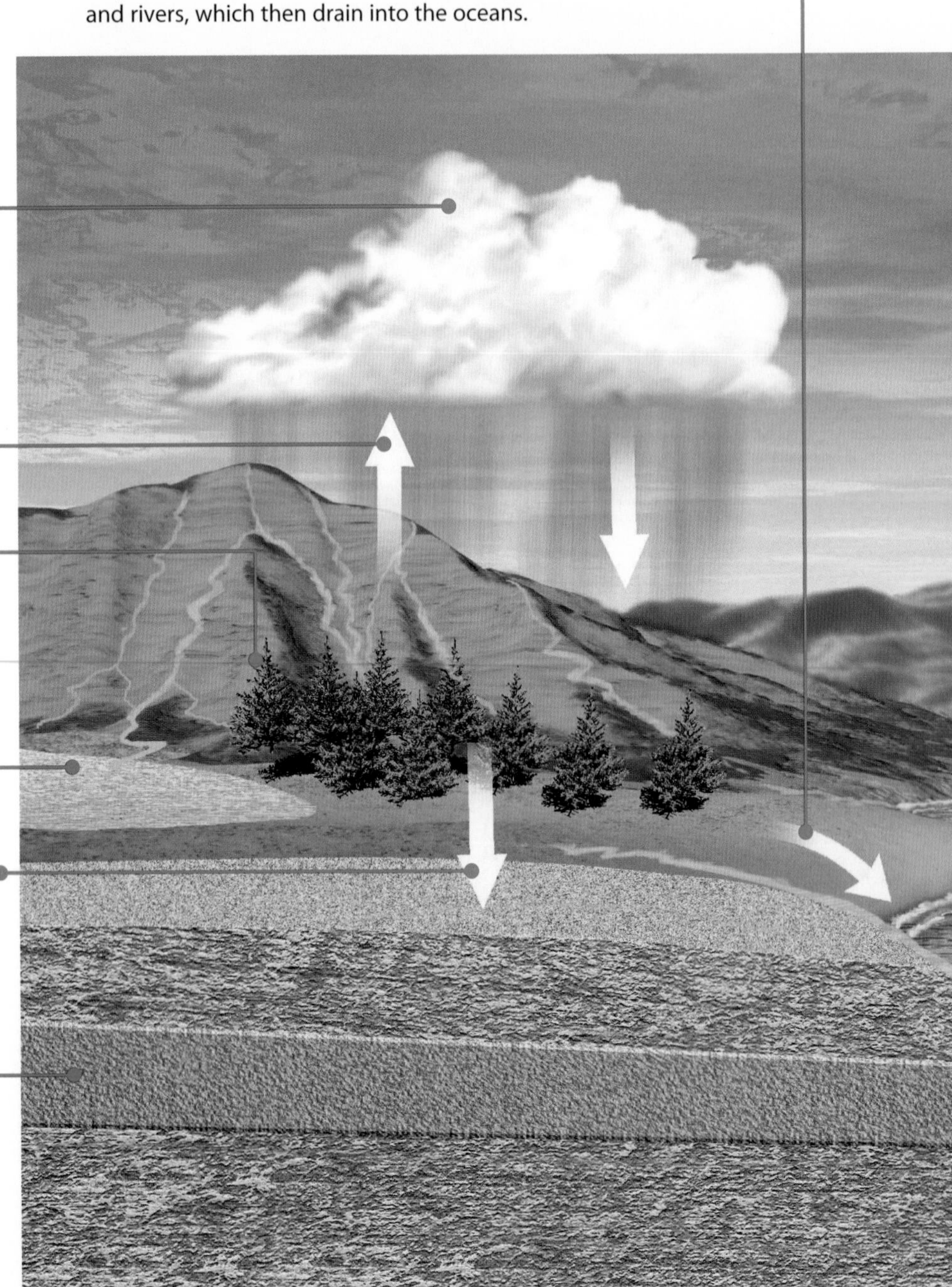

Water moves from oceans and surface waters into the atmosphere through **evaporation**. The main source of energy for evaporation is sunlight.

Water moves from the atmosphere to earth's surface through **precipitation**. Most precipitation falls on the oceans.

The **oceans** are the largest water reservoirs on earth. About 97 percent of the water in the earth system is located in the oceans.

Approximately 2 percent of all water in the earth system is located in **ice** in glaciers and icebergs. This ice makes up the largest freshwater reservoir on earth.

Liquid water turns into ice during the process of **freezing**. Water near the poles and at high elevations freezes to form snow, glaciers, and sea ice.

Illustration and Photo Credits

All illustrations © K12 Inc. unless otherwise noted.

Cover: (ladybug) © Steve Satushek/Getty Images, Inc.; (tree) © Brand X Pictures/Jupiterimages; (jellyfish) © Frederic Pacorel/ Jupiterimages; (nerve cells) © Dennis Kunkel/Phototake.

Illustration Credits

Argosy Publishing: 20, 21, 22, 23, 39; **Kim Battista:** 15, 23, 28, 29, 30, 31, 42, 43, 109; **James Bravo:** 10, 11; **Susan Detwiler:** 81, 82, 83, 84, 85, 124, 125, 143, 175, 178, 179, 189, 202, 203, 204, 205; **DK Images:** 156, 157; **© Peg Gerrity, www.peggerrity.com:** 149, 150, 152, 154, 155, 158, 159, 162, 164, 167, 168, 170; **Garth Glazier/ AA Reps, Inc.:** 3, 7, 40, 41, 70, 90, 91, 92, 93, 94, 95, 96, 97, 98, 99, 100, 101, 104, 105, 106, 107, 110, 111, 112, 113; **Jennifer Horsburgh:** 194, 195; **Julie Jankowski:** 44; **©2006 Lauren Keswick:** 180, 181; **Tim Phelps:** 118, 119, 140, 148, 153, 156, 160, 161, 166, 168, 174; **Precision Graphics:** 46, 47, 48, 49, 50, 51, 52, 53, 54, 55, 56, 57, 58, 59, 60, 62, 63, 64, 65, 66, 120, 121, 163, 165, 168, 169; **Tony Randazzo/AA Reps, Inc.:** 24, 25, 33, 34, 35, 70, 71, 72, 73, 76, 77, 78, 79, 88, 89, 206, 207, 208, 209, 210, 211, 212, 213; **Space Channel/AA Reps, Inc.:** 159, 176, 177, 198, 199.

Photo Credits

Biology Time Line: 2 (cells) © Science VU/Visuals Unlimited; (William Harvey circulatory system) © Bettmann/Corbis; (Carolus Linnaeus) © The Granger Collection, New York; (HMS *Beagle*) © Science Photo Library/Photo Researchers, Inc.; (Gregor Mendel) © Hulton Archive/Getty Images, Inc. **3** (penicillin) © Biophoto Associates/Photo Researchers, Inc.; (leaves) © George D. Lepp/ Photo Researchers, Inc.; (human heart) © Dorling Kindersley/DK Images; (Dolly the sheep) © Reuters/Corbis.

History of Evolution 1: 4 (*Linnaea*) © Valerie Giles/Photo Researchers, Inc.; (crowded street) © Rafael Macia/Photo Researchers, Inc.; (giraffes) © Getty Images, Inc. **5** (*Megalosaurus* fossil) © DK Limited/Corbis; (Grand Canyon) © Getty Images, Inc.; (Charles Darwin) © The Granger Collection, New York.

History of Evolution 2: 6 (Gregor Mendel) © Hulton Archive/ Getty Images, Inc.; (*Archaeopteryx* fossil) © James L. Amos/Photo Researchers, Inc. **7** (Lucy) © John Reader/Photo Researchers, Inc.

Light Miscroscope: 12 (*Euglena*) © Lester V. Bergman/Corbis; (diatoms) © Arthur Siegelman/Visuals Unlimited; (bacteria) © Charles Stratton/Visuals Unlimited. **13** (light microscope) © Getty Images, Inc.

Electron Microscopes: 14 (bacteria) © Dr. David Phillips/Visuals Unlimited; (diatom) © Dr. Dennis Kunkel/Phototake; (*Euglena*) © Visuals Unlimited. **15** (*Euglena*) © Dr. Dennis Kunkel/Visuals Unlimited, Inc.

The Characteristics of Life: 16–17 (snake) © PhotoObjects.net/ JupiterImages.

Biological Compounds: 27 (barnacles) © Kevin Schafer/Corbis; (celery) © Royalty-Free/Corbis; (harp seal) © Tom Brakefield/ Corbis; (lion) © Gallo Image/Corbis.

Monosaccharides: 28 (sugarcane plant) © Greg Ward and James McConnachie/Rough Guides.

Polysaccharides: 30 (mole rats) © Dorling Kindersley; (potatoes) © Dorling Kindersley. **31** (papyrus plants) © Jupiterimages; (papyrus paper) © Science Photo Library/Photo Researchers, Inc.

Proteins: 33 (girl) © Royalty-Free/Corbis.

The Structure of Proteins: 35 (black widow spider) © Steve Maslowski/Visuals Unlimited.

Enzymes: 37 (dog) © Bob Jackson/Alamy.

Lipids: 38 (codfish) © Jupiterimages; (walrus) © Fritz Polking/ Visuals Unlimited; (leaf) © Tracy Knauer/Photo Researchers, Inc. **39** (cheek cell) © Carolina Biological Supply Company/Phototake.

Nucleic Acids: DNA and RNA: 40 (cypress leaf) © Martin B. Withers; Frank Lane Picture Agency/Corbis. **41** (redwood) © Frans Lanting/Minden Pictures.

Water: 43 (water striders) © Gary Zahm/Bruce Coleman Inc.; (marigold) © Photolibrary/Index Stock.

Cell Membranes: 46 (sea star) © Scott Camazine/Alamy.

Cell Organelles: 48 (sea star) © Scott Camazine/Alamy.

Diffusion and Osmosis: 53 (paramecium) © M. I. Walker/Photo Researchers, Inc.

Passive Transport: Simple and Facilitated Diffusion: 54 (amoeba) © PunchStock.

Active Transport: 56 (amoeba) © PunchStock.

Glycolysis: 58 (runners at start) © Getty Images, Inc. **59** (runner at end) © Will McIntyre/Photo Researchers, Inc.

The Krebs Cycle: 60 (runners) © Getty Images, Inc.

The Electron Transport Chain: 62 (runners at finish line) © Comstock Images/PunchStock.

Chloroplasts: 64 (*Monstera*) © Tracy Knauer/Photo Researchers, Inc.

Photosynthesis and Cellular Respiration: 68 (sun) © Mistral Images/Index Stock; (grass) © Market Fresh. **69** (grass) © Market Fresh; (duck) © Photodisc.

Chromosomes: 70 (green onion) © Getty Images, Inc.; (onion root tip) © Biology Media/Photo Researchers, Inc.

Mitosis: 72 (tadpole) © Dwight Kuhn.

Cell Specialization: 74 (blood cells) © Visuals Unlimited; (hair cells) © Steve Gschmeissner/Photo Researchers, Inc.; (bone cells) © BSIP/Photo Researchers, Inc. **74–75** (hand) © Dorling Kindersley. **75** (skin cells) © Eye of Science/Photo Researchers, Inc.; (nerve cells) © Dennis Kunkel/Phototake; (muscle cells) © Visuals Unlimited.

Meiosis I: 76 (stallion) © Kit Houghton/Corbis.

Meiosis II: 79 (horse sperm cells) © Dr. T. E. Thompson/Photo Researchers, Inc.

Pedigrees: 87 (Queen Victoria) © Hulton Archive/Getty Images, Inc.; (Prince Albert) © Bettmann/Corbis.

DNA Structure 1: 90 (wombat) © Theo Allofs/Visuals Unlimited.

Central Dogma of Biology: 96 (polychaete worm) © Natural Visions/Alamy. **97** (polychaete worm) © Natural Visions/Alamy.

The Genetic Code: 102 (mushrooms) © itstock; (cat) © Comstock Images/Jupiterimages; (*Stentor*) © Eric V. Grave/Photo Researchers, Inc.; (plants) © Royalty-Free/Corbis; (bacteria) © Dr. Gary Gaugler/Visuals Unlimited.

RNA Structure: 104 (paramecium) © M. I. Walker/Photo Researchers, Inc.

Plant Cell Differentiation: 106 (onion with roots) © oote boe/Alamy.

Animal Cell Differentiation: 108 (*C. elegans*) © Sinclair Stammers/Photo Researchers, Inc.

Biotechnology 2: 113 (lab technician) © Novo Nordisk.

History of Life on Earth: 117 (Neanderthal) © The Bridgeman Art Library/Getty Images, Inc.; (*Eohippus*) © Tierbild Okapia/Photo Researchers, Inc.; (*Tyrannosaurus rex*) © Tom McHugh/Photo Researchers, Inc.; (magnolia) © Sinclair Stammers/Photo Researchers, Inc.; (*Archaeopteryx* fossil) © James L. Amos/Photo Researchers, Inc.; (*Tiktaalik*) © Zina Deretsky, National Science Foundation; (fossil fish) © Gary Braasch/Corbis; (trilobite) © Ken Lucas/Visuals Unlimited.

Chromosome Mutations: 120 (girl with Williams syndrome) © LWA-Dann Tardif/Corbis. **121** (girl with Down syndrome) © Royalty-Free/Corbis; (karyotype) © Biophoto Associates/Photo Researchers, Inc.

Classification: 128 (bacteria) © Michael Abbey/Visuals Unlimited; (archaebacteria) © Dr. Kari Lounatmaa/Photo Researchers, Inc.; (spiny echidna) © Kevin Schaffer/Corbis. **129** (flamingo) © Arthur Morris/Corbis.

Phylogenetic Tree: 130 (bacteria) © Michael Abbey/Visuals Unlimited; (archaebacteria) © Dr. Kari Lounatmaa/Photo Researchers, Inc.; (paramecium) © M. I. Walker/Photo Researchers, Inc. **131** (daffodils) © Goodshoot/Alamy; (morels) © Rob & Ann Simpson/Visuals Unlimited; (spiny echidna) © Kevin Schafer/Corbis.

Bacteria and Archaeans: 132 (spirochetes) © Larry Mulvehill/Photo Researchers, Inc.; (*Streptococcus*) © David M. Phillips/Photo Researchers, Inc.; (cyanobacteria) © Dr. Robert Calentine/Visuals Unlimited; (*Chlamydia*) © Luis M. de la Maza/Phototake. **133** (Yellowstone hot springs) © Simon Terrey/Photo Researchers, Inc.; (Great Salt Lake) © Pamela Reed/Jupiterimages.

Protists and Fungi: 134 (red algae) © Doug Sokell/Visuals Unlimited; (*Plasmodium*) © Dr. M. A. Ansary/Photo Researchers, Inc.; (*Stentor*) © Eric V. Grave/Photo Researchers, Inc. **135** (corn smut) © Astrid & Hanns-Frieder Michler/Photo Researchers, Inc.; (mushrooms) © Artville; (bread) © Lew Robertson/Jupiterimages; (ringworm) © Biophoto Associates/Photo Researchers, Inc.

Plants: 136 (mosses) © Tom Way/Alamy; (ferns) © Wally Eberhart/Visuals Unlimited. **137** (bristlecone pine) © Jeff Foott/naturepl.com; (cycad) © Dr. Carleton Ray/Photo Researchers, Inc.; (day lilies) © Michael Craven; (oak) © Natural Selection/Jupiterimages.

Animals: 138 (sponges) © Comstock Images/Jupiterimages; (jellyfish) © Frederic Pacorel/Jupiterimages. **139** (*Dugesia* group) © Tom Adams/Visuals Unlimited; (human baby) © Creatas Images/Jupiterimages; (mollusk) © Ken Lucas/Visuals Unlimited; (sea star) © Scott Camazine/Alamy; (grasshopper) © Peter Arnold, Inc./Alamy.

Flatworms: 140 (flatworms) © Sinclair Stammers/Photo Researchers, Inc.; (fluke) © Dennis Kunkel/Phototake; (tapeworms) © Andrew Syred/Photo Researchers, Inc. **141** (*Dugesia*) © M. I. Walker/Photo Researchers, Inc.; (*Dugesia* group) © Tom Adams/Visuals Unlimited; (flatworm) © Nature's Images/Photo Researchers, Inc.

Ferns: 142 (tree fern) © Konrad Wothe/Minden Pictures; (maidenhair fern) © Wally Eberhart/Botanica/Jupiterimages; (*Azolla*) © Tony Wharton; Frank Lane Picture Agency/Corbis. **143** (bracken fern) © Wally Eberhart/Visuals Unlimited.

Primates: 144 (lemurs) © Andy Rouse/Stock Image/Jupiterimages; (golden lion tamarin) © Claus Meyer/Minden Pictures; (bonobo) © Martyn Colbeck/Oxford Scientific/Jupiterimages. **145** (human skeleton) © Alfred Pasieka/Photo Researchers, Inc.; (girl on phone) © BananaStock/Jupiterimages; (graduation ceremony) © Comstock/Jupiterimages.

Excretory Systems: 153 (tree) © Brand X Pictures/Jupiterimages.

Gas Exchange: 156 (*Dugesia* group) © Tom Adams/Visuals Unlimited. **157** (fern) © Wally Eberhart/Visuals Unlimited; (closed stoma) © RMF/Scientifica/Visuals Unlimited; (open stoma) © Dr. Stanley Flegler/Visuals Unlimited.

Human and Flatworm Nervous Systems: 160 (open Venus flytrap) © Barry Rice/Visuals Unlimited; (closed Venus flytrap) © Barry Rice/Visuals Unlimited.

Human Nervous System: 163 (woman with dog) © Royalty-Free/Corbis.

Plant Hormones: 173 (sunflower) © Getty Images, Inc.; (onion with roots) © oote boe/Alamy; (bananas) © Artville; (open stoma) © Dr. Stanley Flegler/Visuals Unlimited; (sapling) © Dwight Kuhn.

Immune System 2: 185 (hand with cut) © image 100/Jupiterimages.

Plant Defenses: 186 (spurge) © Gerald & Buff Corsi/Visuals Unlimited; (cactus) © Creatas Images/Jupiterimages; (rose) © Michael Craven. **187** (pussy willow branch) © Theo Allofs/zefa/Corbis; (poppy with sap) © Dr. Jeremy Burgess/Photo Researchers, Inc.; (redwood burl) © QT Luong/terragalleria.com; (poison ivy) © Wally Eberhart/Visuals Unlimited.

Ecological Levels of Organization: 188 (Earth) NASA.

Ecosystem Diversity: 192 (estuary) © Stephen J. Krasemann/Photo Researchers, Inc. **193** (rain forest) © Royalty-Free/Corbis; (tundra) © blickwinkel/Alamy; (desert) © David Wasserman/Jupiterimages; (lake) © Photodisc/Getty Images, Inc.

Marine Organisms: 198 (ghost crab) © Millard H. Sharp/Photo Researchers, Inc.; (coral reef) © Photodisc/Getty Images, Inc. (octopus) © Brandon Cole Marine Photography/Alamy. **199** (manatee) © Royalty-Free/Corbis; (plankton) © Peter Arnold, Inc./Alamy; (sperm whale) © Photodisc/PunchStock; (tube worms) © Ralph White/Corbis; (anglerfish) © Bruce Robison/Corbis.

Effects of Extinction: 200 (turtle) © Masa Ushioda/Visuals Unlimited; (sea otters) © John Warden/Jupiterimages; (tuna) © Richard Herrmann/Visuals Unlimited. **201** (honeycreeper) © Frans Lanting/Minden Pictures; (frog) © Ken Lucas/Visuals Unlimited.

Food Webs: 204 (plankton) © Peter Arnold, Inc./Alamy.

Pronunciation Guide

The table below provides sample words to explain the sounds associated with specific letters and letter combinations used in the respellings in this book. For example, *a* represents the short "a" sound in *cat*, while *ay* represents the long "a" sound in *day*.

Letter combinations are used to approximate certain more complex sounds. For example, in the respelling of *Celsius*—SEL-see-uhs—the letters *uhs* represent the vowel sound you hear in *shut* and *other*.

Vowels

a	short a: **a**pple, c**a**t
ay	long a: c**a**ne, d**ay**
e, eh	short e: h**e**n, b**e**d
ee	long e: f**ee**d, t**ea**m
i, ih	short i: l**i**p, act**i**ve
iy	long i: tr**y**, m**igh**t
ah	short o: h**o**t, f**a**ther
oh	long o: h**o**me, thr**ow**
uh	short u: sh**u**t, **o**ther
yoo	long u: **u**nion, c**u**te

Letter Combinations

ch	**ch**in, an**c**ient
sh	**sh**ow, mi**ss**ion
zh	vi**s**ion, a**z**ure
th	**th**in, heal**th**
th	**th**en, hea**th**er
ur	b**ir**d, f**ur**ther, w**or**d
us	b**us**, cr**us**t
or	c**our**t, f**or**mal
ehr	**er**ror, c**are**
oo	c**oo**l, tr**ue**, r**u**le
ow	n**ow**, **ou**t
ou	l**oo**k, p**u**ll, w**ou**ld
oy	c**oi**n, t**oy**
aw	s**aw**, m**au**l, f**a**ll
ng	so**ng**, fi**ng**er
air	**Ar**istotle, b**arr**ister
ahr	c**ar**t, m**ar**tyr

Consonants

b	**b**utter, **b**a**b**y
d	**d**og, cra**d**le
f	**f**un, **ph**one
g	**g**rade, an**g**le
h	**h**at, a**h**ead
j	**j**u**dg**e, gor**g**e
k	**k**ite, **c**ar, bla**ck**
l	**l**i**l**y, mi**l**e
m	**m**o**m**, ca**m**el
n	**n**ext, ca**n**di**d**
p	**p**rice, co**pp**er
r	**r**ubbe**r**, f**r**ee
s	**s**mall, **c**ircle, ha**ss**le
t	**t**on, po**tt**ery
v	**v**ase, **v**i**v**id
w	**w**all, a**w**ay
y	**y**ellow, ka**y**ak
z	**z**ebra, ha**z**e

Glossary

actin specialized protein making up the thin muscle filaments

action potential the polarity along a neuron that allows for transmission of an electrical impulse

activation energy the amount of energy needed to start a reaction; the higher the activation energy, the less likely that the reaction will proceed

active transport movement of materials across a membrane that requires an input of energy from the cell

adaptation a structural or behavioral aspect of a living thing that makes it fit for its environment

adhesion an attraction between the molecules of one substance and the molecules of another substance

alcoholic fermentation anaerobic energy-releasing pathway that produces ethanol

allele one of the forms of a gene that codes for a particular trait

alveoli (al-VEE-uh-liy) tiny sacs in the lungs where gas exchange occurs

amino (uh-MEE-noh) acids the basic building blocks of proteins

amylase an enzyme found in saliva that catalyzes the breakdown of starches into simple sugars

anaerobe an organism that does not or cannot use oxygen

angiosperm (AN-jee-uh-spuhrm) a flowering plant; may be in one of two main groups: monocots or dicots

anticodon a sequence of three bases that is complementary to a messenger RNA (mRNA) codon and is part of a transfer RNA (tRNA) molecule

atom the basic building block of all matter; is made up of smaller particles: protons, neutrons, and electrons

ATP (adenosine triphosphate [uh-DEH-nuh-seen triy-FAHS-fayt]) source of usable energy for almost all processes that a cell must undergo to survive

axons long extensions of a nerve cell that carry electrical impulses

bacteriophage a virus that infects bacteria

B cell a lymphocyte that produces antibodies

biome (BIY-ohm) a large area of earth defined by its climate and by the organisms that live there

biosphere (BIY-ih-sfir) the largest and most inclusive level of ecological organization

burl a protective covering that forms over a wound on a tree; a burl may contain clusters of dormant buds that can start to grow if the parent tree is damaged

Calvin cycle a stage of photosynthesis in which carbon dioxide from the atmosphere is assembled into sugars

capillary action the movement of water up a column due to adhesion and cohesion

carbohydrate (kahr-boh-HIY-drayt) an organic compound made of carbon, hydrogen, and oxygen

carrying capacity the largest population that a particular environment can support at a particular time

cell differentiation the process of cell modification from a generalized cell to one that performs a specific task

cellular respiration process in which organisms use oxygen to break down glucose and produce water, oxygen, and energy in the form of ATP

cellulose (SEL-yuh-lohs) a polysaccharide that consists of long, unbranched chains of glucose molecules

centromere the point in a chromosome at which two chromatids are joined

cerebellum (sehr-uh-BEH-luhm) the part of the human brain that governs motor activity and plays an important role in the perception of sensory stimuli

cerebral ganglion a concentrated cluster of nerves that functions as a simple brain for flatworms and some other invertebrates

cerebrum (suh-REE-bruhm) the part of the human brain that is responsible for voluntary movement and conscious thought

chlorophyll (KLOR-uh-fil) a pigment that is a key molecule in photosynthesis; it absorbs sunlight and converts light energy to chemical energy

chloroplast (KLOR-uh-plast) the structure responsible for capturing light energy in photosynthetic organisms; contains chlorophyll

chromatids the two identical strands of a chromosome

chromosome (KROH-muh-sohm) a single long molecule of DNA wound around proteins called *histones*

codon a sequence of three bases that codes for a single amino acid

cohesion an attraction between molecules of the same substance

community all of the populations that live and interact in a particular area

contractile vacuole (VA-kyuh-wohl) a structure in some protists that pumps excess water out of their cells

cotyledon (kah-tuh-LEE-dn) a seed leaf; provides nutrition for the developing plant embryo

covalent (koh-VAY-luhnt) bond a bond formed by electrons shared between atoms

cristae the folds of the inner membrane of a mitochondrion

cross-pollination in flowering plants, the transfer of pollen from an anther of a flower on one plant to a stigma of a flower on another plant

cytokinesis (siy-toh-kuh-NEE-suhs) division of a cell's cytoplasm that produces two separate cells

cytoplasm (SIY-tuh-pla-zuhm) everything, except for the nucleus, that is contained within the cell membrane; contains the organelles and the cytosol

cytosol (SIY-tuh-sahl) the fluid portion of the cytoplasm

decomposers consumers, such as many bacteria and fungi, that break down dead organic matter for energy

deletion mutation mutation in which part of a chromosome breaks off and is lost

dendrites (DEN-driyts) extensions of a nerve cell that receive stimuli

denitrifying bacteria bacteria that convert nitrate into nitrogen gas

deoxyribose (dee-AHK-sih-RIY-bohs) a monosaccharide; the sugar component of DNA

dicot (DIY-kaht) an angiosperm that has seeds with two cotyledons; in general, its leaves have netlike veins, and its flower parts are in multiples of four or five

diffusion process in which atoms and molecules move from an area where they are more concentrated to an area where they are less concentrated

diploid (DIH-ployd) $2n$, containing two sets of chromosomes

directional selection selection that tends to favor one extreme form of a trait over another

disruptive selection selection that tends to favor extreme forms of a trait over the average form of a trait

DNA (deoxyribonucleic [dee-AHK-sih-riy-boh-nyoo-KLEE-ihk] acid) nucleic acid that contains an organism's genetic information

double helix two intertwined coils; describes the twisted double-backbone structure of DNA

ecosystem (EE-koh-sis-tuhm) the community (biotic) and the abiotic factors in a particular area

ectotherm an organism that regulates its internal temperature using external sources of heat

element a substance made up of one kind of atom

endemic species a species that is native to a specific area and is found nowhere else

energy pyramid a representation of the amount of energy available at different trophic levels in the ecosystem

enzymes (EN-ziymz) proteins that speed up the chemical reactions that make life possible

ER (endoplasmic reticulum [EN-doh-plaz-mihk rih-TIHK-kyuh-luhm]) a series of interconnected flattened sacs, tubes, and channels within a cell

estuary (EHS-choo-wair-ee) an ecosystem where freshwater from rivers and streams mixes with seawater

eukaryotic (yoo-KAIR-ee-AH-tihk) cell a cell that has a nucleus, multiple chromosomes, and membrane-bound organelles

evolution broadly, change over time; more precisely, the change in allele frequencies in a population over time

exponential growth model model in which population growth continues indefinitely; has a characteristic J-shaped curve

F1 generation the first filial generation; the offspring of the P generation

F2 generation the second filial generation; the offspring of the F1 generation

facilitated diffusion a kind of passive transport in which small molecules pass through the cell membrane with the aid of proteins

fatty acids long chains of hydrocarbons in fats and phospholipids

fertilization the fusion of a sperm cell and an egg cell

fluke a type of parasitic flatworm

food chain the path of energy flow through organisms in an ecosystem

food web a representation of the feeding relationships in an ecosystem

gamete (GA-meet) a reproductive cell that can fuse with another to form a zygote

genetics (juh-NEH-tihks) the study of heredity

genotype the combination of alleles for a trait or an organism's entire set of alleles

glomerulus a network of capillaries in the upper part of a nephron

glucose (GLOO-kohs) a monosaccharide used by cells for energy

glycerol a three-carbon molecule that forms the backbone of fats and phospholipids

glycogen (GLIY-kuh-juhn) a polysaccharide; a long chain of glucose molecules with many branches; the form in which animals store carbohydrates

glycolysis (gliy-KAH-luh-suhs) "sugar splitting"; process at the beginning of all energy-releasing pathways; takes place in the cytoplasm of both prokaryotic and eukaryotic cells

Golgi (GOHL-jee) body a network of flattened membrane sacs stacked together; receives the products of the ER (mostly proteins), sorts their contents, modifies them, and distributes them throughout the cell

gymnosperm (JIM-nuh-spuhrm) a seed plant that does not produce fruits or flowers

halophile (HA-luh-fiyl) an organism that thrives in extremely salty conditions

haploid (HA-ployd) $1n$, containing only half the usual number of chromosomes for the species

heartwood tissue in the center of a tree trunk where wastes are permanently stored

hemoglobin a protein in red blood cells that brings oxygen from the lungs to cells

heredity passing of genetic information from parents to their offspring

hermaphrodite (hur-MA-fruh-diyt) an organism possessing both male and female reproductive organs

heterozygous (HEH-tuh-roh-ZIY-guhs) having different alleles for a particular trait on homologous chromosomes

histamines chemicals that cause the blood cells around a cut to dilate, which allows more blood to flow to the site of the cut

histones proteins around which a single long molecule of DNA is wound

homeostasis (HOH-mee-oh-STAY-suhs) maintenance of the body's internal conditions within a narrow range, even if outside conditions change; involves controlling the balance of water and minerals in the body, responding to changes in the environment, and controlling metabolism

homologous (huh-MAH-luh-guhs) chromosome one of a pair of chromosomes that have the same genes

homozygous (HOH-muh-ZIY-guhs) having the same alleles on both homologous chromosomes

hormones chemical signals produced by cells in one part of the body that regulate the activity of cells in another part of the body

hydrogen (HIY-druh-juhn) bond a weak force between hydrogen atoms and atoms of oxygen, nitrogen, or fluorine

inversion mutation a mutation in which a chromosome breaks off and reattaches itself backward

ion (IY-ahn) an atom that has gained or lost electrons and is thus a charged particle

ionic (iy-AH-nihk) bond an attractive force between positively and negatively charged atoms that forms when electrons are transferred from one atom to another

karyotype a photograph that displays an individual's paired homologous chromosomes

keratin (KEHR-uh-tn) a protein that forms filament-like structures of hair; also forms feathers, horns, and nails

keystone species a species whose impact on or importance to an ecosystem is greater than its numbers would indicate

Krebs cycle the second stage of aerobic respiration

lactic acid fermentation an energy-releasing pathway that produces two lactic acid molecules

light reactions a series of photosynthesis reactions that take place in the thylakoids

lipid (LIH-puhd) a biological compound that is insoluble in water; includes fats, oils, waxes, and steroids

logistic growth model a model in which a population increases until it reaches its carrying capacity

lymph a clear fluid that contains white blood cells and circulates throughout the body

lymphocyte (LIMP-fuh-siyt) one type of white blood cell that is produced in the spleen; produces antibodies that can destroy viruses and other pathogens

lysosome (LIY-suh-sohm) a vesicle filled with enzymes that break down materials in a cell

meiosis (miy-OH-suhs) a type of cell division that occurs in two stages and results in four haploid cells from one diploid cell

melanin (MEH-luh-nuhn) a protein produced by skin cells that gives skin its color

meristem (MEHR-uh-stem) a localized site of cell division in plants

metabolism (muh-TA-buh-LIH-zuhm) the sum of all chemical processes required to maintain life

mitochondrion (miy-tuh-KAHN-dree-uhn) an organelle that is the site of cellular respiration

mitosis (miy-TOH-suhs) the process by which the nucleus of a cell divides to form two identical nuclei

monocot (MAH-nuh-kaht) an angiosperm whose seeds contain only one cotyledon; in general, its leaves have parallel veins, and its flowers have three parts (or multiples of three)

monohybrid cross a genetic cross of two parents that lets scientists examine inheritance patterns for single characteristics

monosaccharide (MAH-nuh-SAH-kuh-riyd) a simple sugar

motor neurons cells that carry signals from the central nervous system to other cells in the body

myosin specialized protein making up the thick muscle filaments

natural selection the process in which individuals adapted to their environment survive and reproduce at higher rates than other individuals

nematocytes stinging cells in the tentacles of most cnidarians used for stunning and disabling prey

nephrons (NEH-frahnz) structures in the kidney in which blood filtration takes place

net primary productivity (NPP) a measure of energy stored in the bodies of producers that are available to the consumers in an ecosystem

neurons cells that carry information through the nervous system in the form of electrical and chemical signals

neurotransmitter a chemical that transmits a nerve signal across a synapse

nitrogen-fixing bacteria bacteria that convert nitrogen gas into other compounds, such as ammonia and nitrates, that plants can use

nitrogenous base one of a set of bases that are part of nucleic acids

nondisjunction the failure of homologous chromosomes or sister chromatids to separate, resulting in more than two homologous chromosomes in an individual's cells

nuclear membrane the envelope surrounding the nucleus that is made up of two membranes; has many pores that allow the passage of molecules such as RNA from the nucleus to the cytoplasm

nucleic (nou-KLEE-ihk) acids large molecules that are responsible for storing and translating genetic information

nucleolus (nou-KLEE-uh-luhs) a region of the nucleus where ribosomal RNA (rRNA) is produced

nucleotide (NOU-klee-uh-tiyd) a subunit of a nucleic acid that consists of a phosphate group, a five-carbon sugar, and a nitrogenous base

nucleus (NOO-klee-uhs) a cell structure with a double membrane that contains DNA and controls the functions of the cell

oils unsaturated fats that have one or more double bonds between carbon atoms in the fatty acid chains; are liquid at room temperature

organelle (or-guh-NEL) a membrane-bound structure within a eukaryotic cell

organism an individual living thing

osmosis (ahz-MOH-suhs) the diffusion of water across a semipermeable membrane

P generation the parent generation; the first individuals crossed in a breeding study

passive transport movement of materials across a membrane that does not require energy from the cell

pedigree (PEH-duh-gree) a diagram that shows how a trait is passed throughout a group of related individuals over many generations

peptide bond bond formed between two amino acids

permafrost a layer of soil that remains frozen all year

pharynx (FAIR-ingks) the feeding organ in a flatworm; in animals with digestive systems, the passage leading from the mouth to the trachea and esophagus

phenotype an organism's physical or detectable traits

phloem a vascular tissue that carries sugars from the leaves to the rest of a plant

phospholipid a lipid that contains phosphorus

phospholipid bilayer the double layer of phospholipids that makes up the membranes of a cell

photosynthesis (foh-toh-SINT-thuh-suhs) process in which organisms use water, carbon dioxide, and energy from the sun to produce glucose

phototropism the phenomenon of plant stems' growth toward light

phylogenetic (fiy-loh-juh-NEH-tihk) tree a diagram that shows how groups of organisms are related through common ancestry

pith the ground tissue located in the center of vascular plant stems

placenta an organ that allows for the passage of nutrients and wastes between the mother and fetus, while maintaining separation between their blood circulations

plasmid a single, circular, extrachromosomal piece of a bacterium's DNA

pollination the process by which male gametes are carried within pollen grains to a stigma on the same plant or, more commonly, another plant

polypeptide a chain of hundreds or thousands of amino acids

polysaccharide (PAH-lee-SAH-kuh-riyd) a long chain of monosaccharides; a complex carbohydrate

population all the members of the same species in a particular area

population growth an increase in the number of individuals in a population

prokaryotic (proh-KAIR-ee-AH-tihk) cell a cell that lacks a nucleus and membrane-bound organelles

protein a long chain of amino acids or group of polypeptides that play important roles in the structure and function of cells

reabsorption the process by which water diffuses from the fluid in the nephron back into the surrounding capillaries

replication the process in which DNA duplicates, or makes a copy of, itself

reproduction (ree-pruh-DUHK-shuhn) the process of making more of one's kind

respiration the processes in which an organism exchanges gases with its environment

ribose (RIY-bohs) a monosaccharide; the sugar component of RNA

ribosome (RIY-buh-sohm) the site of protein synthesis; may be attached to the ER or suspended within the cytosol

RNA (ribonucleic [RIY-boh-nyoo-KLEE-ihk] acid) a nucleic acid that uses the instructions stored in DNA to build proteins

RNA polymerase (puh-LIM-uhr-ays) an enzyme that binds to a DNA molecule and causes a segment of the two DNA strands to unwind and separate

root cap a group of cells that cover the very tip of a root; protects the tip of a root as it pushes downward through the soil

scavengers consumers that feed on dead plants and animals

selective permeability the ability of the cell membrane to control which substances pass into and out of the cell

self-pollination in flowering plants, the transfer of pollen from the anther to the stigma of the same flower or another flower on the same plant

sensory neurons cells that carry signals from sensory receptors in the body to the central nervous system

SI (Système International d'Unités, or International System of Units) a scientific system of measurement that includes seven base units

stabilizing selection selection that favors the average form of a trait over extreme forms

stomata (STOH-muh-tuh) microscopic pores found on the leaves of most plants

stroma (STROH-ma) the fluid part of a chloroplast that contains DNA, ribosomes, and all enzymes needed during certain stages of photosynthesis

synapse (SIH-naps) the space between adjacent neurons through which signals are transferred chemically

taiga (TIY-guh) biome characterized by long, cold winters and short, cool summers

tapeworm a parasitic flatworm that has no digestive tract; it absorbs nutrients from the gut of its host

T cell a lymphocyte involved in the cell-mediated immune response that can destroy infected body cells

tendons elastic tissues that hold muscles to bones

theory an explanation for a phenomenon supported by a large body of evidence

thermophile (THUHR-muh-fiyl) an organism that thrives in extremely hot conditions

thylakoids a system of interconnected membranes in the chloroplast that are arranged in flat stacks and contain proteins used in the formation of ATP

transcription the process in which instructions for making proteins, carried in a cell's DNA, are written into a strand of mRNA

translation the process in which proteins are produced based on instructions carried by mRNA

translocation mutation a mutation in which a piece of a chromosome breaks off and attaches to a nonhomologous chromosome

triglycerides fats that consist of three fatty acid chains attached to a molecule of glycerol

trophic levels positions in the path of energy transfer among organisms in an ecosystem

tundra biome characterized by long, cold winters; short, cool summers; and little precipitation, with soils that typically have a layer of permafrost below the surface

urethra a tube through which urine passes from the body

valence (VA-luhnts) electron an electron in the outermost shell of an atom

villi (VIH-liy) tiny fingerlike structures in the small intestines that increase surface area to allow for the maximum absorption of nutrients

virus a nonliving particle that reproduces by using a host

xylem (ZIY-luhm) a vascular tissue that carries water and dissolved minerals from a plant's roots to its stems and leaves

zygote (ZIY-goht) a cell that results from the fusion of gametes

Index

SUBJECTS are in all capital letters.

B

C

D

E

N

S